Geared for electronics engineering-technology students, this book deals with the analysis of circuitry as applied to non-sinusoidal signals: pulse, switching, and timing circuits. The approach of the text is both qualitative and quantitative. It covers basic subjects common to radar, computers, television, test equipment, and other devices where non-sinusoidal circuitry is used.

The book reviews basic network methods needed to solve R, L, and C circuits. It introduces tube and semiconductor concepts involving switching circuits, and applies these tools in analyzing the basic pulse and switching circuits used in electronic equipment. Covered also, are recent advances including some of the newer switching devices such as tunnel diodes and zener diodes, and an analysis of a transistorized oscilloscope.

The book employs several unique methods of analyzing RC time constant circuits, and its use of mathematics helps simplify understanding of these circuits. Therefore, the text presupposes a good background of algebra, right-angle trigonometry, and proficiency in the use of the slide rule. In addition, the reader should be familiar with the fundamental laws of electricity and of vacuum tube and semi-conductor theory.

Many types and varieties of classroom-tested problems are used to test the student's comprehension of the material studied. Actual tested circuits are given and analyzed so that the student can build the circuit and check his theoretical calculations against measured values. Answers to odd numbered problems are in the back of the book.

Successful completion of this text will prepare the student for a course in Digital Computers. It can also be used in computer courses or instrumentation classes. Electronics technicians and engineers will find this text especially helpful for enriching their background.

McGRAW-HILL TECHNICAL EDUCATION SERIES

McGRAW-HILL TECHNICAL EDUCATION SERIES

Norman C. Harris, Series Editor

McGRAW-HILL BOOK COMPANY

DONALD J. KETCHUM
Chaffey College, Alta Loma, California

E. CHARLES ALVAREZ
Pierce College, Woodland Hills, California

PULSE and SWITCHING CIRCUITS

NEW YORK · TORONTO · LONDON

TO OUR WIVES, HELEN and PATRICIA

PULSE AND SWITCHING CIRCUITS

PREFACE

The field of electronic science is divided into many specialized categories: Microwaves, television, computers, instrumentation, communications, automatic controls, and industrial machines are but a few. At the base of these various subcategories lie two fundamental approaches to circuit theory—sinusoidal and nonsinusoidal. These two approaches become the cornerstones on which a general approach to circuits is built. They are the intuitive building blocks for most circuit analysis. This book deals with the fundamentals applying to nonsinusoidal pulse, timing, and switching circuits.

The material is presented here in a manner to provide a common denominator of circuits which may lead toward radar, television, test equipment, instrumentation, and/or computers. Complete system analysis of each of these areas is beyond the scope of this book. The final chapter does, however, provide system analysis of four examples from one of the categories mentioned previously: test equipment.

A knowledge of algebra and trigonometry is presupposed. Included in the Appendix are some mathematical derivations making use of the calculus to satisfy the interest of the mathematically minded student who is familiar with some higher mathematics. The student's understanding of devices (vacuum tubes and transistors) should be more than just a mere exposure to the subject. He should possess a sound algebraic and graphic basis of transistor and vacuum-tube theory.

The text has been organized in such a way that the student should gain a real familiarization with each circuit presented. Many of the circuits are presented as practical working models with part values and tube or semiconductor types given. Any such circuit may be built by the student in the laboratory with assurance that the theory presented may be demonstrated by actual measurement and oscilloscope observation. The circuits are analyzed mathematically in detail in the text, and the results will check within normal tolerances when measurements are made on the actual circuits. Answers to odd-numbered problems are given so the student may check his comprehension of the circuit concepts and his ability to make proper calculations.

The authors wish to describe this book as a classroom "tool." The circuits are analyzed in a manner similar to that of classroom presentation. In addition, ample text description is included so the student may use the material as a self-study source. All problems and questions have been "graded" in difficulty, moving from the simple to the complex. The first few problems of any exercise will be within the grasp of even the most casual reader, while the last problems will require considerable analysis.

The authors have intentionally "flavored" the material with examples from industry. In fact, many specific industrial circuits were selected because of their representative and pedagogic value. For this reason, we wish to express our appreciation to the Tektronix Company, Hewlett-Packard, General Radio, Owen Laboratories, and Electronic Instrument Company. Also, we wish to thank all the various transistor and vacuum-tube device manufacturers for their cooperation in providing characteristic curves and engineering data.

As is always the case, no individual ever prepares a technical manuscript without the valuable assistance and encouragement of his colleagues. Our special appreciation goes to Professor John S. Frost and Professor Thomas S. Finnie of Chaffey College, Mr. R. J. Olerich of Rocketdyne, and Professor W. L. Shaw of Pierce College.

Donald J. Ketchum

E. Charles Alvarez

CONTENTS

CHAPTER 1 WAVEFORMS

Electronic devices are of value to mankind in their ability to produce, modify, amplify, and detect changes in voltages and currents. In order to describe the way in which a voltage or current changes with respect to time, the instantaneous values are plotted on a rectangular-coordinate graph, where the vertical axis represents the voltage or current, and the horizontal axis represents time. Such a graph is called the *waveform* of the voltage or current.

1-1 WAVEFORM DEFINITIONS AND DISPLAY

The most common type of change or variation, not only in the field of electronics but also in other areas of science, is represented by a *sine* waveform. In this type of waveform the instantaneous amplitude is a trigonometric sine of time, or some other variable. This text will be concerned with *nonsinusoidal* variations: voltages or currents whose changes are not sine functions of time.

Several devices are available which display the waveforms of rapidly changing voltages. The most common is the oscilloscope, where a dot of light traces out the pattern on the screen. If the horizontal movement of the dot is proportional to time, and the vertical position is proportional to the amplitude of the voltage at that instant of time, the pattern will be the waveform of the voltage.

In a graphic recorder a strip of paper or film is pulled at a constant rate of speed past a pen or other marking device; and the position of the mark-

1

ing device, along a path at right angles to the direction of motion of the paper or film, depends on the instantaneous voltage applied. The pattern formed on the paper or film will be the waveform of the voltage.

Often, the varying voltage will go through a certain pattern of changes, will return to its original value, and then will go through an identical pattern of changes again, repeating these variations over and over. We call the "picture" of such a voltage a *periodic waveform,* and each combination of variations is called a *cycle.* The time it takes for each cycle to be produced is called the *period* of the waveform.

A periodic waveform is easily displayed on an oscilloscope because the dot can be made to trace the same pattern over and over, and the persistence of the screen material will produce a stationary line representing the waveform. Usually the oscilloscope is adjusted to display at least two cycles of the waveform. Because a finite amount of time is required to bring the dot back horizontally to start each new trace, some of the pattern is lost for this short period of time. A display of two or more cycles will allow at least one complete cycle to be observed.

If the time period of the waveform is too long, the dot will not move rapidly enough to appear as a continuous line. The graphic recorder can trace this type of pattern, or a special type of oscilloscope may be used which will cause the path of the dot to glow indefinitely or until it is erased electronically.

If the voltage being observed is *aperiodic* (the "a" is pronounced as in "ate"), that is, not periodic, then a graphic recorder may be used to obtain a continuous picture of the voltage's variation.

Sometimes a voltage variation occurs just once. An example of this occurs when a current, flowing through an inductance, is rapidly changed from one level to another. The changing magnetic field can induce additional voltage changes in the circuit. Such voltage variations are called *transients.* Even though the waveform might be displayed on an ordinary oscilloscope, it would probably occur so rapidly that little information could be obtained. Its single appearance could be photographed, or the special type of oscilloscope mentioned above could preserve it for observation. The graphic recorder might be used if the marking device could respond rapidly enough.

1-2 WAVEFORM ANALYSIS

There are two ways in which nonsinusoidal waveforms may be analyzed. First, it can be shown mathematically that any periodic waveform is a combination of possibly a d-c component and a number of pure sine waves of various amplitudes, phases, and frequencies. The time period of the periodic nonsinusoidal waveform will be a whole-number multiple of the time period of each of its component sine waves. This method of analysis will be discussed in detail in Sec. 1-10.

A second method of analysis is to consider the voltage variation as being made up of a series of consecutive segments, each of which can be classed as one of a small group of simple, basic waveforms. These basic waveforms are the *sine, step, ramp,* and *exponential* (Fig. 1-1). Each of these will now be discussed.

1-3   SINE WAVEFORM

The sine waveform is shown in Fig. 1-1a. Ordinary power-line voltage varies in this way, and pure audio tones have a sinusoidal variation. A sinusoidal signal is the only one which can be applied to circuits consisting of resistors, capacitors, and coils and not be changed in shape—it can be changed only in amplitude and phase. Most a-c circuit theory involves this type of signal. Calculations of reactance, impedance, and resonance have been based on the assumption of a pure sinusoidal signal.

Some nonsinusoidal waveforms have segments which are sinusoidal, for example, the outputs of half- and full-wave rectifiers.

1-4   STEP WAVEFORM

A step voltage (shown in Fig. 1-1b) is a sudden change from one constant voltage level to another. Theoretically, this change takes place in zero time, but in practice a short but finite time is required for the change. This transition time is usually very short compared with the constant-level time periods preceding and following the step. The voltage can either increase or decrease during the step, and the constant levels can be positive, negative, or zero. The *amplitude* of the step is the difference between the two constant levels.

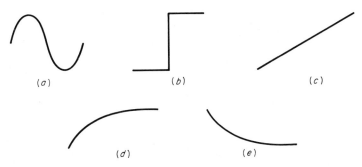

(a)   (b)   (c)

(d)   (e)

Fig. 1-1.   Basic waveforms. (a) Sine. (b) Step. (c) Ramp. (d) Increasing exponential. (e) Decreasing exponential.

1-5 RAMP WAVEFORM

A ramp voltage increases or decreases at a constant rate (Fig. 1-1c). It is represented by a straight line which is other than vertical or horizontal. It can start at zero or at any positive or negative voltage level.

1-6 EXPONENTIAL WAVEFORM

An exponential variation receives its name from the type of equation which may be written to represent this particular kind of variation, for example, $e = E\epsilon^{-t/\tau}$. As can be seen in Fig. 1-1d, the voltage changes rapidly at first, then less and less rapidly, until finally there is no apparent change and the voltage is constant. The graph is a curve with a constantly decreasing slope. The voltage can either increase (Fig. 1-1d) or decrease (Fig. 1-1e). It can start and end at any positive or negative value, or at zero. After a period of time, the voltage apparently stops changing. Theoretically, it never stops changing, but in practice the rate of change becomes so small as to be negligible.

1-7 PULSE WAVEFORM; RECTANGULAR WAVEFORM; SQUARE WAVE

The more common nonsinusoidal periodic waveforms are made up of combinations of the basic waveforms discussed above. The first of these is the *pulse.*

A pulse is defined as a rapid change from one voltage level to another and then a rapid return to the original level. The duration of time at the second level is usually quite short compared with the time at the first level. The pulse is made up of a positive step and a negative step, both of equal amplitudes and occurring at different times. If the positive step occurs first it is a positive pulse, and if the negative step is first it is a negative pulse.

An ideal pulse is shown in Fig. 1-2a. Note the perpendicular sides and horizontal top. The first step is called the *leading edge;* and the second step, the *trailing edge.* The pulse amplitude is equal to the amplitude of each of the steps; the *pulse duration* is the difference in the time at which each step occurs.

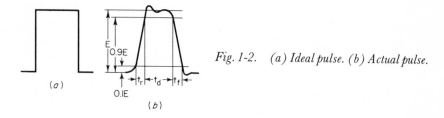

Fig. 1-2.   (a) Ideal pulse. (b) Actual pulse.

In Sec. 1-4 it was stated that a step cannot occur in zero time; likewise, the leading and trailing edges of a pulse cannot be perfectly perpendicular. During the pulse's duration the voltage level may not be constant, but amplitude variations may take place. The actual pulse may have a waveform similar to that shown in Fig. 1-2b. E is defined as the pulse amplitude and is usually the average of the instantaneous amplitudes taken during the pulse's duration. The *buildup time* or the *rise time* is the time it takes for the voltage to change from 10 per cent to 90 per cent of E. This time is shown as t_r in the figure. The *fall time* or *decay time* is designated t_f, and is the time required for the voltage to change from 90 per cent of E back to 10 per cent of E. The pulse duration or pulse width is the time interval during which the amplitude is above a certain percentage of E, usually 90 per cent. The duration time is designated t_d.

Pulses may occur periodically or aperiodically; that is, the time between consecutive pulses may or may not be a fixed value. If the pulses are periodic, their frequency is described by the term *pulse repetition frequency* (prf). If the pulses are aperiodic, the term *pulse repetition rate* (prr) is used. The prr gives the average number of pulses occurring in a certain time, while the prf is the exact number occurring during the time interval.

The term *duty cycle* relates the average ON time to OFF time of the pulses. It is equal to the product of the pulse duration and the pulse repetition frequency or rate.

If the pulse duration is increased, so it is no longer small compared with the time between pulses, we say that the voltage has a *rectangular* waveform.

If the pulse duration equals the time between pulses (the ON time equals the OFF time), we have a *square wave*. The square wave has a duty cycle of 50 per cent. Sometimes the rectangular waveform is called an *asymmetrical* (the "a" is pronounced as in "ate") square wave.

1-8 TRIANGULAR WAVEFORM; SAWTOOTH WAVEFORM

If a positive ramp is followed by a negative ramp with the same slope, and then another positive ramp, then negative, and so on, and if all ramps have the same time duration, we have a *triangular waveform,* as shown in Fig. 1-3a. Note that all amplitudes are equal.

A *sawtooth waveform* (Fig. 1-3b) is formed when the slopes and time durations of the positive ramps are different from those of the negative ramps, but the amplitudes are still equal. Usually the negative ramp has a much shorter time duration than the positive; in fact, for most applications of a sawtooth waveform, it is desirable for the negative ramp to occur in zero time; it will then be a negative step. We designate the longer time duration as the *rise time* t_r, and the shorter as the *fall time* t_f (see Fig. 1-3b).

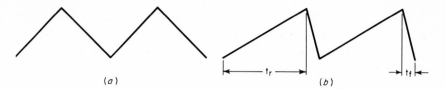

(a) (b)

Fig. 1-3. (a) Triangular waveform. (b) Sawtooth waveform.

1-9 MISCELLANEOUS WAVEFORMS

Many other types of waveforms may be found in certain kinds of equipment. Some of these are the following: a *trapezoidal waveform* (Fig. 1-4a), formed from a positive step, positive ramp, and a negative step; a *staircase waveform* (Fig. 1-4b), a series of positive steps and one negative step; a *differentiated square wave* (Fig. 1-4c), a positive step, a negative exponential, a negative step, and a positive exponential; and an *integrated square wave* (Fig. 1-4d), a series of alternate positive and negative exponentials.

1-10 HARMONIC ANALYSIS

Section 1-2 stated that any periodic nonsinusoidal waveform is a combination of a number of pure sine waves and possibly a d-c component. This method of analyzing waveforms will now be discussed.

Sine waves whose frequencies are whole-number multiples of one given frequency are called *harmonics* of the given frequency, and the sine wave which has the given frequency is called the *fundamental*. The ratio of the frequency of the harmonic to the frequency of the fundamental is the *number* of the harmonic. For example, if the fundamental frequency is 200 cps, the second harmonic frequency is 400 cps, and the fifth harmonic frequency is 1 kc.

Through a mathematical process called *Fourier analysis,* the component parts of a periodic waveform may be determined. This not only will show what harmonics make up the waveform but will give the amplitude and phase of each harmonic as well as the amplitude of the d-c component.

(a) (b) (c) (d)

Fig. 1-4. (a) Trapezoidal waveform. (b) Staircase waveform. (c) Differentiated square wave. (d) Integrated square wave.

This information can be presented in the form of an equation, consisting of a constant and a series of sine or cosine terms; or the information can be taken from the equation and shown in a graphic form called the amplitude spectrum.

The equations of several of the common waveforms are given below; the waveforms themselves and the amplitude spectra are shown in Fig. 1-5.

SQUARE WAVE

The waveform shown in Fig. 1-5a is represented as

$$e = \frac{4}{\pi}\left(\sin \omega t + \frac{1}{3}\sin 3\omega t + \frac{1}{5}\sin 5\omega t + \cdots + \frac{1}{n}\sin n\omega t\right)$$

where e = voltage amplitude at any time t
n = number of the harmonic
ω = angular velocity of the fundamental

Note that only odd harmonics are present. There is no d-c component present because this waveform is symmetrical about the horizontal axis; the average amplitude is zero.

SAWTOOTH WAVEFORM

The waveform shown in Fig. 1-5b is represented as

$$e = \frac{2}{\pi}\left[\sin \omega t - \frac{1}{2}\sin 2\omega t + \frac{1}{3}\sin 3\omega t + \cdots - \frac{(-1)^n}{n}\sin n\omega t\right]$$

We see that all harmonics are present; odd harmonics have positive amplitudes and even harmonics have negative amplitudes. As with the square wave above, this waveform is symmetrical about the horizontal axis, so there is no d-c component present.

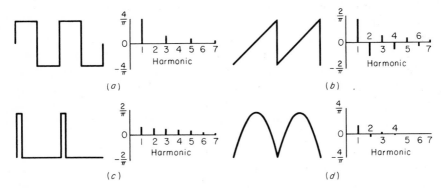

Fig. 1-5. Amplitude spectra. (a) Square wave. (b) Sawtooth waveform. (c) Pulse with 10 per cent duty cycle. (d) Output of full-wave rectifier.

The waveform shown in Fig. 1-5c is represented as

$$e = \frac{\theta}{\pi} + \frac{2}{\pi}\left(\sin\theta\cos\omega t + \frac{\sin 2\theta\cos 2\omega t}{2} + \frac{\sin 3\theta\cos 3\omega t}{3} + \cdots + \frac{\sin n\theta\cos n\omega t}{n}\right)$$

where $\theta = (\pi)$(duty cycle)

All harmonics are present. Although the terms of the equation are presented as cosine functions, they have the same waveform as sine functions. A d-c component is present because none of the waveform occurs below the horizontal axis. The waveform and amplitude spectrum in Fig. 1-5c are for a duty cycle of 10 per cent; therefore $\theta = 0.314$ rad $= 18°$.

OUTPUT OF FULL-WAVE RECTIFIER

The waveform shown in Fig. 1-5d is given as

$$e = \frac{2}{\pi} + \frac{4}{\pi}\left[\frac{1}{3}\cos\omega t - \frac{1}{15}\cos 2\omega t + \frac{1}{35}\cos 3\omega t + \cdots - \frac{(-1)^n}{4n^2-1}\cos n\omega t\right]$$

Note how rapidly the higher harmonics drop in amplitude.

Note also that all four of these waveforms are theoretically made up of an infinite number of harmonics; the n in each equation extends to infinity. In practical situations the amplitudes of the higher-numbered harmonics are so small that they can be neglected. Usually, no more than 15 to 20 sine waves are needed to form a reliable waveform.

The number of sine-wave components needed to form a pulse waveform depends on the duty cycle. In fact, a good estimate of the number needed is equal to the reciprocal of the duty cycle. A duty cycle of 10 per cent means that approximately ten sine-wave components are needed. A pulse with a duration time of 2 μsec and a prf of 1 kc has a duty cycle of 0.2 per cent. The number of harmonics needed is 500. These calculations apply for small duty cycles only. For example, a square wave has a duty cycle of 50 per cent, but it takes more than just two harmonics to produce a good square wave.

Probably the most important idea to remember from this harmonic concept of nonsinusoidal waveforms is that to amplify or transmit one of these signals without changing its shape, the equipment must be able to pass all the necessary harmonics with little phase, frequency, or amplitude distortion.

Ordinary audio amplifiers are generally designed to amplify frequencies from about 20 cycles to 20 kc. In the design of these circuits, little concern is given to phase distortion or harmonic distortion since up to 5 per cent of distortion is just barely discernible by the human ear. The frequency pass characteristic of the audio amplifier need not extend beyond 20 kc, since the human ear cannot detect frequencies above that. The conventional audio amplifier cannot be used as a pulse amplifier because of the narrow pass characteristic. If a nonsinusoidal wave requires that the amplifier pass at least the first 15 harmonics, the amplifier's response must extend up to 75 kc for a 5-kc square wave. Similar problems are encountered in phase and harmonic distortion as well.

DISTORTION

Three types of distortion are of importance in pulse amplifiers.

Harmonic Distortion. Amplitude or harmonic distortion causes a sine-wave input to be changed in shape so that the output is no longer a perfect sine wave. The output contains additional harmonics which distort the waveform. This type of distortion is caused by the input signal's overdriving the amplifier or by operating on a nonlinear portion of the dynamic characteristic curve.

Frequency Distortion. Frequency distortion causes different frequencies to be amplified with different gains, so that a nonsinusoidal periodic waveform is distorted. This type of distortion is not evident when a single-frequency sine wave is amplified.

Phase Distortion. Phase distortion is evident only during amplification of sine waves of more than one frequency or of nonsinusoidal periodic waveforms. There is almost always some phase shift between the input and output signals of an amplifier. If this causes the phase relationships of the different harmonic components in the output signal to be different from those of the input signal, phase distortion results. Frequency and phase distortion are caused by reactive components in the coupling circuits and by the interelectrode and junction capacitances of tubes and transistors.

Figure 1-6*a* shows a waveform made up of two sine waves: a fundamental and a third harmonic whose amplitude is one-third that of the fundamental. Figure 1-6*b* illustrates amplitude distortion; the positive portion of the waveform is amplified more than the negative portion. In Fig. 1-6*c* the waveform is made up of the same two components with the same phase as in Fig. 1-6*a*, but here the third harmonic has an amplitude less than one-third that of the fundamental. This is the result of frequency distortion. In Fig. 1-6d the third harmonic is shifted in phase with respect to the fundamental, resulting in phase distortion. There has been no change in the relative amplitudes of the two components.

COUPLING CIRCUITS

When more than one stage of amplification is required, the signal must be coupled from the output of one stage to the input of the next. These two points in a circuit are usually at different d-c voltage levels; therefore, the coupling circuit must not pass direct current.

A coupling capacitor, which is a reactive component in series with the signal, can introduce both frequency and phase distortion. It will normally pass high frequencies better than low, so it is usually a factor in the low-frequency response of an amplifier. Its physical size can have a bearing on the high-frequency response of an amplifier; it can form a shunting capacitance between itself and the chassis of the amplifier and at high frequencies can lower the effective load of the previous stage. The voltage gain of an amplifier drops off with decreased load impedance; so the larger the shunting capacitance in the circuit, the faster the voltage gain drops at high frequencies.

Transformer coupling has the advantage that the output impedance of the first stage can be matched to the input impedance of the second. This is of particular importance in power amplifiers. If desired, the transformer can be used to step up the signal voltage or current, and thus can increase the overall gain. Transformers have the disadvantage of higher cost and weight; and, unless very carefully designed and built, they have poor frequency response. At low frequencies, the reduced impedance of the primary reduces the load impedance of the previous stage, and thus its gain. At high frequencies the interwinding capacitances increase the total shunt capacitance in the circuit, and thus the load impedance on the previous stage is reduced.

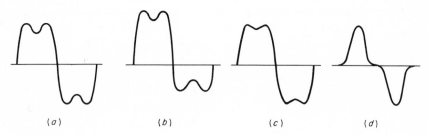

(a)   (b)   (c)   (d)

Fig. 1-6. Distortion. (a) Undistorted input. (b) Harmonic distortion. (c) Frequency distortion. (d) Phase distortion.

In order to amplify nonsinusoidal waveforms without distortion, the amplifier must have good frequency response and little phase distortion. These two requirements are usually interdependent; an amplifier designed for good frequency response will also have good phase characteristics.

The analysis of nonsinusoidal waveforms has been discussed from two viewpoints: the waveform made up of a series of consecutive segments and the waveform made up of a number of sine waves. The second concept was used in stating that an amplifier must have good frequency response in order to faithfully reproduce nonsinusoidal signals. Another approach will now be taken to discuss the consecutive segments of the waveform. The frequency response of an amplifier has a very definite relationship to the various segments of a particular waveform, which will be distorted or faithfully reproduced.

For example, in order to reproduce a ramp signal, there is a direct relationship between the slope of the ramp and the frequency response needed in the amplifier. To reproduce a ramp with a large slope (rapid voltage change) requires good high-frequency response. For a ramp with a small slope (slow voltage change), good low-frequency response is necessary. To extend this idea, a step waveform can be thought of as a combination of the two limits of a ramp signal: infinite slope and zero slope. An ideal step waveform would require an amplifier with flat frequency response from direct current to infinity. The low-frequency end could extend to direct current (discussed in Sec. 1-14); however, there is always a limit to the high-frequency response.

A square-wave signal, being made up of a series of step waveforms, is often used to check the frequency response of amplifiers. Rounding of the leading and trailing edges (as shown in Fig. 1-7*a*) is caused by poor high-frequency response; and a tilt of the horizontal portion (Fig. 1-7*b*) shows a lack of low-frequency response. An amplifier with a flat frequency response from 10 cps to 1 Mc will pass a 50-cps square wave with sharp leading and trailing edges, because even the 19,999th harmonic will pass through the amplifier.

The lowest frequency harmonic of the square wave is 50 cps, and the amplifier will pass signals down to 10 cps; hence, it would be expected that the low-frequency response is adequate. Here is where the phase characteristics of the amplifier become important; and if the low-frequency response is not good enough, the corresponding phase distortion will give the horizontal part of the square-wave tilt, as shown in Fig. 1-7*b*. The per cent of tilt is defined by

$$\text{Per cent of tilt} = \frac{E_2 - E_1}{E} \ (100\%) \tag{1-1}$$

where E is the halfway point between E_2 and E_1. $E_2 - E = E - E_1$, so $E = (\frac{1}{2})(E_2 + E_1)$; and substituting into Eq. (1-1) gives

$$\text{Per cent of tilt} = \frac{2(E_2 - E_1)}{E_2 + E_1} \quad (100\%) \tag{1-2}$$

It can be shown mathematically (see Jacob Millman and Herbert Taub, "Pulse and Digital Circuits," p. 33, McGraw-Hill Book Company) that the per cent of tilt can be calculated from

$$\text{Per cent of tilt} = \frac{\pi f_L}{f} \quad (100\%) \qquad \text{1-3}$$

where f_L = low-frequency 3-db point
f = frequency of square wave

In the example above, the per cent of tilt would be $\pi(10/50)$ $(100\%) = 20\pi\% = 62.8\%$.

If the low-frequency 3-db point of the amplifier is reduced to one one-hundredth of the square-wave frequency, the output waveform will have a tilt of 3.14 per cent.

Even with the best design, an RC-coupled circuit will not have sufficient bandwidth to amplify many of the nonsinusoidal waveforms we are considering. The circuit can be improved so that the voltage gain of an RC-coupled amplifier may be caused to vary with frequency in such a way as to counteract other variations. This modification is called *frequency compensation.*

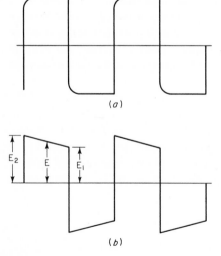

(a)

(b)

Fig. 1-7. Square waves applied to an amplifier. (a) Poor high-frequency response. (b) Poor low-frequency response.

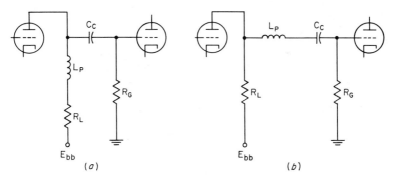

Fig. 1-8.   High-frequency compensation circuits.

The main reason for drop in voltage gain at high frequencies is the shunting effect of stray and tube or transistor capacitances. If an inductor is connected in series with the load resistor, the resulting load is a parallel *LC* circuit. As the frequency is increased, instead of the shunt capacitance reducing the effective load impedance, the *LC* combination maintains a high impedance up to the resonant frequency of the combination. It is important to consider the Q of the circuit since a high-Q circuit can "ring" (see Sec. 3-7) when a step voltage is applied to it. The impedance at resonance is equal to Q times the capacitive reactance, and we do not wish the load impedance to rise too much with frequency—just enough to keep the amplifier's gain from dropping. Because this type of compensation increases or "peaks" the high-frequency response of the amplifier, the coil is called a peaking coil; in this case a *shunt* peaking coil, because it is in shunt with the signal.

Most of the shunt capacitance which reduces the high-frequency response is the input capacitance of the following stage (see Sec. A-9). Putting a coil in series with this input capacitance will cancel out a portion of the capacitive reactance and improve the response of the circuit. This type of coil is called a *series* peaking coil. Again, the Q must be kept low, and often the coil is shunted with a *damping resistor* to keep the circuit from ringing. Circuits with shunt and series peaking coils are shown in Fig. 1-8.

The decrease in voltage gain at low frequencies is due mainly to the increased reactance of the coupling capacitor. One solution would be to eliminate the coupling capacitor altogether, and have a direct connection between stages. This can be done, but leads to a more complicated power-supply arrangement (see Sec. 1-14).

Attenuation through the coupling circuit can be compensated for by causing the gain of the amplifier itself to increase as the frequency is decreased. The amplifier gain is dependent upon the load impedance; the higher the load impedance, the higher the gain. Figure 1-9*a* shows the

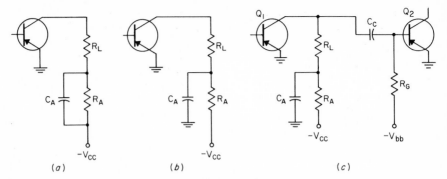

Fig. 1-9. *Low-frequency compensation circuits. (a) Low-frequency compensation. (b) Modified low-frequency compensation. (c) Phase compensation.*

parallel $R_A C_A$ circuit forming part of the load impedance with R_L. As the frequency decreases, the capacitive reactance increases, so the total load impedance increases, and so does the voltage gain. Because V_{cc} is at a-c ground potential, one end of the capacitor C_A is usually grounded, as shown in Fig. 1-9*b*.

The circuit component which contributes most to phase distortion is the coupling capacitor between amplifier stages. The compensation circuit for low-frequency distortion will minimize phase distortion if one additional design precaution is observed. Refer to Fig. 1-9*c*. In ordinary design the value of R_A is made small compared with that of R_L. Thus the effective a-c load on Q_1 is the parallel combination of R_L, C_A and C_C, R_G. Low-frequency phase distortion can be compensated (as well as frequency) if the product $R_L C_A$ is made to equal the product $C_C R_G$.

Compensation at both high and low frequencies can be accomplished with the load of the amplifier as shown in Fig. 1-10, where both a shunt peaking coil and a low-frequency RC circuit are connected as part of the load impedance.

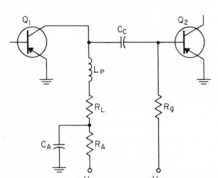

Fig. 1-10. *High- and low-frequency compensation.*

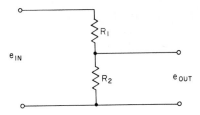

Fig. 1-11. *Simple resistance attenuator.*

1-13 COMPENSATING AN ATTENUATOR

Amplifier circuits often involve *attenuators,* which are circuits designed to decrease the signal level. A simple voltage divider, as shown in Fig. 1-11, will accomplish this, and the amount of attenuation is given by

$$a_R = \frac{R_2}{R_1 + R_2} \qquad (1\text{-}4)$$

where a_R = ratio of output voltage to input

In a purely resistive circuit such as this, the amount of attenuation is independent of frequency.

If the output of the simple attenuator feeds into a reactive load, such as the input capacitance of an amplifier circuit, it becomes necessary to compensate the attenuator, in order to again make its attenuation independent of frequency. If we call the amplifier's input capacitance C_2, the circuit is that shown in Fig. 1-12. Compensation is accomplished by shunting R_1 with a capacitor C_1, so that $R_1C_1 = R_2C_2$. This will make Eq. (1-4) hold for signals at all frequencies including direct current. The circuit is shown in Fig. 1-13a.

To prove that the attenuation is independent of frequency, we first modify the attenuator circuit slightly, as shown in Fig. 1-13b. If the output is taken from the junction of R_1 and R_2, the attenuation will be $a_R = R_2/$

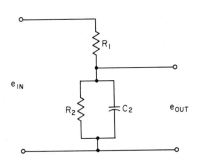

Fig. 1-12. *Attenuator with input capacitance.*

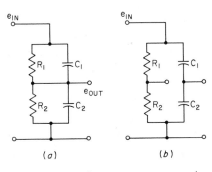

Fig. 1-13. *Attenuator compensation circuits.*

$(R_1 + R_2)$. If it is taken from the junction of C_1 and C_2, the attenuation will be

$$a_C = \frac{X_2}{X_1 + X_2} = \frac{1/\omega C_2}{1/\omega C_1 + 1/\omega C_2} = \left(\frac{1}{C_2}\right)\frac{C_1 C_2}{C_1 + C_2}$$

$$a_C = \frac{C_1}{C_1 + C_2} \tag{1-5}$$

We see that a_R and a_C are both independent of frequency. If the attenuations are equal, the two junctions can be connected, and the result is the original circuit of Fig. 1-13a:

$$a_R = a_C = \frac{R_2}{R_1 + R_2} = \frac{C_1}{C_1 + C_2}$$

$$R_2 C_1 + R_2 C_2 = R_1 C_1 + R_2 C_1$$

$$R_1 C_1 = R_2 C_2 \qquad\qquad \text{1-6}$$

Therefore, when the circuit values are such that Eq. (1-6) is true, the circuit is compensated and the attenuation, given by Eq. (1-4), is independent of frequency.

A practical example of a compensated attenuator is the use of oscilloscope probes. The vertical input amplifier possesses a given input capacitance. When an attenuator probe is connected to the scope, the probe must be matched to the scope. This process is accomplished by adjusting a small capacitor within the probe connected in parallel with the attenuator resistor. A square wave is generally used to make this adjustment.

1-14 D-C AMPLIFIERS

As stated earlier, the low-frequency response of an amplifier could be improved by eliminating the coupling capacitor and having direct coupling from one stage to the next; hence, the name *direct-coupled* amplifier. This would make the frequency response flat to 0 cps, or direct current. Remember that when a direct-current amplifier is required, we are talking in terms of amplifying a direct-current level which changes very slowly, or else is at one level for a period of time and then changes to another level; we therefore wish to amplify slowly changing signals, or step functions.

The one difficulty in trying to design a direct-coupled amplifier is that the grid of one stage will have to be at the same potential as the plate of the previous stage. The plate of an amplifier tube has to be positive with respect to its cathode, and the grid is usually negative with respect to the cathode. Therefore, the cathodes of two adjacent stages will have to be at different potentials. This can be done, as shown in Fig. 1-14. Notice that

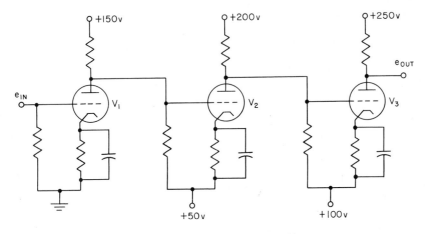

Fig. 1-14. *Direct-current coupling.*

five different positive voltage sources are required for three stages of amplification, whereas one positive source is usually sufficient when a-c coupling is used.

Consider briefly the function of the coupling capacitor in an *RC*-coupled circuit. The capacitor charges up to a fixed value of voltage, the difference in potential between the plate of one stage and the grid of the following. Then, as the plate voltage of the first tube varies in accordance with the signal, this variation is transferred to the grid of the next stage, because the capacitor's voltage cannot change rapidly. The difficulty arises when the signal-voltage changes are slow enough that the capacitor's voltage can change, and then a modified signal is transferred to the grid. If the capacitor is replaced with a battery, as shown in Fig. 1-15, the same effect is present as with a capacitor except that the coupling voltage will not change, even for slowly varying signals. As the plate voltage of V_1 increases above and decreases below 100 volts, the grid of V_2 will go positive and negative, correspondingly. The drawbacks of this circuit are as follows: first, an extra battery or power supply is required for each coupling circuit;

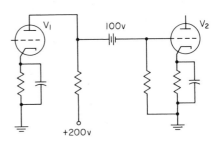

Fig. 1-15. *Example of d-c coupling compared with RC coupling.*

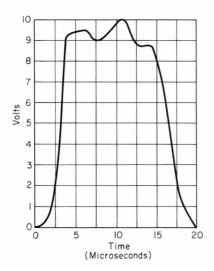

Fig. 1-16.   *Typical pulse with varying amplitude.*

second, any changes in the d-c characteristics of V_1 will transfer as a change in bias of V_2; and third, the shunt capacitance between the coupling battery or power supply will reduce the high-frequency response of the amplifier.

A modification of battery coupling is the use of a gas diode, such as a neon bulb, in place of the battery. When the gas ionizes, the voltage drop across the diode is fairly constant; thus variations in the potential on one side will be transferred to the other side.

PROBLEMS

1-1   Find the following characteristics of the pulse shown in Fig. 1-16: (*a*) rise time; (*b*) fall time; (*c*) pulse duration time; (*d*) pulse amplitude.

1-2   A given pulse signal has a duty cycle of 2 per cent and a prf of 1,350 kc. (*a*) What is the pulse duration? (*b*) How many harmonic components are needed for a good reproduction of the wave?

1-3   A pulse type of signal has a prf of 25 kc and a duty cycle of 2 per cent. Find: (*a*) the pulse duration; (*b*) the number of harmonic components needed for a good waveform; (*c*) the frequency response of the amplifier needed to faithfully reproduce this signal.

1-4   The secondary winding of a power transformer has 300 volts, 60 cps, each side of the center tap. If it is connected to a full-wave rectifier, with no filtering, find the amplitude of the 600-cps sine-wave component of the output waveform.

1-5   Show that for a good pulse waveform the highest frequency component needed should be equal to or greater than the reciprocal of the pulse duration.

1-6   In the circuit of Fig. 1-9c, assume that $C_c = 4$ μf, $R_g = 1$ kilohm, $R_L = 5$ kilohms. What value of C_A is required for low-frequency phase compensation?

1-7   If the input capacitance to an oscilloscope is 12 pf and the input resistance is 10 megohms, what capacitance must shunt the 1-megohm resistor in the attenuator probe?

1-8   A 5-kc square wave whose amplitude is 10 volts has what magnitude of fifth harmonic?

1-9   A given periodic pulse has a duration time of 10 msec, a rise time of 50 μsec, a fall time of 65 μsec, and a period of 78 msec. What is the duty cycle?

1-10   A given pulse has a duration time of 50 μsec and a duty cycle of 60 per cent. What is the pulse repetition period? (Assume zero rise and fall times.)

1-11   Find the bandwidth needed to amplify an 800-cps square wave. Assume that all harmonics up to the twenty-fifth are needed and that the per cent of tilt will be 2.5 per cent.

1-12   An amplifier has an input capacitance of 88 pf and a 470-kilohm input resistance. We wish to apply a 1.3-volt signal from a 15-volt source. Calculate (a) the series resistor needed to drop this voltage and (b) the capacitance needed in shunt with this resistor to compensate the attenuator.

1-13   An amplifier has a high-frequency pass limitation up to 150 kc. A pulse generator is driving the amplifier with a 1-kc signal whose pulse width is variable. What is the minimum pulse width which can be faithfully amplified?

1-14   Refer to Prob. 1-13. If the frequency of the applied pulse is doubled, how will the minimum pulse width be influenced?

CHAPTER 2 NETWORKS

This chapter is a review of those network theorems and circuit processes directly related to the methods of circuit analysis presented in this text. Included in the chapter are such topics as the ratio method of solving simple circuits, Thévenin's and Norton's theorems, and the application of circuit theorems.

2-1 RATIO METHOD

The ratio method of solution is essentially an Ohm's law process of solving parallel and series circuits. The method, however, affords a considerable saving of time compared with the conventional method. There are two theorems, one for voltage calculations in series circuits and one for current calculations in parallel circuits.

VOLTAGE

Consider the circuit of Fig. 2-1a. Assume that the known values are those given in the figure. Assume further that the potential across resistor R_3 is to be determined:

$$e_3 = i_t R_3$$

$$i_t = \frac{e}{R_1 + R_2 + R_3}$$

$$e_3 = \frac{R_3 \, e}{R_1 + R_2 + R_3} \tag{2-1}$$

The voltage across any resistor in a series loop containing any number of series resistances may be determined by the ratio method from the following general equation:

$$e_n = \frac{R_n e}{\Sigma R}$$
2-2

where n refers to the particular resistor whose voltage is desired. ΣR is the sum of all the resistances in the loop, and e is the applied voltage.

CURRENT

A similar manipulation of Ohm's law provides a useful statement for the currents in a parallel circuit. The current through R_2 of Fig. 2-1b, according to Ohm's law, is

$$i_2 = \frac{e}{R_2}$$

$$e = i_t R_t = \frac{i_t R_1 R_2}{R_1 + R_2}$$

$$i_2 = \frac{i_t R_1}{R_1 + R_2}$$
2-3

A generalized statement for the current ratio method may be developed for any number of parallel branches. However, when the ratio method is applied to more than two parallel branches, the process becomes as time-consuming as the conventional Ohm's law method. Whenever circuits involving more than two branches are encountered, the Ohm's law method should be employed.

EXAMPLE What is the voltage across the 3-kilohm resistor of Fig. 2-2?

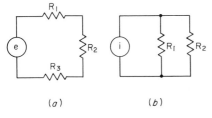

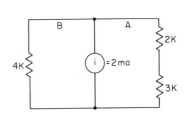

Fig. 2-1. Ratio method of solving simple circuits.

Fig. 2-2. Current ratio method of solving simple circuits.

Application of the ratio method gives the current through branch A as

$$i_A = \frac{(4)(2)}{4 + (2 + 3)}$$

$$= 0.899 \text{ ma}$$

$$e_3 = (0.899)(3) = 2.667 \text{ volts}$$

2-2 VOLTAGE AND CURRENT SOURCES

The methods of circuit analysis require that a convention be established regarding the identification of voltage and current sources. The convention in regard to voltage sources, which is standard throughout the field, states that all ideal voltage sources have a zero internal impedance. The concept is easy to understand when a battery is involved, since a fully charged storage battery actually possesses a negligible amount of internal resistance. A lead acid cell has an internal resistance of the order of a few tenths of an ohm. On the other hand, a vacuum tube has a finite value of internal resistance identified as r_p. A rectifier and filter circuit designed to supply d-c power should ideally have a zero internal impedance; however, in practical circuits this impedance is of the order of 50 to 100 ohms, depending upon the circuit. In circuit-analysis work involving vacuum tubes, transistors, and a-c or d-c power sources, the device is shown as a voltage source with zero internal impedance, and the actual internal impedance is shown in series with the voltage source. Figure 2-3a shows a vacuum-tube voltage source.

The ideal current generator is one that supplies a current from a source which possesses an infinitely high impedance. The transistor does not represent an ideal current source since it has a finite value of resistance. Practical current sources are shown in equivalent circuits as ideal sources with the finite value of internal resistance in parallel. (This internal resistance is often shown as a conductance.) Figure 2-3b illustrates an example.

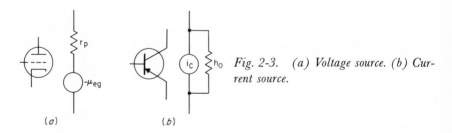

Fig. 2-3. (a) Voltage source. (b) Current source.

(a) (b)

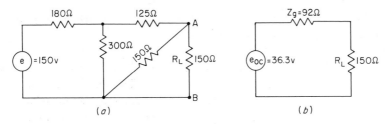

Fig. 2-4.   Illustration of Thévenin's theorem.

2-3   THÉVENIN'S THEOREM

Thévenin's theorem states that the current through a load connected to a complex network is the same as that existing when the load is connected to a simple network, where the simple network is developed from the complex network after the load is removed. The simple network consists of a constant-voltage source whose value is the open-circuit voltage of the complex network. The simple network's impedance is the impedance looking into the open circuit after all sources have been replaced by their respective internal impedances.

The theorem is best illustrated by a numerical example. Consider the elementary circuit shown in Fig. 2-4a. The circuit can easily be analyzed by using simple series-parallel methods; however, the circuit serves as a good introduction to the theorem.

The network to the left of points A and B is considered the complex network. When the load resistance is removed, the voltage between points A and B becomes 36.3 volts. This open-circuit potential (e_{oc}) is the Thévenin-generator voltage as shown in Fig. 2-4b.

The Thévenin-generator impedance Z_g is determined from the open-circuit impedance looking into points A and B when the voltage source is replaced by a zero impedance (or short circuit). Z_g is 92 ohms.

If the 150-ohm load is connected to the Thévenin network, the voltage across the load is 22.5 volts.

The procedure of converting a complex network to a Thévenin equivalent circuit is summarized as follows:

1. Remove the load (if present) from the complex network.
2. Calculate or measure the voltage at the open-circuit terminals.
3. The potential of step 2 is the Thévenin-generator voltage e_{oc}.
4. Replace all voltage and current sources with their internal impedances.
5. Calculate or measure the total impedance looking into the open-circuit terminals.
6. The impedance of step 5 is the Thévenin-generator impedance Z_g.

7. Reconnect the load to the Thévenin equivalent circuit and perform any required calculations or measurements.

EXAMPLE   Determine the voltage across the 40-ohm resistor in the network of Fig. 2-5a. Use the method of Thévenin's theorem. When the 40-ohm resistor is removed, the resultant circuit is shown in Fig. 2-5b. The polarities across each of the remaining resistors result from the effective 30 volts in the series loop. The open-circuit potential will be the algebraic sum of the voltages across the 60-ohm resistor, the generator e_1, and the 20-ohm resistor. According to the ratio method, the voltage across the 60-ohm resistor is

$$e_{60} = \frac{(60)(30)}{120} = 15 \text{ volts}$$

The voltage across the 20-ohm resistor is

$$e_{20} = \frac{(20)(30)}{120} = 5 \text{ volts}$$

The open-circuit potential is

$$0 = 15 - 40 + 5 + e_{oc}$$
$$e_{oc} = 20 \text{ volts or } -20 \text{ with respect to ground}$$

When e_1 and e_2 are replaced by their zero internal impedances, the resultant circuit is a parallel combination, as shown in Fig. 2-5c. The Thévenin-generator impedance is

$$Z_g = \frac{(40)(80)}{120} = 26.67 \text{ ohms}$$

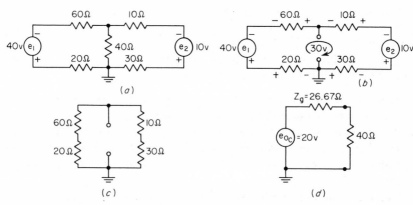

Fig. 2-5. Example of Thévenin's theorem.

When the 40-ohm resistor is connected across the equivalent Thévenin generator of Fig. 2-5d, the voltage across it, determined by the ratio method, is

$$e_{40} = \frac{(40)(20)}{66.67} = 12 \text{ volts}$$

The techniques of Thévenin's theorem are rarely used for simple solutions as illustrated in the previous examples. The method becomes particularly useful when complex circuits involving vacuum tubes and transistor elements are employed in switching circuits. The theorem does find some application to simple networks when it is used in conjunction with other theorems. For example, the *maximum power transfer theorem* states that maximum power is developed in a load when the load impedance is equal to the internal impedance of the source. It is not immediately apparent what value of load resistance should be substituted for the 40-ohm resistor in the network of Fig. 2-5a in order to develop a maximum transfer of power. However, when the equivalent circuit of Fig. 2-5d is examined, it is apparent that a load of 26.67 ohms will develop maximum power.

2-4 NORTON'S THEOREM

Norton's theorem is related to Thévenin's theorem in a number of ways. Both provide methods of reducing complex networks to simple networks, and both utilize the same method of determining the equivalent impedance Z_g.

Norton's theorem states that the current through a load connected to a complex network is the same as that existing when the load is connected to a simple network, where the simple network is developed from the complex network after the load is removed. The simple network consists of a constant-current source whose value is the short-circuit current of the complex network. The simple network's impedance is determined by the same methods used in Thévenin's theorem.

Examine the circuit of Fig. 2-6b. Norton's theorem will be used to calculate the current through the 10-ohm resistor. If the 10-ohm load resistor is removed and a short circuit is connected in its place, the current through the short circuit is 1.333 amp (i_{sc}). The equivalent Norton-generator current source is 1.333 amp as shown in Fig. 2-6b. If the short circuit is removed and the voltage source replaced with a short circuit, the impedance looking into the open-circuit terminals is 30 ohms. The Norton generator's impedance is 30 ohms. If the 10-ohm load is reconnected to the equivalent Norton generator and the current through it is solved by the ratio method, the result is 1 amp.

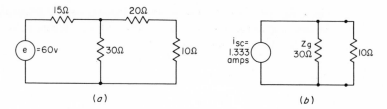

Fig. 2-6. Example of Norton's theorem.

Once the two network theorems are learned, the time of solution is greatly decreased as a result of a developed insight into working with networks. The decision as to when a given network should be reduced to a Norton generator or to a Thévenin generator will most often be indicated by the circuit components involved. Often with transistor circuit analysis, the calculations involve both constant-current and constant-voltage sources. When this is the case, it is sometimes faster to first solve for the Thévenin generator and then convert the Thévenin generator to its equivalent Norton generator.

EXAMPLE Assume that the load resistor (R_L) of Fig. 2-7a is to vary in value. An equivalent Norton network will simplify the number of calculations. In this problem it is faster to reduce the circuit to an equivalent Thévenin network and then convert the Thévenin network to a Norton network.

Remove the unknown load resistance and calculate the open-

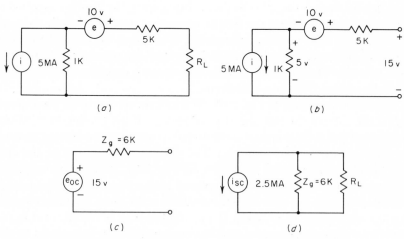

Fig. 2-7. Conversion from Thévenin to Norton circuit.

circuit potential. This voltage will be the sum of the constant-voltage generator potential and the potential across the 1-kilohm resistor. The current flowing through the resistor is 5 ma, the output of the constant-current generator. Therefore, the open-circuit potential is 15 volts (Fig. 2-7b).

The equivalent impedance is found by replacing the current source with an open circuit and replacing the voltage source with a short circuit. The result is the series combination of the 5- and 1-kilohm resistors: 6 kilohms. The equivalent network is shown in Fig. 2-7c.

To convert the Thévenin network to a Norton network, place a short circuit across the terminals of the Thévenin network. By Ohm's law the current through the short circuit is 2.5 ma. This becomes the Norton constant-current generator. The Thévenin and Norton equivalent impedances are the same. The Norton circuit is as shown in Fig. 2-7d. The various values of load resistance may now be connected to the circuit and all necessary calculations completed.

A useful relationship between the two theorems is

$$Z_g = \frac{e_{oc}}{i_{sc}}$$

where e_{oc} = open-circuit voltage
$\quad i_{sc}$ = short-circuit current

PROBLEMS

2-1 Refer to the circuit of Fig. 2-8. Determine: (a) the value of the load resistor; (b) the voltage across R_L; (c) the equivalent Thévenin voltage and impedance between points x and y with R_L removed; (d)

Fig. 2-8. Figure for Probs. 2-1 through 2-6.

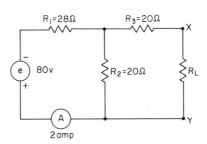

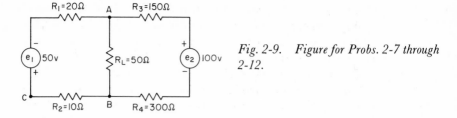

Fig. 2-9.   Figure for Probs. 2-7 through 2-12.

the voltage across R_L if connected across the Thévenin equivalent circuit.

2-2   In the circuit of Fig. 2-8, if the value of R_3 is increased to 60 ohms, what is the Thévenin voltage between x and y? Compare this Thévenin generator with the one in Prob. 2-1.

2-3   If the value of e in the circuit of Fig. 2-8 is doubled, what is (a) the Thévenin voltage; (b) the Thévenin impedance?

2-4   If R_1 of Fig. 2-8 increases, does the Thévenin equivalent voltage increase, decrease, or remain the same?

2-5   (a) If the load resistor of Fig. 2-8 is removed, terminals x and y represent what equivalent Norton generator? (b) Solve for voltage across R_L if connected across the Norton equivalent circuit.

2-6   If the value of R_3 in Prob. 2-5 is increased from 20 to 60 ohms, what new equivalent Norton circuit will result?

2-7   In the bridge circuit of Fig. 2-9, what is the voltage and impedance of the equivalent Thévenin circuit looking into the circuit at points A and B with R_L removed?

2-8   Refer to the bridge circuit of Fig. 2-9. (a) What current flows through the 50-ohm load? (b) The electron flow through the 50-ohm load is toward which terminal, A or B?

2-9   What is the Norton equivalent of the Thévenin generator for the circuit of Fig. 2-9, looking into terminals A and B, if R_L is removed?

2-10   Refer to Fig. 2-9. If the polarity of e_2 is reversed, what is the resultant Thévenin circuit seen by the 50-ohm load?

2-11   What value of resistance should be connected in place of the 50-ohm resistor of Fig. 2-9 in order to develop maximum power at the resistor?

2-12   Refer to the circuit of Fig. 2-9. What Thévenin equivalent circuit is seen at points B and C with R_2 removed?

2-5   ADDITIONAL NETWORK THEOREMS

The sections on Thévenin's and Norton's theorems illustrated how complex networks can be reduced to simple networks. It should not be assumed that *all* networks are reducible by all methods and theorems. As an example, consider the circuit of Fig. 2-10. The circuit is driven by two constant-current generators and one constant-voltage source. If the 2-kilohm resistor is considered the load, what voltage is developed across it?

If a solution using Thévenin's theorem is attempted, it becomes obvious that the impedance looking into the terminals from where the 2-kilohm resistor is removed is infinite. With an infinite internal impedance there would presumably be no voltage across the load resistor. In reality, the voltage across the 2-kilohm load is 12 volts. The solution must be approached from the point of view of one of the other network theorems.

SUPERPOSITION THEOREM

The principle of superposition is applied in many areas of electronics. It is useful in network considerations where the complex network consists of multiple generators. The theorem states: The current through a given load in a complex network is the same as the vector sum of the currents which would result if each generator were connected into the network alone with all other generators replaced by their respective internal impedances. A numerical example best illustrates the theorem.

EXAMPLE   Consider the circuit of Fig. 2-10. Assume that i_1 is left in the circuit, e_1 is replaced by a short circuit, and i_2 is replaced by an open circuit. The result is a series circuit; hence the current i_1 flowing down through R_L is 2 ma. If i_2 is connected into the circuit, e_1 is replaced by a short circuit, and i_1 is replaced by an open circuit, again the result is a series circuit and i_2 is 4 ma. Since the current from i_2 is flowing in the same direction as the current from i_1 (when it was in the circuit), these two currents carry the same sign. If e_1 is replaced into the circuit and the two current sources are replaced by open circuits, the result is an incomplete circuit; hence no current flows through the load. The actual current flowing through R_L is the sum of three superposition currents:

$$i_L = i_1 + i_2 = 2\text{ ma} + 4\text{ ma} = 6\text{ ma}$$

The voltage across the load, according to Ohm's law, is 12 volts.

Fig. 2-10. Multiple-generator network.

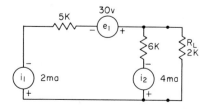

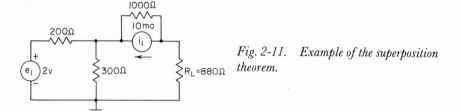

Fig. 2-11. *Example of the superposition theorem.*

The circuit of Fig. 2-11 is taken from transistor circuitry. The network can be solved by Thévenin's theorem, Norton's theorem, or the superposition theorem. The following example uses the superposition method; however, the student should verify the results by using the other two.

EXAMPLE   What current flows through the 300-ohm resistor of Fig. 2-11? Replace the current generator with an open circuit. The current through the 300-ohm resistor is 3.76 ma flowing away from the ground terminal. Return the current generator to the circuit and replace the voltage source with a short circuit. According to Ohm's law, the current through the 300-ohm resistor is 2 ma flowing toward the ground terminal. The resultant current through the 300-ohm resistor is 1.76 ma flowing away from the ground terminal.

DELTA-WYE NETWORKS

Frequently the solution of networks by Thévenin's and Norton's methods involves bridge circuits. Such is the case where a vacuum tube is driving a

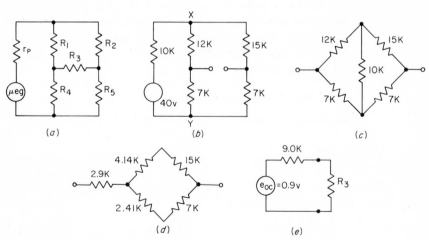

Fig. 2-12.   *Vacuum tube with a bridge-circuit load.*

bridge network. If the internal impedance of the vacuum tube were zero, the solution would be relatively simple. However, vacuum tubes possess a finite value of resistance. Consider the circuit of Fig. 2-12a. Assume the load resistance to be R_3. The process of reducing the remaining network to an equivalent Thévenin circuit results in another bridge circuit. In order to evaluate the impedance of a bridge circuit, a delta-to-wye transformation is of value.

The presentation of delta-to-wye and wye-to-delta transformations is given here as a review. The equations are presented without derivations.

Consider the delta circuit of Fig. 2-13a. The equivalent three-terminal wye circuit is shown in Fig. 2-13b. Transformation from a delta to its wye equivalent employs the following equations:

$$R_x = \frac{R_1 R_2}{\Sigma R}$$

$$R_y = \frac{R_2 R_3}{\Sigma R}$$

$$R_z = \frac{R_1 R_3}{\Sigma R}$$

where $\Sigma R = R_1 + R_2 + R_3$

Transformation from a wye to a delta employs the following equations:

$$R_1 = \frac{\Sigma R'}{R_y}$$

$$R_2 = \frac{\Sigma R'}{R_z}$$

$$R_3 = \frac{\Sigma R'}{R_x}$$

where $\Sigma R' = R_x R_y + R_x R_z + R_y R_z$

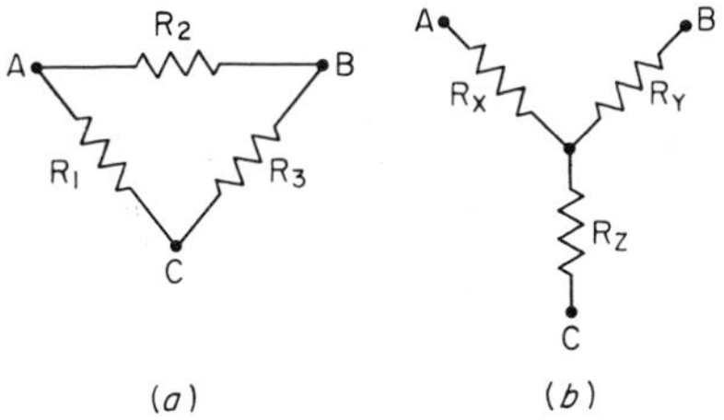

Fig. 2-13. Delta-wye transformation.

(a)

(b)

EXAMPLE   Refer to the circuit of Fig. 2-12a. Assume that the value of R_3 will take on a number of different values. Under these conditions it is best to reduce the circuit seen by R_3 to an equivalent Thévenin circuit. If $R_1 = 12$ kilohms, $R_2 = 15$ kilohms, $R_4 = 7$ kilohms, $R_5 = 7$ kilohms, $r_p = 10$ kilohms, $\mu = 20$, and e_g is 2 volts, what is the equivalent Thévenin circuit? When R_3 is removed, the resultant circuit is shown in Fig. 2-12b. According to Ohm's law, the voltage between points x and y is 20.2 volts. If the ratio method is applied to the two parallel branches, the voltage across the 12-kilohm resistor is 12.8 volts. The voltage across the 15-kilohm resistor is 13.7 volts. The open-circuit potential is 0.9 volt.

The open-circuit impedance results in a bridge circuit when the voltage source is replaced by a short circuit (Fig. 2-12c). In order to solve for the total impedance, one of the two delta combinations—either 12, 7, and 10 kilohms or 10, 15, and 7 kilohms—must be converted to a wye equivalent. If the first one is selected, the circuit is that shown in Fig. 2-12d. The circuit can now be solved for total resistance of 9 kilohms by series-parallel methods. The equivalent Thévenin generator with the R_3 load connected is shown in Fig. 2-12e.

PROBLEMS

2-13   If the values of R_1, R_2, and R_3 in Fig. 2-13 are each 25 ohms, what is the value of R_x?

2-14   If $R_1 = 30$, $R_2 = 40$, and $R_3 = 50$ ohms in Fig. 2-13, what is the value of R_z?

2-15   If $R_x = 10$, $R_y = 30$, and $R_z = 60$ ohms, what is the value of R_1?

2-16   In the circuit of Fig. 2-13, if R_x is 17 ohms, R_y is 14.3 ohms, and R_z is 3 ohms, what is the impedance between terminals A and B if terminals A and C are short-circuited?

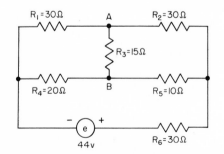

Fig. 2-14.   Figure for Probs. 2-20 through 2-24.

2-17   In the equivalent delta circuit of Prob. 2-16, if the terminals A and C are short-circuited, what is the impedance between terminals A and B?

2-18   Refer to Fig. 2-13. If $R_x = 20$, $R_y = 40$, and $R_z = 60$ ohms, and if 10 volts is applied between points B and C, and a 10-ohm resistor is connected between points A and C, what is the Thévenin equivalent looking into points A and B?

2-19   If R_1, R_2, R_3, R_x, R_y, and R_z in Fig. 2-13 are each 10 ohms, and the two A terminals are connected together and the two B terminals are connected together, what is the impedance between the two C terminals?

2-20   In the circuit of Fig. 2-14, what is the equivalent Thévenin circuit at points A and B with R_3 removed?

2-21   In the circuit of Fig. 2-14, what current flows through R_3?

2-22   What is the equivalent Norton generator seen by R_3 in the circuit of Fig. 2-14?

2-23   Refer to Fig. 2-14. If R_5 is increased in value by 10 ohms, does the current through R_3 increase, decrease, or remain unchanged?

2-24   If R_6 in Fig. 2-14 is decreased to zero, does the equivalent Thévenin voltage seen by R_3 increase, decrease, or remain unchanged?

CHAPTER 3 *RESISTANCE—*

CAPACITANCE–INDUCTANCE

Capacitors and inductors cannot change the shape of a sine waveform; they can change only the amplitude and phase. The amount of change in amplitude and phase depends on the frequency. This is the theory of operation of filter networks containing these components: changing the amplitudes of signals of different frequencies by differing amounts.

Chapter 1 described how nonsinusoidal periodic waveforms are made up of sine waves of different frequencies. Therefore, inductive and capacitive circuits would be expected to change the amplitudes and phases of these harmonic components, and thus the resulting waveform could be quite different from the original. This chapter discusses how the process occurs.

3-1 CAPACITOR CHARGE AND DISCHARGE

The charge on a capacitor is defined as the quantity of electrons transferred from one plate (or set of plates) to the other. Because the potential difference between the plates is proportional to this charge ($E = Q/C$), the charge of a capacitor is sometimes referred to in terms of the voltage across the plates. When the capacitor's voltage is increasing, the capacitor is charging; and if the voltage is decreasing, the capacitor is discharging. Remember that the charging or discharging of a capacitor is actually accomplished by electrons flowing onto or off the plates.

To increase or decrease the number of electrons on the plates of a capacitor, it takes a finite amount of time; electrons cannot flow at an in-

34

finite rate because that would result in an infinite current $(I = Q/T)$. Therefore, it takes time to charge or discharge a capacitor; its voltage cannot change instantaneously.

Assume in Fig. 3-1a that the capacitor has no charge when the switch is open. When the switch is closed, a current will flow. According to Kirchhoff's law the battery voltage E equals the sum of e_R and e_C. If the current is zero, $e_R = i_R = 0$, so $e_C = E$. But the capacitor had no charge immediately before the switch was closed, and its charge cannot change instantaneously, so the charge must be zero immediately after the switch is closed, and $e_C = 0$. Therefore, $e_R = E$ and $i = e_R/R = E/R$.

Because the dielectric of the capacitor is an insulator, electrons cannot flow across from one plate to the other; they flow onto one plate and off the other, leaving a charge on the capacitor. This charge results in the potential difference between the plates, e_C. The voltage across the capacitor opposes the battery voltage; therefore, the resistor's voltage e_R equals $E - e_C$. The current flow i will equal $e_R/R = (E - e_C)/R$. As current flows and builds up the charge on the capacitor, the difference $E - e_C$ will decrease, decreasing i. This continues until e_C is so close to E that $(E - e_C)/R$

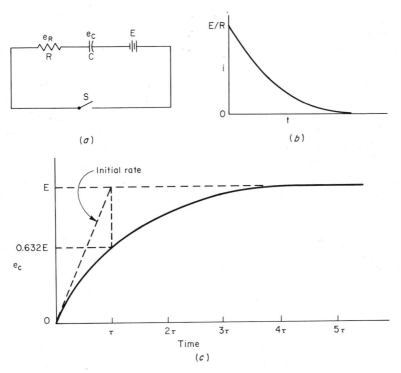

Fig. 3-1. Change in current with time in an RC circuit (during the charge conditions).

is practically zero. A graph showing how this current decreases with time is given in Fig. 3-1b; the increase of the capacitor's voltage with time is shown in Fig. 3-1c.

GENERAL EQUATION

If the capacitor already had some charge when the switch was closed, it would continue to charge or discharge until $e_C = E$. The general equations for the charge or discharge of a capacitor are derived in Sec. A-1 and are given below.

$$e_C = E - (E - E_{C0})\, \epsilon^{-t/RC} \qquad\qquad \textbf{3-1}$$

$$e_C = E - (E + E_{C0})\, \epsilon^{-t/RC} \qquad\qquad \textbf{3-2}$$

where E_{C0} is the initial voltage across the capacitor. If the initial capacitor voltage is in series opposing E, Eq. (3-1) is used (Fig. 3-2a and b). If the initial capacitor voltage is in series aiding E, Eq. (3-2) is used (Fig. 3-2c).

Note that the product of R and C is involved in these equations. This product is called the *time constant* of the circuit and is indicated as τ (tau). It allows us to compare various circuits in regard to how fast the capacitor will charge or discharge. It should be obvious that the amount of current flow will depend on the resistance in the circuit ($I = E/R$); the larger the resistance, the smaller the current. The amount of charge needed on a capacitor for it to reach a certain voltage depends on its capacitance ($Q = C/E$); the larger the capacitance, the more charge needed. The time it takes for the capacitor to charge varies directly with how much charge is needed, Q, and inversely with the rate at which this charge is put into the capacitor, I. The ratio of these two quantities is $t = Q/I = CE/(E/R) = RC$, the time constant.

More specifically, the product of R and C, both in their fundamental units of measure, equals the time required, in seconds, for the capacitor's

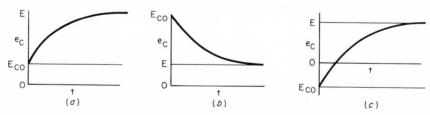

Fig. 3-2. (a) The charge of the capacitor from one voltage to a higher value of the same polarity. (b) The discharge of the capacitor from one voltage to a lower value of the same polarity. (c) The discharge of the capacitor to zero and then the charging to a voltage of opposite polarity.

voltage to change 63.2 per cent of the total change which would take place in infinite time; this applies whether the capacitor is charging or discharging.

During a time period equal to $2RC$, the capacitor's voltage will change 63.2 per cent during the first time-constant interval; then during the second period of time the voltage will change 63.2 per cent of the remaining amount. The total change will be $0.632 + 0.632 (1 - 0.632) = 86.4$ per cent. During a third time-constant interval the voltage will change 63.2 per cent of the remaining amount: $(0.632)(0.136) = 8.6$ per cent. During five time constants the total change is more than 99 per cent of the possible change; therefore, we can usually assume that after five time constants the change is completed. These various changes are shown in Fig. 3-1c.

If a capacitor continued to charge at its initial rate, shown by the dashed line in Fig. 3-1c, it would be completely charged after a time period equal to one time constant. Because its rate of charge is constantly decreasing, it actually reaches only 63.2 per cent of its full charge during this time.

The following examples illustrate the use of the equations and concepts which have been presented.

EXAMPLE 1 A 0.05-μf capacitor, with no initial charge, is connected to a 45-volt battery through a 22-kilohm resistor. Find the capacitor's voltage after 0.5 msec.

Because E_{C0} is zero in this problem, either Eq. (3-1) or Eq. (3-2) could be used. First, the time constant of the circuit will be calculated. Then its value, along with the other given values, will be substituted into Eq. (3-1).

$$\tau = RC = (2.2 \times 10^4)(5 \times 10^{-8}) = 11 \times 10^{-4} \text{ sec}$$
$$e_C = E - (E - E_{C0})\epsilon^{-t/\tau}$$
$$= 45 - 45\epsilon^{-(5\times10^{-4})/(11\times10^{-4})}$$
$$= 45 - 45\epsilon^{-0.455}$$

To evaluate the exponential equation, let $y = \epsilon^{-0.455}$. Take the log of both sides of the equation:

$$\log y = \log \epsilon^{-0.455} = -0.455 \log \epsilon$$
$$= (-0.455)(0.434) = -0.198 = 0.802 - 1$$

Take the antilog of both sides:

$$y = 0.634$$

Substitute this value for y back into the original equation:

$$e_C = 45 - (45)(0.634) = 45 - 28.5$$
$$= 16.5 \text{ volts}$$

EXAMPLE 2 A 4-μf capacitor is initially charged to 20 volts and then is connected in series opposing a 100-volt power supply, through a 56-kilohm resistor. How long will it take for the capacitor's voltage to increase to 60 volts?

Here the capacitor's initial voltage is in series opposing the supply voltage, so Eq. (3-1) is used.

$$\tau = RC = (5.6 \times 10^4)(4 \times 10^{-6}) = 0.224 \text{ sec}$$

Substituting into Eq. (3-1) gives

$$60 = 100 - (100 - 20)\epsilon^{-t/0.224}$$
$$80\,\epsilon^{-t/0.224} = 40$$
$$\epsilon^{-t/0.224} = 0.5$$

Taking the logs of both sides gives

$$-\frac{t}{0.244}\log\epsilon = \log 0.5$$

$$-\frac{t}{0.244}0.434 = 0.699 - 1 = -0.301$$

$$t = \frac{(0.301)(0.224)}{0.434}$$

$$= 0.1555 \text{ sec}$$

EXAMPLE 3 A 385-pf capacitor is initially charged to 127 mv and then connected through a 2.2-megohm resistor to a 1-volt source. If the capacitor and source are in series aiding, how long will it take for the capacitor to discharge to zero?

Equation (3-2) must be used because of the aiding connection of the capacitor and source.

$$\tau = (2.2 \times 10^6)(3.85 \times 10^{-10}) = 8.47 \times 10^{-4} \text{ sec}$$
$$0 = 1 - (1 + 0.127)\epsilon^{-t/(8.47 \times 10^{-4})}$$
$$1 = 1.127\epsilon^{-t/(8.47 \times 10^{-4})}$$
$$0.888 = \epsilon^{-t/(8.47 \times 10^{-4})}$$

$$\log 0.888 = \frac{t}{8.47 \times 10^{-4}}\log\epsilon$$

$$0.948 - 1 = \frac{t}{8.47 \times 10^{-4}}0.434$$

$$t = \frac{(8.47 \times 10^{-4})(0.052)}{0.434}$$

$$= 0.103 \text{ msec}$$

PROBLEMS

3-1 A series RC circuit consists of a 5-megohm resistor and a 0.05-μf capacitor. What voltage will be developed across the resistor 100 msec after 40 volts is applied to the circuit?

3-2 Refer to Prob. 3-1. What is the capacitor voltage 200 msec after the 40 volts is applied?

3-3 How much time is required to fully charge the capacitor of Prob. 3-1?

3-4 Assume that the capacitor of Prob. 3-1 is fully charged. If the voltage source is replaced by a short circuit, how long will it take for the capacitor to discharge to 20 volts?

3-5 If a 45-volt battery, a 0.22-μf capacitor, and a resistor are connected in series, what will be the resistor's value if the capacitor charges to 30 volts in 10 msec?

3-6 Refer to Prob. 3-5. What will be the resistor's value if an 80-volt battery is used instead of the 45-volt battery?

3-7 A 0.05-μf capacitor has an initial charge of 20 volts. It is in series with a 10-kilohm resistor. If a 30-volt source is connected in series in such a way that it will discharge the capacitor and then charge it up in the reverse polarity, how long will it take for the capacitor's voltage to equal zero?

3-8 If the value of R in Prob 3-7 is doubled, what will be the time required to discharge the capacitor to zero?

3-9 Refer to Prob. 3-7. How long will it take the capacitor to charge to 30 volts in the reverse polarity?

3-10 Refer to Prob. 3-7. The 10-kilohm resistor would have to be changed to what value to cause the capacitor's voltage to drop to zero in 0.5 msec?

INCREMENT EQUATION

An analysis will show that in all these problems a capacitor is trying to change in value by an amount equal to the initial voltage across the resistor; and, if $t = \infty$, or at least t is large compared with τ, the change in capacitor voltage will equal this initial resistor's voltage.

In Example 1, the resistor's initial voltage is 45 volts; and, if t were large, the capacitor would charge up to 45 volts, a change of 45 volts.

In Example 2, the resistor's initial voltage is 100 volts minus 20 volts, which is 80 volts. The capacitor is trying to charge up to 100 volts, which would be a change from 20 to 100 volts, an 80-volt change.

In Example 3, the battery voltage and the capacitor's initial voltage are in series aiding, so the resistor's initial voltage is 1.127 volts. The capacitor is trying to change from 0.127 to 1 volt of opposite polarity, or a total change of 1.127 volts.

These relationships can be expressed mathematically. The resistor's initial voltage E_{R0} is equal to the difference between the supply voltage and the capacitor's initial voltage:

$$E_{R0} = E - E_{C0} \tag{3-3}$$

The change in the capacitor's voltage is the difference between its final voltage and its initial voltage:

$$\Delta e_C = e_C - E_{C0} \tag{3-4}$$

Substituting e_C from Eq. (3-1) into Eq. (3-4) gives

$$\Delta e_C = E - (E - E_{C0})\epsilon^{-t/\tau} - E_{C0}$$
$$\Delta e_C = (E - E_{C0}) - (E - E_{C0})\epsilon^{-t/\tau} \tag{3-5}$$

Now, substituting Eq. (3-3) into Eq. (3-5) gives

$$\Delta e_C = E_{R0} - E_{R0}\epsilon^{-t/\tau}$$

$$\Delta e_C = E_{R0}(1 - \epsilon^{-t/\tau}) \tag{3-6}$$

E_{R0} can be easily calculated from looking at the circuit. It should be obvious from the problem whether the capacitor's voltage will increase or decrease. Therefore, the main concern is with the resistor's initial voltage and how much change there will be in the capacitor's voltage.

Solving exponential equations involves taking logs of both sides and then solving the resulting logarithmic equations. A simpler method of solving these problems is to change Eq. (3-6) into a logarithmic equation. First, Eq. (3-6) is rearranged:

$$E_{R0}\epsilon^{-t/\tau} = E_{R0} - \Delta e_C$$
$$\frac{E_{R0}}{E_{R0} - \Delta e_C} = \frac{1}{\epsilon^{-t/\tau}}$$
$$= \epsilon^{t/\tau}$$

Taking logs of both sides of this equation gives

$$\log \frac{E_{R0}}{E_{R0} - \Delta e_C} = \log \epsilon^{t/\tau} = \frac{t}{\tau} \log$$

$$\log \frac{E_{R0}}{E_{R0} - \Delta e_C} = \frac{0.434t}{\tau} \tag{3-7}$$

Some examples will illustrate the use of this simplified equation.

EXAMPLE 4   A 4-μf capacitor is charged to 20 volts and then connected in series with a 75-volt battery and a 15-kilohm resistor. The battery is opposing the capacitor's voltage. Find the capacitor's voltage after 25 msec.

Because the two voltages are opposing, the resistor's initial voltage is the difference, 55 volts.

$$\tau = RC = (1.5 \times 10^4)(4 \times 10^{-6}) = 60 \text{ msec}$$

Substituting these values into Eq. (3-7) gives

$$\log \frac{55}{55 - \Delta e_C} = \frac{(0.434)(25 \times 10^{-3})}{60 \times 10^{-3}} = 0.181$$

Taking antilogs of both sides of the equation gives

$$\frac{55}{55 - \Delta e_C} = 1.518$$

$$\Delta e_C = 18.8 \text{ volts}$$

Because the supply is trying to increase the capacitor's charge,

$$e_C = e_{C0} + \Delta e_C = 20 + 18.8 = 38.8 \text{ volts}$$

EXAMPLE 5   A 2,500-pf capacitor is charged to 0.75 volt and then is connected in series aiding with a 1.5-volt battery and a 680-kilohm resistor. How long will it take for the capacitor's voltage to (a) drop to 0.25 volt; (b) drop to zero; (c) equal 0.25 volt with a polarity opposite to its initial value?

Δe_C can easily be calculated for each of the three parts of this problem:

(a) $\Delta e_C = 0.75 - 0.25 = 0.5 \text{ volt}$
(b) $\Delta e_C = 0.75 - 0 = 0.75 \text{ volt}$
(c) $\Delta e_C = 0.75 - (-0.25) = 1.0 \text{ volt}$

$$\tau = (6.8 \times 10^5)(2.5 \times 10^{-9}) = 1.70 \text{ msec}$$

E_{R0} is the sum of the supply voltage and the capacitor's initial voltage:

$$E_{R0} = E + E_{C0} = 1.5 + 0.75 = 2.25 \text{ volts}$$

Substituting the values for part a into Eq. (3-7) gives

$$\log \frac{2.25}{2.25 - 0.5} = \frac{0.434t}{1.7 \text{ msec}}$$

$$\log 1.285 = \frac{0.434t}{1.7 \text{ msec}}$$

$$0.109 = \frac{0.434t}{1.7 \text{ msec}}$$

$$t = \frac{(0.109)(1.7 \text{ msec})}{0.434}$$

$$= 0.427 \text{ msec}$$

In like manner, the answers for parts b and c can be shown to be:

(b) $t = 0.690$ msec
(c) $t = 1.00$ msec

INITIAL-RATE-OF-CHANGE EQUATION

It can be noted from the graphs showing the charge or discharge of a capacitor (Fig. 3-1) that the curve has almost a linear slope during the initial portion. The initial slope of the curve can be calculated; then, for values of time much shorter than one time constant, a simplified equation can be derived. This is done in Sec. A-2, and the resulting equation is

$$\Delta e_C = \frac{E_{R0} t}{\tau} \qquad \qquad \boxed{3\text{-}8}$$

The accuracy of this equation will be checked by working a problem in two ways: first with Eq. (3-7) and then with Eq. (3-8).

EXAMPLE 6   A capacitor with no initial charge is connected to a 100-volt battery through a resistor. What will be its voltage after a time equal to 0.1τ?
Using Eq. (3-7) gives

$$\log \frac{100}{100 - \Delta e_C} = (0.434)(0.1) = 0.0434$$

$$\frac{100}{100 - \Delta e_C} = 1.105$$

$$\Delta e_C = 9.5 \qquad e_C = 9.5 \text{ volts}$$

Using Eq. (3-8) gives

$$\Delta e_C = (100)(0.1) = 10 \text{ volts}$$

For shorter periods of time, using Eq. (3-8) will be more accurate than using Eq. (3-7) because of the difficulty of taking the antilog of very small numbers.

For example, if the time period in Example 6 were 0.001τ, Eq. (3-8) would very easily give an answer for Δe_C of 0.1 volt. Using Eq. (3-7) would require finding the antilog of 0.000434, which could not be found on the slide rule but would require six-place log tables.

PROBLEMS

3-11   A 0.5-μf capacitor is charged to 50 volts and then is connected in series with a 27-kilohm resistor and a 30.8-volt battery, so the battery voltage and the capacitor's voltage are in series aiding. How long will it take for the capacitor to discharge to 0 volts?

3-12   A 350-pf capacitor is charged to 712 mv and then is connected in series with a 470-kilohm resistor and a 0.5-volt battery, so the battery voltage and the capacitor's voltage are in series opposing. Find the capacitor's voltage after 125 μsec.

3-13   If a 0.005-μf capacitor has no charge and a 30-volt potential is applied through a 100-kilohm resistor, what is the voltage across the capacitor 5 μsec after the voltage source is connected?

3-14   Assume that a capacitor has a charge of 20 volts across it and is connected in series aiding to a 40-volt supply through a 1-megohm resistor. Find the value of C if the capacitor's voltage drops to zero in 10 msec.

3-15   Refer to Prob. 3-14. What value of C would cause the capacitor's voltage to drop to zero in 5 msec?

3-16   A series circuit consists of a 0.1-μf capacitor, a 0.01-μf capacitor, and a 200-kilohm resistor. If 50 volts is applied to the circuit, what voltage will appear across the 0.01-μf capacitor after 3 msec?

3-17   Refer to Prob. 3-16. What is the maximum voltage which will build up on the 0.01-μf capacitor?

3-18   A 130-pf capacitor has an initial charge of 270 mv and is connected in series aiding to a 1.5-volt source, through a 680-kilohm resistor. How long will it take for the capacitor's voltage to drop to 250 mv?

3-19   Assume in Fig. 3-3 that S_1 has been open and S_2 has been closed for a long period of time. Now, S_1 is closed and S_2 is opened. How long will it take for the voltage at e_o to equal -15 volts? (*Hint:* make a Thévenin equivalent circuit out of R_1, R_2, and the battery.)

3-20   Work Prob. 3-19, assuming that the bottom end of R_3 is connected to the positive side of the battery instead of the negative side.

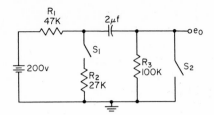

Fig. 3-3. Figure for Probs. 3-19 and 3-20.

3-2 RC CIRCUIT RESPONSE TO STEP INPUT

Figure 3-4a shows an *RC* series circuit connected to a signal source, consisting of a switch and a battery. If it is assumed that no time is required to switch between the two positions, the signal source generates a step waveform with the two voltage levels being zero and *E*. The response of the circuit to this step voltage will now be determined.

If the switch is initially at position *A* and then is switched to position *B* and is left for at least five time constants, we find the voltage across the capacitor rises exponentially from zero to *E*. The voltage across the resistor is equal to $E - e_C$, at any instant of time; it rises instantaneously to *E* at the time the switch is changed to *B*, and then it drops exponentially to zero. The three voltages involved are shown in Fig. 3-4b. Note that at any instant of time $e_{in} = e_R + e_C$.

After the switch has been in position *B* for at least five time constants, $e_C = E$. If the switch is returned to position *A,* the input voltage immediately goes to zero. The capacitor cannot discharge immediately but drops exponentially to zero. It discharges through the resistor, and the discharge current is opposite in direction to the charging current, so the resistor's voltage has reversed polarity. The capacitor and resistor are actually in parallel during this time, so their voltages drop to zero together. The three voltages involved are shown in Fig. 3-4c. Notice that the voltage across the capacitor changes in the same way for both polarities of step inputs: no sudden change, but an exponential change to the new input level. The re-

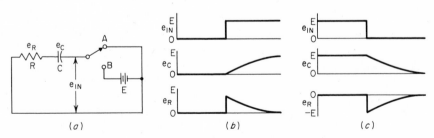

Fig. 3-4. Response of an RC circuit to a step input signal.

sistor's voltage also changes in the same way for both polarities: a sudden and instantaneous change from zero to the total circuit voltage and then an exponential drop to zero.

3-3 RC CIRCUIT RESPONSE TO PULSE INPUT

If the switch in Fig. 3-4a is changed from position A to position B at time t_1, and then is switched back to A at time t_2, where $t_2 - t_1$ is a much shorter period of time than five time constants, the input signal can be considered to be a pulse (see Fig. 3-5). If there is no initial charge on the capacitor at time t_1, there will not be time enough, while the switch is at B, for the capacitor to charge completely. Assume $t_2 - t_1 = 0.25\tau$. The capacitor has charged to only 22 per cent of E. On the other hand, the voltage across the resistor increased to a value equal to the pulse amplitude and then dropped to 78 per cent of E or ($e_R = E - e_C$).

At t_2 the input voltage drops to zero and the capacitor's voltage drops to zero in about five time constants. The resistor's voltage reverses to 22 per cent of E with opposite polarity and then drops exponentially to zero. The three voltages are shown in Fig. 3-5. Notice that the voltage across the resistor is similar to that of the input signal.

3-4 RC CIRCUIT RESPONSE TO SQUARE-WAVE INPUT

If the switch of Fig. 3-3a is continuously switched back and forth so the time intervals in each position are equal, the input to the circuit will be a square wave. The period of the square wave is equal to twice the time interval that the switch is left in each position. An RC circuit's response to square waves with different periods will now be considered. First, when the period is equal to five time constants, the circuit will be described as having a *medium time constant*. Second, when the period is fifty times the time constant, the circuit has a *short time constant*. Third, if it is assumed that the period is only one-tenth of a time constant, the circuit has a *long time constant*. The supply voltage, and therefore the peak-to-peak amplitude of the square wave, will be assumed to be 100 volts.

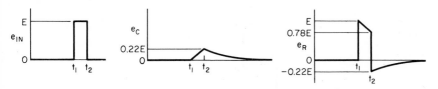

Fig. 3-5. Response of an RC circuit to a pulse input signal.

For a medium-time-constant circuit, the switch is left in each position for a time equal to 2.5τ (one-half a period). When the switch of Fig. 3-5 is changed from position A to position B, the change in capacitor voltage can be calculated from Eq. (3-7). Note in Fig. 3-6 that the capacitor's voltage has risen exponentially from 0 to 91.8 volts, while the resistor's voltage jumped to 100 volts and then dropped exponentially to 8.2 volts. The switch is changed back to A, dropping the input to zero. The resistor's voltage reverses polarity to -91.8 volts and drops as the capacitor's voltage drops. In order to solve for the change in the capacitor's voltage during this second time interval, the value for E_{R0}, 91.8 volts, and the value for t, 2.5τ, are both substituted into Eq. (3-7). Δe_C is found to be 84.25 volts. The voltage across C has dropped to 7.55 volts. The resistor's voltage also equals this value but with opposite polarity.

Again throwing the switch to B results in an increase in the capacitor's voltage. By applying Eq. (3-7), $\Delta e_C = 84.85$ volts; hence, $e_C = 92.4$ volts. The capacitor's voltage has risen exponentially from 7.55 to 92.4 volts, and the resistor's voltage has gone abruptly from -7.55 to 92.45 volts and then dropped exponentially to 7.6 volts.

During the next time interval the capacitor's voltage will drop exponentially from 92.4 to 7.6 volts, while the resistor's voltage reverses polarity to -92.4 volts and then changes exponentially to -7.6 volts.

Succeeding calculations will just repeat these values; the voltages are now varying between fixed peak values. The voltage waveforms shown in Fig. 3-6 start before the time the switch was first changed from position A to position B and continue for two complete cycles.

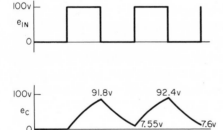

Fig. 3-6. Response of a medium-time-constant RC circuit to a square-wave input.

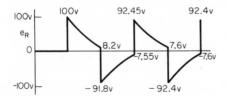

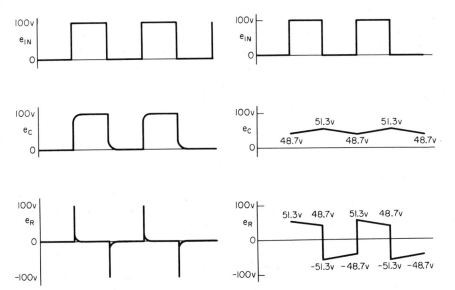

Fig. 3-7. Response of a short-time-constant RC circuit to a square-wave input.

Fig. 3-8. Response of a long-time-constant circuit to a square-wave input.

Now, a circuit with a short time constant will be considered. If the time period is equal to fifty times τ, the capacitor will be charging and discharging in time periods each equal to 25 time constants. A capacitor is considered to be completely charged after five time constants; therefore, the three voltage waveforms will be as shown in Fig. 3-7; the capacitor charges up and discharges in only about one-fifth of the time the switch is in each position. The resistor's voltage, being the difference between the input signal and the capacitor's voltage, rises instantaneously to a peak and then drops exponentially to zero in about one-fifth of the time the switch is in each position.

For a long-time-constant circuit, with the period of the square wave only one-tenth of τ, it takes a number of cycles for the waveforms to settle down to identical consecutive cycles. By calculation (Sec. A-3) it can be shown that e_C will eventually vary between 48.7 and 51.3 volts and will take on the appearance of a triangular waveform (see Fig. 3-8). Each time the switch changes position the capacitor starts to charge from 48.7 volts toward 100 volts, or to discharge from 51.3 volts toward zero, but just gets started changing when the switch again changes position.

Because each time interval is short compared with the time constant of the circuit, it can be assumed that the capacitor charges and discharges at a linear rate; thus, the waveform is made up of a series of ramp segments.

The variation in the resistor's voltage for the circuit can be determined by subtracting the capacitor's voltage from the input signal. When the input is 100 volts, e_C rises from 48.7 to 51.3 volts, so e_R drops from 51.3 to 48.7 volts. When the input drops to zero, e_R drops to -51.3 volts and then changes to -48.7 volts. When the input rises to 100 volts again, e_R reverses polarity to 51.3 volts.

3-5 DIFFERENTIATING AND INTEGRATING CIRCUITS

The two main processes in the field of mathematics called *calculus* are *differentiating* and *integrating*. Differentiating is the process of finding the *derivative* of some function. The derivative of a function is the instantaneous rate of change of the function, usually with respect to time.

One of the circuits which has been discussed has the ability to differentiate a signal; that is, the output signal is proportional to the derivative or the rate of change of the input. This circuit is the simple RC circuit with the output taken from across the resistor. One important restriction is that the time constant of the circuit must be short compared with the period of the input signal. It can be proved mathematically (Sec. A-4) that

$$e_{out} = \tau \frac{de_{in}}{dt} \qquad \text{3-9}$$

where de_{in}/dt is the derivative or the instantaneous rate of change of the input signal with respect to time.

If the input signal is not changing, $de_{in}/dt = 0$, and there will be no output. If the input signal is changing very rapidly—for example, a step waveform—de_{in}/dt will be very large, and the output signal will be a narrow pulse with high amplitude. If the step could change levels in zero time, the output pulse would actually be infinite in amplitude, but this is not possible in actual circuits. If the input is a ramp, de_{in}/dt is constant, and the output will be a constant voltage level. It is important to remember that a differentiating circuit must have a short time constant.

Integrating is a process in calculus of finding the *integral* of a function. The integral of a function is just the reverse of the derivative, in the same way that the square of a number is just the reverse of a square root, or that the antilog is the reverse of the log. If the derivative of X is Y, then the integral of Y is X. An integral of something might be thought of as a *sum* of all its parts.

If an RC circuit has a long time constant, the voltage across the capacitor is proportional to the integral of the input signal; that is, the capacitor's voltage at any instant of time is proportional to the sum of all the instantaneous input amplitudes up to that instant of time. It can be shown mathematically (Sec. A-5) that

$$e_{out} = \frac{1}{\tau} \int e_{in}\, dt$$

3-10

where $\int e_{in}\, dt$ is the time integral of the input signal. (The integral sign $\int$ evolved from the letter "S," standing for sum.)

If the input signal is zero, the output is zero. If the input is a constant value greater than zero, the output will be a positive ramp. The reason for this can easily be seen. If the input amplitudes are continuously added up, the sum grows at a constant rate. If the constant input level were a negative value, the output would be a negative ramp, decreasing at a constant rate. A square wave, with one level positive and the other level negative, will give a triangular-wave output.

A ramp input to an integrating circuit will result in an output which is proportional to the sum of the instantaneous input amplitudes, but here each amplitude added on is larger than the previous one, so the sum is not increasing linearly but at an increasing rate; this gives a hyperbolic waveform. Remember that the integrating circuit must have a long time constant.

Figure 3-9 shows the relationship between four waveforms. If a particular waveform is differentiated, the resulting waveform is the next lower

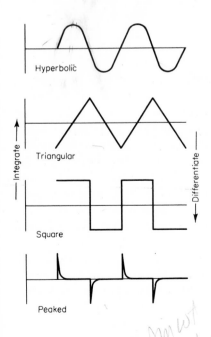

Fig. 3-9. *Differentiation and integration of waveforms.*

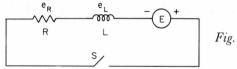

Fig. 3-10. RL circuit.

one. If a waveform is integrated, its new form is the next higher one in the figure. Differentiating and integrating circuits are often of great value in obtaining desired waveforms.

3-6 RL CIRCUITS

A coil has a tendency to try to keep its current flow from changing. When the switch of Fig. 3-10 is open, the current flow is zero. When the switch is closed, the current through the coil cannot change instantaneously, so it is still zero. There will be no voltage drop across the resistor, so e_L will equal E.

A differentiating circuit can be formed of a resistor and a coil in series, if the circuit has a short time constant and if the output signal is taken from across the inductor. An integrating circuit will have a long time constant, and the output will be the resistor's voltage. RL integrating circuits are not too practical, because a long time constant means a large inductance and a small resistance. A large coil is expensive, and the small-value resistor will give a small output voltage. It is more practical to use RC integrating circuits.

PROBLEMS

3-21 In the circuit of Fig. 3-10, if $R = 5$ kilohms and $L = 15$ mh, what steady-state current will flow if 75 volts is applied to the circuit?

3-22 In the circuit of Prob. 3-21, what voltage will appear across the resistor 2 μsec after the 75 volts is applied? [The time constant equations which define e_L and e_R are similar to those of RC circuits. The time constant $\tau = L/R$. Hence $e_R = E(1 - \epsilon^{-t/\tau})$ where E is the applied voltage.]

3-23 In the circuit of Prob. 3-21, what voltage will be developed across the coil 1.5 μsec after the 75 volts is applied? (Hint: $e_L = E\epsilon^{-t/\tau}$.)

3-24 Refer to Prob. 3-21. At what time will the voltage across the resistor be 50 volts?

3-25 If a 100-cps square wave, 0 to +75 volts, is applied to the circuit of Prob. 3-21, what voltage will appear across the coil at the end of the second period? (Assume that the period begins at the leading edge of the square wave.)

3-26 If a series circuit consists of a 500-kilohm resistor and a 0.2-μf capacitor, with a square-wave signal applied, what is the largest frequency which will allow the capacitor to charge and discharge completely with each input period?

3-27 If a square wave whose pulse duration is 100 msec and whose amplitude is 200 volts is applied to the circuit of Prob. 3-26, what voltage will appear across the capacitor at the end of the second period? (Assume that the period begins at the leading edge of the square wave.)

3-28 If the frequency at the input of the circuit of Prob. 3-27 is doubled, what will be the voltage across the capacitor after three complete periods?

3-29 A series circuit consists of a 0.001-μf capacitor, a 100-kilohm resistor, and a 25-kilohm resistor. Suppose that 200 volts is applied. (*a*) What is the steady-state current flow? (*b*) What is the instantaneous current through the circuit when $t = 100$ μsec? (*c*) What current flows into the capacitor when the voltage across it is 60 volts? (*d*) What is the voltage across the 25-kilohm resistor when the voltage across the 100-kilohm resistor is 50 volts?

3-30 A series RC differentiating circuit consists of a 0.05-μf capacitor and a 4-kilohm resistor. If the input signal varies as shown in Fig. 3-11, sketch the output waveform, giving voltage values.

3-31 A delay relay has an inductance of 20 mh and a resistance of 200 ohms. If the relay closes at 3.13 ma, and a time delay of 500 μsec is desired, find the value of voltage which must be applied.

3-32 A circuit consists of a 100-mh coil and a 10-kilohm resistor. What will be the voltage across the resistor 5 μsec after 20 volts is applied to the circuit?

3-7 RLC CIRCUITS

If a circuit has both inductance and capacitance, as well as resistance, its response to a step voltage is quite different from that of the circuits

Fig. 3-11. Figure for Prob. 3-30.

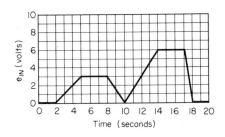

which have been discussed. If R is less than $2\sqrt{L/C}$, the equation for the resulting current can be derived (Sec. A-7), and is rather complicated.

$$i = \frac{2E}{\sqrt{(4L/C) - R^2}} \ \epsilon^{-Rt/2L} \left[\sin \frac{\sqrt{(4L/C) - R^2}}{2L} t \right] \tag{3-11}$$

Note the three main parts to the equation: the constant, the exponential, and the sine function. The resulting current waveform can be described as a sine wave with an angular velocity equal to

$$\omega = \frac{\sqrt{(4L/C) - R^2}}{2L} \tag{3-12}$$

but whose peak amplitude starts out at $2E[(4L/C) - R^2]^{-1/2}$ when $t = 0$, and then decreases exponentially with time according to

$$F = \epsilon^{-Rt/2L} \tag{3-13}$$

where F is a multiplying factor. This kind of waveform, shown in Fig. 3-12, is not a true sine wave but is called a *damped sine wave*.

If R, in the circuit, is zero, Eq. (3-12) becomes $\omega = (LC)^{-1/2}$, which is the equation for resonance and shows that the circuit will oscillate at its resonant frequency. Equation (3-13) becomes $F = 1$, which means that there is no damping and the circuit will continue to oscillate with no decrease in amplitude; the current will have a true sine waveform. The amplitude will equal $E(L/C)^{-1/2}$.

If R is greater than $2(L/C)^{1/2}$, the circuit is said to be *overdamped*, and the current rises and then falls to zero as shown in Fig. 3-13.

Therefore, the resulting waveform depends on the relationship between R, L, and C. This can be expressed in terms of the circuit Q:

$$Q = \frac{X_L}{R} \qquad Q^2 = \frac{X_L^2}{R^2} \qquad X_L = X_C$$

$$Q^2 = \frac{X_L X_C}{R^2} = \frac{\omega L}{R^2 \omega C} = \frac{L}{R^2 C}$$

$$Q = \frac{1}{R} \sqrt{\frac{L}{C}} \tag{3-14}$$

If R is less than $2(L/C)^{1/2}$, the oscillations are damped:

$$R < 2\sqrt{\frac{L}{C}} \qquad \frac{1}{2} < \frac{1}{R}\sqrt{\frac{L}{C}}$$

Substituting Eq. (3-14) into this gives $\frac{1}{2} < Q$, which states that if the Q of the circuit is greater than 0.5, the circuit is underdamped, and damped oscillations result.

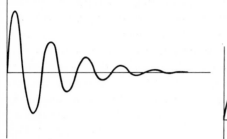

Fig. 3-12. Damped sine wave; under-
damping.

Fig. 3-13.   Current in an overdamped
RLC circuit.

If R is greater than $2(L/C)^{1/2}$, it can be shown that the Q of the circuit is less than 0.5, and the circuit is overdamped, resulting in no oscillations.

The larger the Q of the circuit, the less is the damping; if $Q = \infty$ ($R = 0$), there is no damping, and the circuit continues to oscillate with constant peak amplitudes.

If an RLC circuit has a Q slightly greater than 0.5, a step input signal will give a high-amplitude pulse, representing one half-cycle of the sine wave, and then the rest of the sine wave will damp out rapidly. This is called a *peaking circuit*. The output waveform is shown in Fig. 3-14.

If the Q of the circuit is large, the circuit is called a *ringing circuit*. Here, a single step input will start the circuit oscillating, or ringing, and the circuit will continue to oscillate for several cycles until the energy is dissipated in the resistor. It can be shown (Sec. A-8) that the number (N) of cycles of oscillation, which will take place before the peak amplitude drops to $1/\epsilon$ of its initial value, is related to the Q of the circuit by

$$N = \frac{Q}{\pi}$$

3-15

Fig. 3-14.   Output of RLC peaking
circuit.

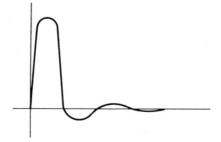

The characteristics of an underdamped *RLC* ringing circuit are used in a device manufactured by Owen Laboratories for calibrating the horizontal scale of an oscilloscope in "time" units. A simplified circuit diagram is shown in Fig. 3-15. Four different combinations of L and C may be switched into the circuit to give resonant frequencies with time periods of 1, 10, 100, and 1,000 μsec. For example, the 10-μsec values are 2.5 mh ± 3 per cent and 0.001 μf ± 5 per cent. The terminal marked "sweep" is connected to a source of the sweep voltage of the oscilloscope, and the return portion of the sawtooth sweep voltage starts the circuit oscillating. The "scope" terminal is connected to the vertical input of the oscilloscope, and the damped sine wave may be observed on the screen. The distance between adjacent peaks of this pattern will equal the time period to which the instrument is set, and then the horizontal scale of the oscilloscope may be calibrated in "time."

PROBLEMS

3-33   A series circuit consists of a 2.5-kilohm resistor, a 0.1-henry coil, and a 0.01-μf capacitor. When a d-c voltage is applied to the circuit, what is the period of the damped oscillation?

3-34   Refer to Prob. 3-33. If the resistance value is doubled, will the damped oscillation period increase, decrease, or remain unchanged?

3-35   If a series circuit consists of a 50-ohm resistor, a 1-mh coil, and a 0.1-μf capacitor, how long after 20 volts is applied will the current oscillations damp out? (Compare with the five-time-constant rule discussed in Sec. 3-1.)

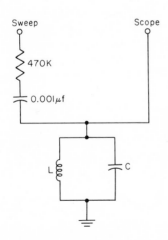

Fig. 3-15. Simplified diagram of Owen type 160 time calibrator. (Owen Laboratories, Pasadena, California.)

3-36 Refer to Prob. 3-35. What is the current the first instant after the d-c voltage is applied?

3-37 Is the circuit of Prob. 3-33 underdamped? Prove your answer.

3-38 Refer to Prob. 3-33. What is the circuit Q?

3-39 A 150-mh coil has an effective resistance of 2 kilohms and is connected in series with a 0.002-μf capacitor. A step voltage with amplitude of 100 volts is applied. Prove that this circuit is underdamped and find: (a) the frequency at which oscillations occur; (b) the peak current amplitude immediately after the voltage step occurs; (c) the time it takes for the exponential multiplying factor [Eq. (3-13)] to equal $1/\epsilon$; (d) the number of cycles of oscillation occurring during the time calculated in part c; (e) the value of N, calculated from Eq. (3-15), and compare this with the answer for part d.

3-40 When the Owen type 260 time calibrator is set to 10 μsec, about 12 cycles occur before the amplitude drops to $1/\epsilon$. Find the effective resistance of the coil.

CHAPTER 4 DIODE SWITCHING CIRCUITS

A diode, with its characteristics of low forward resistance and high reverse resistance, can be used as a switch. It has the advantages of simplicity of operation and usually low cost. It has disadvantages of loading down the circuit and no amplification.

4-1 VACUUM-DIODE CHARACTERISTICS

Ideally, a diode would have a voltage-current characteristic curve like that shown in Fig. 4-1a. It would have zero resistance with forward voltage applied and infinite resistance with reverse voltage. In actual practice, vacuum diodes have characteristics like that shown in Fig. 4-1b. The variation in plate current of a 6AL5 is shown as plate voltage is varied from -3 to $+3$ volts. Notice the variation from the ideal diode. The forward resistance varies from about 300 ohms at $+0.3$ volt to about 250 ohms at $+2$ volts.

Figure 4-1b shows that as the applied voltage drops to zero, there is still plate current flowing, due to the *Edison effect*. The velocity of the electrons emitted from the cathode is sufficient to allow them to reach the plate. This results in a current of about 150 μa for the 6AL5. It takes a negative plate voltage of about 1 volt to oppose this effect and to cut the current to zero.

With reverse voltages higher than 1 volt, the vacuum diode behaves like an open circuit, and for all practical purposes has infinite resistance.

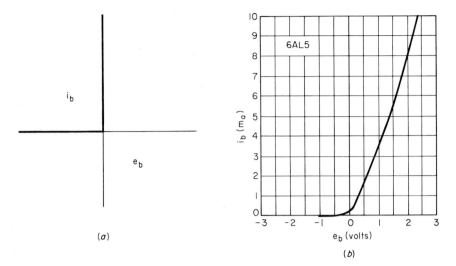

Fig. 4-1. (a) Ideal diode characteristic curve. (b) Actual diode characteristic curve.

Because the diode consists of two conductors (plate and cathode) separated by an insulator (vacuum), it has a capacitance. This is usually small, of the order of a few picofarads. In switching circuits, this capacitance can be an undesirable factor in the circuit's operation.

4-2 IDEAL VACUUM DIODE

A 6AL5 is to be used in the switching circuit shown in Fig. 4-2a. It is desirable to have the full 3 volts appear at the output when the diode switch is turned on. A 300-ohm load line is shown on the characteristic curve of the 6AL5 in Fig. 4-2b. It is seen that the output will be 1.5 volts when the 3 volts is applied to the input. The output voltage is e_{R_L}, as shown in Fig. 4-2b. This condition is less than ideal. If the load resistance is doubled, the load line (Fig. 4-2b) shows that the output voltage is increased to 2 volts, an improved condition.

The high-vacuum diode can be made to approach an ideal diode by operating the tube into a high value of load resistance. As an example, refer again to the characteristics of Fig. 4-2b. Note that a 3-kilohm load results in an output of about 2.8 volts, a condition which approaches the ideal. If the diode is operated into a much larger load, 100 kilohms or more, the tube acts as an ideal switch.

Since no plate current can flow from the plate to the cathode, the tube is an ideal switch with reverse bias under any load conditions.

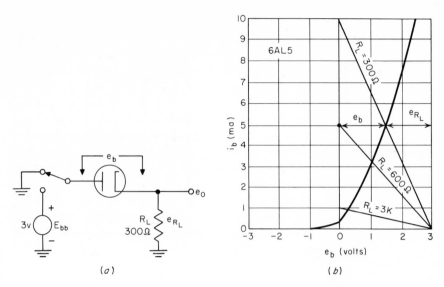

Fig. 4-2. (a) Diode circuit. (b) Load line for current.

4-3 CRYSTAL DIODE

The crystal diode differs from the vacuum diode in the following ways. No heater is required; hence there is a great saving in power, size, and weight, and there is a reduction in heat problems. The crystal diode has a finite resistance in the reverse direction. It has a lower and more nearly constant forward resistance than the vacuum diode. The crystal diode has lower internal capacitance, but its characteristics are more dependent on the ambient temperature.

The two common types of crystal diodes are the *point-contact* diode and the *junction* diode. The junction diode can handle larger forward currents and has a smaller, more nearly constant reverse current, up to a certain value of reverse voltage. At this particular voltage, called the *zener voltage,* the reverse current begins to rise rapidly and gives the crystal diode characteristics similar to those of the gas diode. Special *zener diodes* can be used as voltage reference or control devices. The point-contact diode has lower capacitance, and therefore is sometimes used in high-speed switching circuits.

The semiconductor material used is either germanium or silicon. Silicon has the advantage of lower reverse current, a higher peak-inverse-voltage rating, higher forward-current capability, and a reduced effect of temperature on its characteristics. It has the characteristics of a very high forward impedance up to about 0.7 volt forward voltage, but low impedance at higher voltages.

4-4 IDEAL SEMICONDUCTOR DIODE

The ideal semiconductor diode, like the high-vacuum diode, would be one which presented a zero impedance in the forward direction and an infinite impedance in the reverse direction. Figure 4-3 shows an example of an ideal curve and an actual curve. Unlike the vacuum diode, the semiconductor diode cannot be made to approach an ideal switch by operating the device into a large value of load resistance. Inserting a large value of load resistance would produce ideal conditions under forward-bias conditions, but would render the circuit less than ideal in the reverse direction. As an example, refer to Fig. 4-3b. Note that a 1-megohm load line, plotted on the reverse characteristics, causes a voltage drop of 7 volts across the load resistor. Ideally, this value should be zero. In order for a semiconductor diode to approach the conditions of an ideal switch, an optimum value of load resistance must be chosen, depending upon the characteristics of the diode.

4-5 DIODE SWITCHING

Diode switching is divided into four groups: vacuum-diode, semiconductor-diode, zener-diode, and tunnel-diode switching.

VACUUM-DIODE SWITCHING

Consider the circuit of Fig. 4-4a. While a negative 10-volt pulse is applied to the circuit, the diode is reverse-biased; hence, the output should

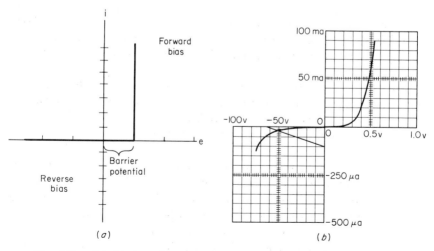

Fig. 4-3. (a) *Ideal-semiconductor-diode curve.* (b) *1N191 characteristic.*

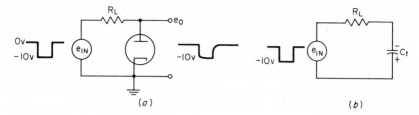

Fig. 4-4. *(a) Diode switching circuit. (b) Equivalent diode circuit.*

be a negative 10-volt pulse. Even if the input pulse has an infinitely fast rise time, the output will not rise to maximum in zero time, since the tube's capacitance cannot charge instantaneously.

The circuit can be reduced to a simple RC circuit, as shown in Fig. 4-4b. The time constant of this equivalent circuit is $\tau = R_L C_t$. The voltage across the capacitor is given as

$$e_C = E(1 - \epsilon^{-t/\tau}) \tag{4-1}$$

where Eq. (4-1) is Eq. (3-1) with $E_{C0} = 0$.

The rise time of the output pulse is considered to be the time required for the voltage to pass from the 10 per cent point to the 90 per cent point. In this circuit the voltage will rise 10 per cent in 0.11τ, and it would take 2.31τ to rise from zero to 90 per cent of E. Therefore, the time required for the voltage to rise from 10 to 90 per cent of E is $2.31\tau - 0.11\tau = 2.2\tau$:

$$t_r = 2.2\tau \qquad \textbf{4-2}$$

Equation (4-2) is a general equation for the rise time of a vacuum diode switching to the reverse-bias direction. When the input voltage drops to zero, the capacitor cannot discharge instantaneously, so a finite fall time results.

Diode switching in the forward direction presents no problem since the circuit reduces to an equivalent circuit involving only resistive elements. If the load is large compared with the resistance of the diode, the switching time is essentially the same as the input switching time.

EXAMPLE   If a 6AL5 diode is to operate into an 800-kilohm load resistor, what is the reverse switching time if a -10-volt pulse is applied? The time constant of the circuit is 2.4 μsec, since the tube capacitance for a 6AL5 is 3 pf. The actual switching time is 2.2τ, or about 5.304 μsec. (Note that the magnitude of the applied pulse does not influence the switching time of a particular vacuum-diode–load combination.)

It has been shown that a vacuum diode's capacitance is the factor that most affects its switching speed. The junction capacitance in a semiconductor diode is one important factor which affects its switching speed, but there are additional properties which can also be contributing factors. The most significant of these is called *minority-carrier storage*.

Consider the circuit of Fig. 4-5a. When the input pulse goes to +10 volts, the diode is switched on (forward-biased). The leading edge of the output signal follows the input with negligible delay. (In very fast switching circuits this delay should not be neglected.)

Over the interval of t_d a heavy forward current flows through the diode, and an excess of minority carriers is built up at the junction. The density of these carriers is determined by the doping of the diode and the amount of forward bias. At t_1, the input to the diode switches to −10 volts. It might be assumed that in the reverse direction, the diode would offer a high impedance, no current would flow, and therefore there would be no output voltage across the load resistor. This, however, is not the case, since minority carriers, stored at the junction, must be swept away. The result is that a large reverse current flows over the interval t_1 to t_2. Once the carriers have been swept from the junction, the voltage across the resistor drops to zero as the junction capacitance becomes charged to the applied voltage. The waveshape at the output, over this time interval from t_2 to t_3, is shown in Fig. 4-5b.

The time interval from t_1 to t_2 is known as the *recovery time* t_{rt}. The magnitude of the recovery time is a function of the forward current I_f, the reverse current I_r, and a constant K, determined by the type of diode used. In general, the larger the forward current, the greater the minority-carrier storage. An acceptable approximation for the recovery-time relationship is given in an empirical equation

$$K = \frac{t_{rt}}{\ln\left[(I_f + I_r)/I_r\right]} \tag{4-3}$$

where t_{rt}, I_f, and I_r are determined from an experimental test setup.

In the vacuum-diode circuit, it was found that the magnitude of the applied voltage did not influence the rise or the fall time. In the junction

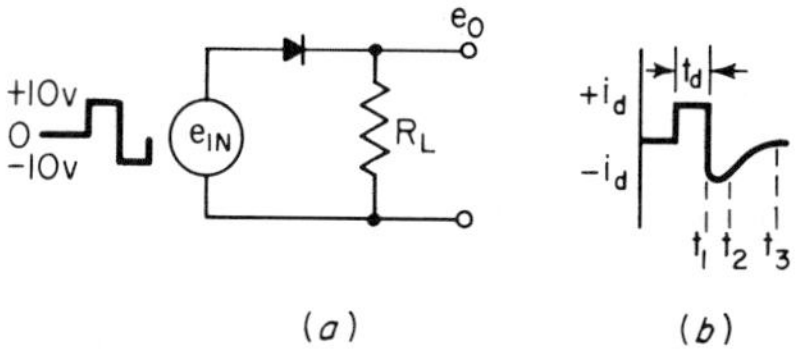

Fig. 4-5. (a) *Semiconductor-diode switching circuit.* (b) *Output waveshape.*

(a)

(b)

diode, such is not the case since the reverse voltage developed across the diode influences the junction capacitance. The reverse potential changes the width of the depletion region, changing the distance between the charge concentrations. This has an effect similar to that of varying the distance between the plates of a capacitor. The value of this capacitance can be determined from the equation

$$C = \frac{K}{(-E_r - E_{ba})^n} \tag{4-4}$$

where E_r = reverse voltage
E_{ba} = barrier voltage
n = a constant ranging from $\frac{1}{3}$ to $\frac{1}{2}$, depending upon doping

Three basic guideposts should be observed when designing circuits employing semiconductor diodes. Adherence to these conditions will provide the fastest possible switching speeds.

1. The forward current should be maintained as low as possible and for as short a time as feasible.
2. The circuit should operate into a low impedance.
3. The reverse bias should be as large as possible.

The point-contact diode has the advantage of having a relatively small depletion region. This condition reduces the problem of minority-carrier storage and significantly reduces the junction capacitance. However, its current-handling ability is extremely low compared with that of the junction diode. It can be used successfully in high-speed low-current switching applications.

ZENER-DIODE SWITCHING

In switching from forward to reverse and from reverse to forward, the conventional semiconductor diode's major drawbacks are minority-carrier storage and junction capacitance. Together, these contribute to the undesirable characteristics of a long switching time. In some applications the conventional diode can be replaced with a zener diode, and the switching can be performed at the zener point. Examine the zener characteristic curve of Fig. 4-6a. Note that in the reverse direction the diode exhibits a high impedance to potentials up to E_z volts. At the zener point, the reverse impedance becomes low and the current increases rapidly. This portion of the characteristic curve is similar to the ideal curve shown in Fig. 4-3a. Two advantages are realized: (a) There is no minority-carrier storage, hence no problem of recovery time. (b) The diode capacitance is lower and reasonably constant; hence the switching time is decreased.

Examine the circuit of Fig. 4-6b. Assume that the 10-volt pulse train

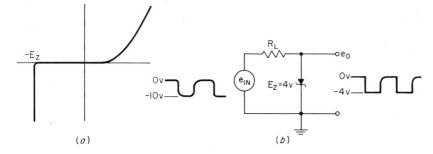

Fig. 4-6. (a) Zener characteristic. (b) Zener-diode switching circuit.

applied to the circuit has lost some of its high-frequency components. If the pulse train is applied to a zener switching circuit, where the diode's zener potential is 4 volts, the lost harmonic components will be restored, and the magnitude of the output pulses will be −4 volts.

Zener diodes are available with reverse breakdown voltages ranging from a few volts to as high as 200 volts. In most circuits employing zener diodes, some form of surge protection is required. Care must be taken not to exceed the peak power rating of the diode. Manufacturers provide ample information regarding zener potentials, duty-cycle ratings, maximum allowable peak power, and, in some cases, recommended circuits.

TUNNEL-DIODE SWITCHING

The characteristics of a semiconductor diode indicate that current does not flow in the forward direction for low values of forward voltage. It takes at least 0.3 volt or more for the germanium diode and about 0.7 volt or more for the silicon diode (see Fig. 4-7).

By increasing the density of the majority current carriers, the diode can be made to start conducting as soon as a forward bias is connected across it. As this bias voltage increases, the current will increase until a *peak point* is reached, when suddenly the current will drop rapidly to a low value

Fig. 4-7. Comparison of germanium and silicon diode characteristics.

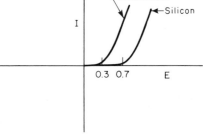

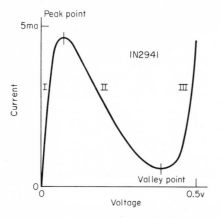

Fig. 4-8. Tunnel-diode characteristics.

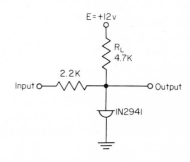

Fig. 4-9. Tunnel-diode switching circuit.

called the *valley point*. A further increase in bias voltage will again increase the current in the normal way. This device is called a *tunnel diode*. Its name comes from the *tunnel effect,* where current carriers apparently tunnel through a potential barrier.

The characteristics of a typical tunnel diode are shown in Fig. 4-8. The portion of the current-voltage curve marked II has negative resistance characteristics and is an unstable region of operation. Once operation starts into this region, the operating point will continue to move across it into one of the two stable regions, I or III.

A tunnel-diode switching circuit is shown in Fig. 4-9. Its operation can be explained by drawing a load line on the characteristic curve, as shown in Fig. 4-10. The load line crosses the curve in three points, but only points

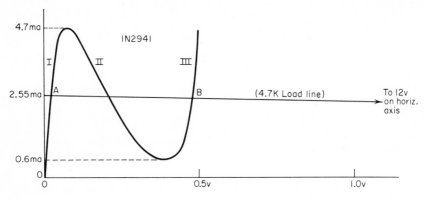

Fig. 4-10. Load line plotted on tunnel-diode characteristic.

A and *B* are stable points of operation. Assume that the circuit is operating at point *A*. If an input pulse of 6 volts is applied to the circuit, a positive current of 6/2.2 kilohms or 2.72 ma is added to the 2.55 ma, and the rise in current to the peak point drives the circuit into the unstable region. The negative resistance characteristics of this region will carry the operation into region III and to the *B* operating point. Operation continues at this point until a negative 6-volt pulse reduces the current below 0.6 ma. The diode is again driven into region II and on into region I, where it assumes stable operation at point *A*.

The currents at points *A* and *B* are practically equal, but the voltages are about 0.02 and 0.48 volt; one point can be the OFF position and the other the ON state.

The problem of minority-carrier storage is eliminated, and switching speed is on the order of a few nanoseconds.

4-6 OR AND AND CIRCUITS

Computer logic circuits such as OR gates and AND gates utilize diodes as switches. Figure 4-11*a* shows an example of an OR circuit. The objective of the circuit is to produce an output pulse at e_0 whenever a pulse appears at *A* OR *B*. An equivalent network of the OR gate is shown in Fig. 4-11*b*. If a positive pulse is applied at *A*, diode D_A becomes forward-biased and D_B is reverse-biased. The voltage developed across *R* is the voltage of the pulse at *A*. The same analysis results if a voltage is applied at *B* instead of *A*. A positive pulse will occur at the output if a pulse is applied to either *A* or *B* or to both.

Figure 4-12 shows an AND gate and its equivalent circuit. Note from the equivalent circuit that with no positive pulses at either *A* or *B*, both diodes are forward-biased. A voltage drop *E* appears across *R*. Since the output is the sum of the voltages across *R* and *E*, the output is 0 volts.

Assume that a positive pulse applied at *A* has a magnitude of *E* volts.

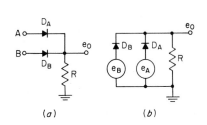

Fig. 4-11. (a) OR *circuit. (b) Equivalent network of* OR *circuit.*

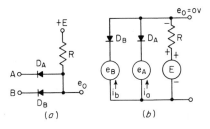

Fig. 4-12. (a) AND *circuit. (b) Equivalent network of* AND *circuit.*

Diode D_A is no longer forward-biased. The effective current through D_A is zero. However, diode D_B remains forward-biased and the voltage drop across R does not change. The output remains at zero.

If a positive pulse, with magnitude E, is applied at both A AND B, neither diode is forward-biased and diode currents are zero. No load current flows, and the voltage across R is reduced to zero. The output potential rises to E volts. The circuit requires a pulse at both A and B to produce a pulse at the output. These and other gating circuits will be covered in detail in Chap. 10.

4-7 CLIPPER CIRCUITS

The preceding sections discussed the use of vacuum tubes and semiconductor devices as switches. These electronic switches can pass or reject certain signals and can be activated by separate control signals, or they can be controlled by the signals which are to be turned on or off. If the latter is the case, and if the switch is activated at a particular reference-voltage level, the circuit is called a *clipper*. Sometimes these circuits are also referred to as *limiters*. The term clipper comes from the idea that all the signal above or below the reference voltage is "clipped" and the remaining signal appears at the output. Or the circuit can be considered to "limit" the signal amplitude from exceeding the reference-voltage level, hence the name limiter.

DIODE CLIPPERS

Consider a diode and a resistor to be connected in series across a sine-wave signal source, as shown in Fig. 4-13a. Assume the diode to be ideal. On the positive half-cycle of the input signal the diode conducts and the full input signal appears across the resistor R. On the negative half-cycle, the diode is an open circuit; and, there being no current flow through the resistor, all the input signal appears across the diode terminals. The half-wave rectifier is essentially a clipper where either the positive or the neg-

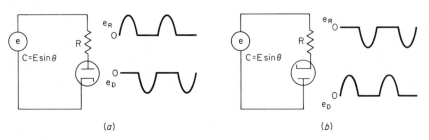

Fig. 4-13. Diode clipper circuits.

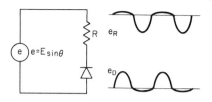

Fig. 4-14. *Semiconductor-diode clipper circuit.*

ative half of the input is clipped, depending upon the circuit connection. The output signal could be either that across the resistor or that across the diode, the only difference being in the polarity and the inversion of the waveform. If the diode's connections are reversed, as in Fig. 4-13*b*, the output signals are reversed, as shown.

This circuit is either a shunt or a series diode clipper, depending on the position of the diode in relationship to the output signal. If the diode is across, or in shunt with, the output signal, we call it a shunt clipper. If the diode is in series with the output terminals, it is a series clipper. There is a significant difference in the characteristics of the two types of circuits when the signal is transmitted. In the series clipper, it is a direct connection, which sometimes makes this circuit preferred. In the shunt clipper, the tube's interelectrode capacitance may be a factor in affecting the output signal at high frequencies. In a series circuit the tube's capacitance may provide a coupling path when the diode switch is reverse-biased.

We have assumed a perfect diode. In practice the diode has some finite resistance during conduction. These resistances alter the output waveshapes slightly from those shown in Fig. 4-13 to those of Fig. 4-14. When the diode conducts, a small portion of the input signal is dropped across the diode, the remaining part across the resistor. When the semiconductor diode is nonconducting, a small current flows, so a small portion of the input signal appears across the resistor and the rest across the diode.

BIASED CLIPPERS

The preceding circuits clipped at zero voltage level. This clipping point can be set at any other desired value by using an additional d-c voltage source in the circuit (refer to Fig. 4-15). The bias voltage must be included in the shunt part of the circuit, or the position of the clipped waveforms will be shifted. The output waveforms of Fig. 4-15 result when the bias voltage is equal to about one-half the peak amplitude of the input signal, and if the output is obtained from between points *A* and *C* or between points *B* and *D*.

DUAL-DIODE CLIPPERS

It has been shown how either shunt or series diode clippers can remove any portion of an input signal above or below a certain voltage level. A

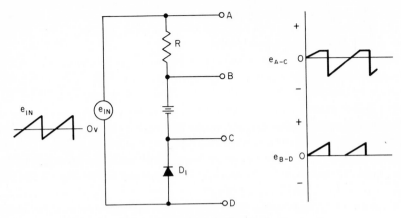

Fig. 4-15. Biased clipper circuit.

combination of two diodes in either a shunt circuit (Fig. 4-16a) or a series clipper (Fig. 4-16b) will remove portions of both positive and negative peaks.

A practical use for this type of clipper would be in a simple type of square-wave generator. Assume that a sine-wave oscillator produces a signal with a peak amplitude of 10 volts. Then a dual clipper could remove about 9.5 volts from each peak, leaving a signal with a peak-to-peak value of 1 volt. If this output were amplified 20 times, the result would be a fairly good square wave, with a peak amplitude of 10 volts and with rise and fall times each less than 1 per cent of the period.

EXAMPLE   Refer to the circuit of Fig. 4-16a. Assume that the input a-c signal is 20 volts peak-to-peak at 2 kc. If E_1 and E_2 are each 0.5 volt, what is the period of the output square wave and what are the rise and fall times of the output pulse? What is the peak-to-peak amplitude of the output?

$$T = \frac{1}{f} = \frac{1}{2 \times 10^3} = 0.5 \text{ msec}$$

The rise time of the output pulse is equal to twice the time required for the sine wave to change from 0 to 0.5 volt:

$$e = E_m \sin \omega t$$
$$0.5 = 10 \sin (12.56 \times 10^3 \times t)$$
$$0.05 = \sin (1.256 \times 10^4 \times t)$$
$$1.256 \times 10^4 \times t = 0.05 \text{ (radians cancel)}$$
$$t = 3.97 \text{ } \mu\text{sec}$$
$$t_r = 7.94 \text{ } \mu\text{sec}$$

The peak-to-peak amplitude of the output square wave will be twice the bias of E_1 or E_2, or 1 volt p-p.

Zener diodes, operating back to back, can be used as dual-diode clippers. Refer to the circuit of Fig. 4-16c. Assume that a 60-volt signal is applied to the circuit. The 1N1522 zener potential is 7.66 volts. When the input signal passes through its positive excursion, diode D_1 is forward-biased and D_2 remains reverse-biased up to 7.66 volts. At this potential, D_2 conducts and the output remains at 7.66 volts. During the negative half of the input cycle, D_1 is reverse-biased and conducts at 7.66 volts. The output amplitude is equal to the sum of the two zener potentials, 15.32 volts.

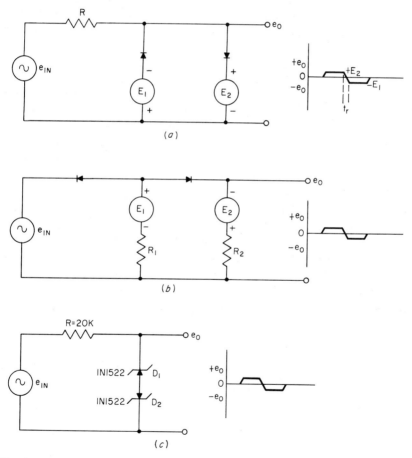

Fig. 4-16. (*a*) *Shunt dual-diode clipper.* (*b*) *Series dual-diode clipper.* (*c*) *Zener-diode clipper.*

A *clamping circuit* is designed to connect one part of a circuit to a fixed reference voltage for a period of time and to disconnect it the rest of the time. Therefore, it is a switch, similar to those which have been discussed.

Some clamping circuits are designed to shift a waveform so that it is all above or all below a certain voltage—often 0 volts. In this process a d-c voltage has been added to the signal. The d-c voltage added to the signal may equal a d-c component which was lost by passing the signal through an *RC-* or transformer-coupled circuit. This circuit is called a *d-c restorer.*

DIODE CLAMPING

Figure 4-17*a* shows a simple clamping circuit. On the positive half-cycle of the input, the diode conducts, charging C to a value equal to the peak value of the input signal. From then on we have essentially a d-c voltage source in series with the input signal, shifting its position, as shown by the output signal in Fig. 4-17*b*.

The purpose of R is to make this circuit a *self-adjusting* d-c restorer. If the amplitude of the input signal should decrease, C will discharge through R, until the capacitor's voltage is equal to the new value of the input signal. The positive peak of the output signal will again be clamped at the 0-volt level. If the input signal level should increase, the diode will conduct, charging the capacitor to the new level, maintaining the clamping action.

Actually, capacitor C discharges slightly during each cycle. Then, on positive peaks of the input signal, the diode conducts, recharging the capacitor. Because of this, there is a slight clipping action on the positive peaks; but if R and C have a long time constant compared with the period of the input signal, this clipping is negligible.

On the other hand, if the RC time constant is too long, the circuit will not adjust readily to changes in the signal's amplitude. That is, if the signal level is decreased, the positive peaks will not quite reach the zero level until the capacitor's voltage has discharged to the new level. The choice of R and C values is often a compromise between a short time constant for

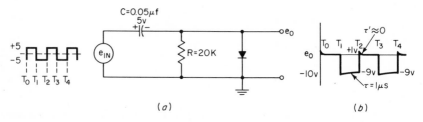

Fig. 4-17. (*a*) *Diode clamping circuit.* (*b*) *Semiconductor-diode clamping.*

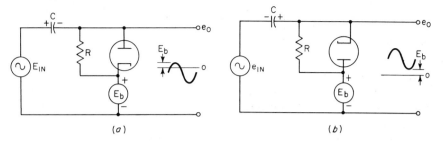

Fig. 4-18. Biased clamping circuits.

following changes in amplitude and a long time constant for least distortion of the signal.

If the diode connections are reversed, the voltage across the capacitor will be reversed in polarity and the negative peaks of the waveform will be clamped at the zero level.

EXAMPLE   Assume that a 10-volt peak-to-peak square wave is applied to the circuit of Fig. 4-17a. If the pulse repetition frequency of the input signal is 5 kc, what is the waveform of the output voltage? (Assume the diode to be ideal.)

The duration time of the positive half of the output is equal to $0.5 \times \text{prf} = 0.1$ msec. From t_0 to t_1, there is no output voltage; the capacitor charges to the 5 volts applied. When the input switches to -5 volts, the diode is reverse-biased and the output voltage drops to -10 volts, the sum of the input voltage and the capacitor's voltage. From t_1 to t_2, the capacitor discharges through R. (The parallel resistance of the reverse-biased diode can be neglected, as its value is much larger than R.)

$$\tau = RC = 1.0 \text{ msec}$$

The change in capacitor voltage, according to Eq. (3-6), is 1 volt.

The output voltage changes to -9 volts during the negative half of the input signal. When the input voltage switches to $+5$ volts, the capacitor charges almost instantaneously because of the forward-biased diode.

Adding a fixed bias voltage in series with the diode will shift the clamping level from 0 volts to the bias voltage. Two examples are shown in Fig. 4-18. Note that the capacitor's voltage, which determines how much shift there is in the waveform, is a combination of the fixed bias voltage and the peak value of the input signal. In Fig. 4-18a, the bias voltage opposes the input signal on the conduction half-cycle, charging the capacitor to a smaller value than would be the case with no bias voltage. Thus the output signal is shifted less than if there were no bias voltage. In Fig. 4-18b, with the diode connection reversed, the negative peak of the signal is clamped. The bias voltage aids the input signal on the conduction half-cycle, so the capacitor is charged to a value larger than the peak value of the input signal, and the output signal is shifted more than it would have been with no fixed bias voltage.

Note that the polarity of the diode determines which peak is clamped, and the clamping level is determined by the value and polarity of the bias voltage. The waveshape and amplitude have not been altered by any significant amount.

FIXED-LEVEL CLAMPING

The circuits discussed previously were self-adjusting—that is, the amount of d-c voltage added was dependent upon the amplitude of the input signal. In order to clamp one peak of the input signal to a fixed level, just the right amount of d-c voltage was added.

Sometimes, instead of adding a d-c voltage to shift the position of the waveform, we wish merely to keep the signal from rising above a certain fixed level or from dropping below a certain level, without regard to any change in the form of the signal. It can readily be seen that this was exactly the function of the clipper or limiter. The purpose here is not to duplicate that discussion, but just to add the idea that a limiter may be considered a clamper.

Consider, for example, a vacuum triode with its plate connected through a load resistor to B+ (refer to Fig. 4-19). As plate current varies, the plate voltage changes. Suppose a grid signal is trying to vary the plate voltage between 50 and 150 volts, but it is necessary to limit the variation so the plate voltage varies between 75 and 100 volts. V_2 clamps this point to 75 volts whenever it tries to drop below this value, and V_3 clamps it to 100

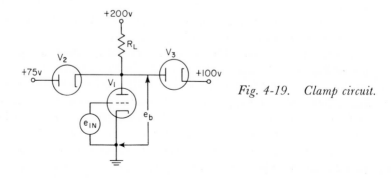

Fig. 4-19.   Clamp circuit.

volts when it tries to exceed 100 volts. For any value of e_b below 75 volts, the plate of V_2 is more positive than its cathode, the diode conducts, and the plate of V_1 is clamped to 75 volts. If e_b is greater than 75 volts, the cathode of V_2 is positive with respect to its plate, so V_2 is nonconducting. If e_b is less than 100 volts, the plate of V_3 is negative with respect to its cathode, so V_3 is nonconducting. If e_b tries to exceed 100 volts, the plate of V_3 becomes more positive than its cathode, and V_3 conducts, clamping the plate of V_1 to 100 volts. Thus, the plate voltage of V_1 may be varied between the two clamping levels.

PROBLEMS

4-1   If, in Fig. 4-4a, $R = 200$ ohms and the tube is a 6AL5, what is the output voltage when $+3$ volts d-c is applied as forward bias at the input?

4-2   If R of Prob. 4-1 is changed to 2 kilohms, what is the voltage across R?

4-3   The resistor of Prob. 4-1 is increased to 1 megohm. The manufacturer gives the interelectrode capacitance of the 6AL5 as 3.4 pf. What total time is required to charge the tube's capacitance?

4-4   A semiconductor diode is found to have a 5-μsec recovery time with a forward current of 3 ma and a reverse current of 2 μa. If the forward current is doubled and the reverse current is maintained at 2 μa, what is the new recovery time?

4-5   Refer to the diode of Prob. 4-4. How much should the reverse current be increased or decreased to maintain a 5-μsec recovery time?

4-6   Refer to the circuit of Fig. 4-9. If the value of E is reduced to 1 volt, what minimum value of R_L will maintain the switching characteristic of the tunnel diode?

4-7   Refer to Prob. 4-6. What will be the stable voltage points if the load is maintained at 300 ohms?

4-8   Refer to Fig. 4-12a. If the polarity of E is reversed to $-E$, what is the output voltage when no signals appear at A or B?

4-9   Refer to the circuit of Fig. 4-15. If a 25-volt sine wave is applied and $E = 3$ volts, $R = 100$ kilohms, plot the voltage output at terminals AC, BD, and AB. (Assume the diode to be ideal.)

4-10   Refer to Prob. 4-9. What quiescent voltage appears between terminals CA?

4-11   With the bias battery in Prob. 4-9 reversed, plot the output waveshapes at terminals AC, BD, and AB, with a 25-volt sine wave applied to the circuit. Compare these waveshapes with those of Prob. 4-9.

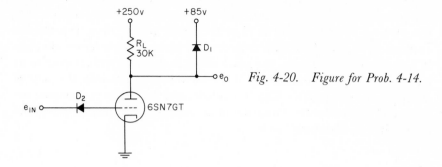

Fig. 4-20. Figure for Prob. 4-14.

4-12 With a 20-volt p-p 400-cps sine wave applied to the circuit of Fig. 4-16*a*, determine the output period, the peak-to-peak output voltage, and the rise time of the output signal. Assume R to be 500 kilohms and $E_1 = E_2 = 1.5$ volts.

4-13 With the pulse train applied to the circuit of Fig. 4-17 positive for 30 μsec and negative for 10 μsec, draw the output waveshape. $C = 0.01$ μf and $R = 10$ kilohms. What is the pulse repetition frequency at the output? (Assume an instantaneous rise and fall time of the input.)

4-14 Refer to the circuit of Fig. 4-20. What is the quiescent output potential? If a 60-volt p-p 1-kc signal is applied at the input, what is the amplitude of the output signal?

4-15 If the value of R_L in Prob. 4-14 is increased 50 kilohms, what is the new output amplitude?

4-16 Refer to Prob. 4-14. If the diode is reversed (so that the cathode is connected to the plate of the triode), what is the new peak-to-peak output? Assume that the input signal is the same as that in Prob. 4-14.

CHAPTER 5 TRIODE SWITCHES

A triode, either vacuum tube or semiconductor, can be used as a switch because it can be caused to either conduct heavily or not conduct at all. The particular "open" or "closed" state can be selected by applying the proper input voltage or current. The triode switch has the advantage over the diode in that amplification of the signal is possible.

5-1 VACUUM-TRIODE REGIONS

ACTIVE REGION

Figure 5-1 illustrates a typical triode amplifier and its corresponding graphic representation. The *active region* of the device is defined as the operating region between saturation and cutoff. It is in this region that the tube acts as an amplifier. Note from Fig. 5-1b that a grid voltage of -2 volts gives a value of 115 volts for the plate voltage e_b. If the grid voltage is changed to -6 volts, the plate voltage increases to 165 volts. The 4-volt change in grid voltage results in a 50-volt change in plate voltage. The triode is amplifying, and the voltage gain is equal to $50/4 = 12.5$. Often the active region between the cutoff value and 0 volts grid bias is called the *grid base;* and in the case of Fig. 5-1, it is equal to 20 volts. For a triode vacuum tube the grid-base value is approximately E_{bb}/μ. For a pentode it is given as E_{bb}/A, where A is the voltage gain of the stage.

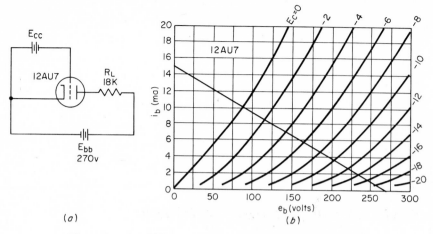

Fig. 5-1. (a) Triode amplifier. (b) Graphic representation.

SATURATION REGION

In many of the circuits discussed in this text, the grid voltage is driven into the saturation region. When the grid voltage goes positive, the plate current increases above the value for zero grid voltage. Figure 5-2 shows a family of e_b-i_b curves for positive grid voltages. It can be seen that they are very similar to the other curves except that they are at low values of plate voltage. The shaded area of Fig. 5-2 represents the saturation region. Whenever the tube is operating at positive grid potentials (with respect to its cathode) in this shaded region, it is said to be operating in the saturation region.

When grid current flows, the grid-cathode circuit is acting as a diode, with the grid acting as the anode. With forward voltage, the "diode's" resistance drops from infinity to a comparatively small value. Figure 5-3 shows how grid current varies with plate voltage, for various values of grid voltage. For example, when $E_b = 50$ volts, the grid-cathode resistance is about 1.3 kilohms; and at $E_b = 150$ volts, this resistance is about 1.6 kilohms. Thus the input impedance to the device is about 1.6 kilohms.

Edison effect is also present in this grid-cathode type of diode circuit. For zero grid voltage, approximately 0.2 ma of grid current may flow, and there can even be a small grid current flowing for small negative values of grid voltage. This current will flow through a resistor connected between the grid and cathode, and can develop some negative bias. If a 500-kilohm grid resistor is connected in the circuit, 1 μa of grid current could develop 0.5 volt; or a grid current of 0.5 μa could develop 2.5 volts across a 5-megohm grid resistor.

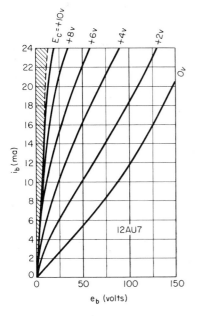

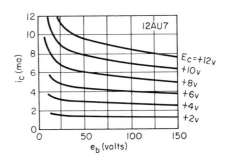

Fig. 5-2.   Positive-grid-voltage curves.

Fig. 5-3.   Plate-voltage–grid-current characteristic for positive grid voltages.

This effect can be minimized by connecting a large resistor to B+ instead of B−. Figure 5-4 shows such a circuit. With a positive grid voltage, a grid-to-cathode resistance of about 1.5 kilohms is present. This resistance forms a voltage divider with the 5-megohm resistor, and the resulting grid-cathode voltage is $300[1.5/(1.5 + 5{,}000)] = 0.09$ volt, compared with the 2.5 volts obtained with the grid resistor connected to B−.

When the grid is positive with respect to the cathode, and the grid current flowing reduces the grid-cathode resistance to a small value, we say the grid-cathode potential is clamped to the cathode potential.

Fig. 5-4.   Positive grid return.

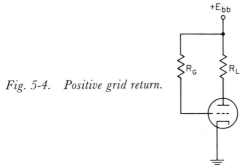

The vacuum tube is in the cutoff region whenever the grid voltage is more negative than the cutoff potential. The grid cutoff potential is determined by the B supply voltage. The 12AU7 of Fig. 5-1 has a grid cutoff potential of about -20 volts. If the B supply is reduced to 100 volts and the load is maintained at 18 kilohms, the tube cuts off at -10 volts. For triodes the grid-base equation is an approximate measure of cutoff potential:

$$E_{co} = \frac{E_{bb}}{\mu}$$

5-1

EQUIVALENT CIRCUITS

Analysis of triode vacuum-tube circuits requires the use of equivalent circuits which represent the three regions of operation. In order to simplify calculations, these equivalent circuits should be shown as Thévenin equivalent circuits.

Refer to the circuit of Fig. 5-5a. Assume e_{in} to be a negative voltage larger than E_{bb}/μ. With the tube cut off, r_p is infinite, and the equivalent circuit is equal to the load resistance in series with the B supply (Fig. 5-5b).

The equivalent circuit for the active region is derived from the equivalent *linear model* of the tube. Refer to the output characteristics of Fig. 5-6a. Note that an "ideal" set of characteristics has been superimposed on the actual characteristics. Each of these ideal linear characteristics intersects the voltage ordinate with a separation of 40 volts. Note that the $e_c = 0$ volts curve intersects the voltage ordinate at $+20$ volts. For the ideal triode the $e_c = 0$ volts curve should pass through the origin. The voltage E_s in Fig. 5-6a is identified as the *compensation potential*. The equivalent circuit of the compensated circuit is shown in Fig. 5-6b. (The circuit of Fig. 5-6b is the linear model of the actual circuit where E_s compensates for nonlinear characteristics.)

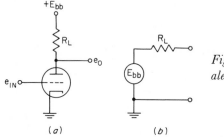

$+E_{bb}$

e_{IN}

e_0

R_L

(a)

R_L

E_{bb}

(b)

Fig. 5-5. (a) Triode circuit. (b) Equivalent cutoff circuit.

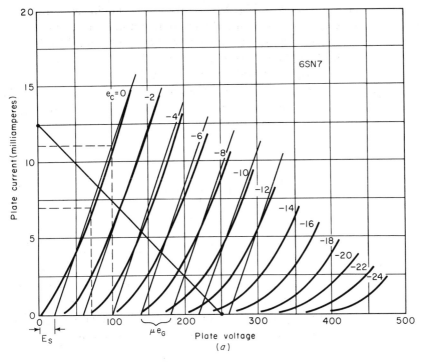

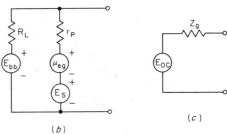

Fig. 5-6. (a) Linear equivalent characteristics. (b) Equivalent circuit showing compensation voltage. (c) Thévenin equivalent of active region.

The Thévenin equivalent circuit (Fig. 5-6c) is derived from the circuit in Fig. 5-6b, where

$$E_{oc} = E_s + \mu e_g + \frac{r_p}{r_p + R_1}(E_{bb} - E_s - \mu e_g) \qquad (5\text{-}2)$$

$$Z_g = \frac{r_p R_L}{r_p + R_L} \qquad (5\text{-}3)$$

EXAMPLE Assume that the circuit of Fig. 5-5a is to operate with a grid bias of −2 volts. If the load is 20 kilohms, $E_{bb} = 250$ volts, and the tube is a 6SN7, what is the Thévenin equivalent circuit?

The value of r_p in Fig. 5-6b is taken from the linear characteristic of Fig. 5-6a. The line chosen to determine r_p is the linearized $e_c = 0$ volts characteristic. (Any of the lines could have been used.) The plate resistance $r_p = \Delta e_p/\Delta i_b = 30/(4)(10^{-3}) = 7.5$ kilohms. E_s is determined from the characteristics of Fig. 5-6a. $E_s = 20$ volts. Since the μ of a 6SN7 is 20, the μe_g voltage is 40 volts. The equivalent circuit is shown in Fig. 5-7a. According to the ratio method, the voltage across r_p becomes

$$E_{r_p} = \frac{r_p E_x}{R_L + r_p}$$

where E_x is the equivalent potential in the network.

$$E_{r_p} = \frac{(7.5)(190)}{(20)(103) + (7.5)(10^3)} = 51.8 \text{ volts}$$

The open-circuit output voltage, and hence the Thévenin generator voltage, is 111.8 volts (Fig. 5-7b). The impedance looking into the open-circuit terminals, with all voltages replaced with short circuits, is 5.45 kilohms. The circuit of Fig. 5-7b is the equivalent circuit representing the active region of the triode when the grid is maintained at -2 volts.

The equivalent circuit for the saturated region of the tube depends upon the circuit in which the tube is operating. If the circuit is designed so that the grid cannot be driven positive, there exists no saturation region. The equivalent circuit becomes the equivalent circuit of the active region with e_g indicated as zero. Most circuits are designed in this manner. In those circuits where the grid is allowed to go positive, the equivalent circuit is determined from the linear model of the positive-grid output characteristics.

Figure 5-8 is a linear equivalent of the characteristics of Fig. 5-2. The saturation region is shown as a shaded area. The circuit associated with

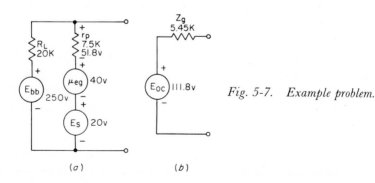

(a)   (b)

Fig. 5-7. Example problem.

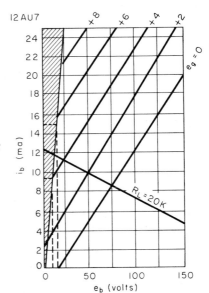

Fig. 5-8. Linear equivalent characteristics for the positive region of a 12AU7.

Fig. 5-8 has an $E_{bb} = 250$ volts and a 20-kilohm load line. Note that the active region of this circuit extends to a positive voltage of 4.5 volts. Beyond that value the circuit is operating in the saturation region. Any increase in the grid voltage beyond $+4.5$ volts does not appreciably change the plate potential. The r_p of the equivalent circuit becomes the increment of plate voltage to the increment of plate current along the saturation line. For the 12AU7 this r_p is about 1.5 kilohms. The equivalent Thévenin circuit for the saturation region is determined by substituting the new r_p and e_g into the linear equivalent circuit for the active region. Remember to reverse the polarities of the μe_g and E_s voltage sources in the equivalent circuit for the positive-grid-voltage regions.

5-2 TRIODE CLIPPERS

If the grid of a triode is maintained negative with respect to its cathode, the input can be likened to that of a reverse-biased diode. If the grid is driven positive, the "diode" conducts. This application of the triode can be used as a shunt clipper, as shown in Fig. 5-9. As in the case of the diode, this type of clipper can also be biased to change the clipping level. If the plate of the triode is connected through a load resistor to a positive power-supply voltage, the clipped signal will be amplified and inverted and a d-c component added to it. This is called *grid-current limiting*.

Clipping action could still take place if the grid resistor were eliminated. Referring to Fig. 5-1b, note that no matter how positive the grid is driven,

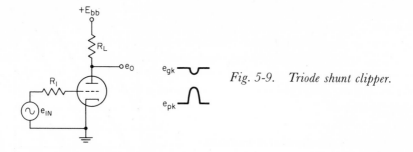

Fig. 5-9.   Triode shunt clipper.

the plate current can never exceed 15 ma because it is limited by the 18-kilohm plate load resistor. If a dynamic characteristic curve is plotted for the 12AU7 circuit shown in Fig. 5-1a, it can be seen how plate current varies with grid voltage. Referring to such a curve in Fig. 5-10, note that any instantaneous grid-cathode voltage higher than about $+8$ volts has no effect on plate current. This condition is identified as *saturation limiting*.

It can also be seen from Fig. 5-1b that for any grid-cathode voltage more negative than about 22 volts, the plate current will remain at zero. This shows a third way in which the triode can be used as a clipper, and is called *grid-cutoff limiting*. Figure 5-10 is a dynamic characteristic curve of the plate current plotted against the input signal (solid line). The curve would follow the dashed line for positive input voltages with grid-limiting resistor R_1 in the circuit (Fig. 5-9).

Of these types of triode clippers, the grid-current type provides the most predictable response. In addition, the output impedance for this type of limiting is lower than that for cutoff clipping, and therefore the shunt

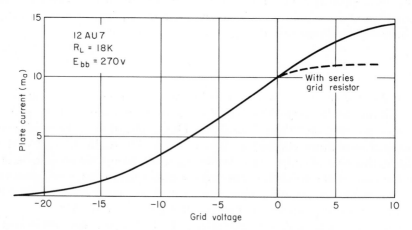

Fig. 5-10.   Grid-voltage–plate-current characteristic.

capacitance effects in the output circuit will have less effect at high frequencies. With cutoff limiting, the input capacitance is much lower, thus effecting an improved response. Saturation limiting requires a higher positive grid signal before clipping occurs and is less stable than the other types. With proper selection of the plate supply voltage, the plate load resistor, and the grid-bias voltage, signals with a wide range of amplitudes may be clipped.

5-3 DUAL CLIPPING WITH TRIODES

Triodes may be used for dual clipping by grid-current limiting of the positive peak of the input signal and cutoff limiting of the negative peak. Suppose, for example, it is desired to clip the peaks off an input signal whose peak value is 4 volts. If the clipping levels are to be at $+3$ and -3 volts, the circuit can be designed using a 12AU7 tube in the following way. A total swing of 6 volts on the load line is desired, with the grid voltage going from 0 volts for grid clipping to -6 volts for cutoff clipping. This means that cutoff should occur at -6 volts; and according to the characteristic curves for 12AU7 (Fig. 5-1b), cutoff will occur at -6 volts grid voltage when the plate voltage is about 80 volts. This fixes one point of the load line at 80 volts. Any value of plate load resistor could theoretically fulfill the clipping requirements; but the larger the load resistor, the higher the voltage gain and therefore the higher the output signal. A 40-kilohm load resistor would give a 65-volt peak-to-peak signal, while a 4-kilohm load resistor would provide a 25-volt peak-to-peak output. The smaller the load resistor, the better the high-frequency response, because of the relative value of shunt resistance and capacitance.

5-4 SQUARING CIRCUIT

The dual-clipping circuit of Sec. 5-3 is also identified as a squaring circuit. It is so called because the circuit produces squared pulses at the output for various waveshapes applied at the input. This characteristic is best illustrated in a numerical example.

EXAMPLE Assume that a 6SN7 is to be used as a source of square waves when a 50-volt peak-to-peak 1-kc sine wave is applied at the input. The amplitude of the output must have zero volts as a reference and a peak value of $+100$ volts. Refer to Fig. 5-11b. Since the main criterion is the amplitude, point A is arbitrarily selected at the $e_c = 0$ volts curve at the e_b voltage point of 100 volts. The second point is chosen at $e_b = 200$ volts. The load line intersects the 20.5-ma point; hence, the load resistance is $200/(20.5)(10^{-3}) = 9.77$ kilohms.

The switching time for this example can be determined from the load line and the output characteristics of the 6SN7. Section 5-3 illustrates how the grid voltage in Fig. 5-11a remains at zero during the positive half of the input cycle; hence,

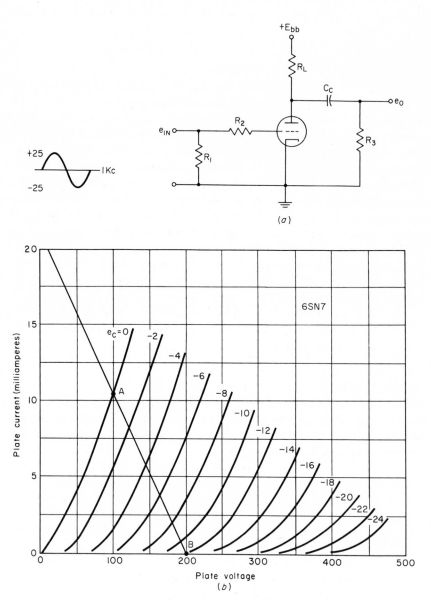

Fig. 5-11. (a) Squaring circuit. (b) Load-line characteristic.

the output remains at the quiescent value. During the negative half of the input cycle, the tube is driven from 0 to -12 volts, where the tube is cut off. The rise time of the output square wave becomes the time required for the input signal to change from 0 to -12 volts. This, too, can be determined from the equation

$$E = E_m \sin 2\pi ft$$
$$12 = 25 \sin [(360°)(10^3)t]$$
$$0.48 = \sin (360°)(10^3)t$$
$$\sin^{-1} 0.48 = \sin^{-1} [\sin(360°)(10^3)(t)]$$
$$28.7° = (360°)(10^3)t$$
$$t = (28.7°)/(360°)(10^3) = 80 \ \mu\text{sec}$$

It becomes apparent that the higher the input frequency the shorter the rise and fall times of the output square wave. The maximum input frequency is limited by the inherent switching time of the circuit.

Triode switching time is determined from the load connected to the triode and the tube's output capacitance paralleled by the circuit's distributed capacitance.

5-5 TRIODE CAPACITANCE

Just as the diode has interelectrode capacitance, the triode has three interelectrode capacitances to consider: grid-cathode, plate-cathode, and grid-plate. As in the diode, these are small, just a few picofarads; but at high frequencies, they can affect the circuit's operation. For example, the grid-plate capacitance can couple signal energy from the output circuit back into the input; and if this energy is of sufficient amplitude and of the right phase, a feedback-type oscillator can result.

At frequencies where a tube's capacitive reactance is a factor, the shunting effects of the grid-cathode and the plate-cathode capacitances can reduce the input and output impedances of an amplifier. In pulse circuit applications, the switching time of the stage is influenced. The actual reduction in input impedance is more than might be expected, because the Miller effect (Sec. A-9) makes the input capacitance much higher than just the grid-cathode capacitance:

$$C_{in} = C_{gk} + (1 + A)C_{gp} \qquad \text{5-4}$$

where C_{in} = input capacitance
C_{gk} = grid-cathode capacitance
C_{gp} = grid-plate capacitance
A = voltage gain of amplifier

Figure 5-12a is the circuit of a standard triode amplifier. Note that the input capacitance has virtually no resistance in series. Any negative step function applied to the circuit will be developed across the input capacitance instantaneously. Theoretically, there is no switching-time limitation. Its equivalent input circuit is shown in Fig. 5-12b.

The input circuit of Fig. 5-11a, however, has a series resistance connected in the grid circuit. The equivalent input now has a finite switching time determined by R_z and C_{in}, the Miller input capacitance. This time can be determined from the equation

$$e_{co} = E(1 - \epsilon^{-t/\tau})$$

where e_{co} = cutoff potential and E is the maximum amplitude of the applied pulse.

OUTPUT-CIRCUIT SWITCHING TIME

The output switching time is limited by the tube's output capacitance, the distributed capacitance of the circuit, the input capacitance of the following stage (if any), and the total load resistance on the tube. The larger the capacitance and load, the longer the switching time. In the following numerical example, assume that the triode of Fig. 5-13 has an output capacitance of 2 pf and a distributed capacitance of 20 pf. If a step function at the input cuts off the tube instantaneously, what are the rise and fall times of the output? The equivalent circuit for the triode in the cutoff region (shown in Fig. 5-13b) is connected to the equivalent capacitance C_{pk} paralleled by the distributed capacitance C_d. $C_{pk} + C_d = 22$ pf. According to Eq. (4-2), the rise time of the output pulse becomes

$$t_r = 2.2\tau_r$$
$$= (2.2)(22)(10^{-12})(35)(10^3) = 1.7 \ \mu sec$$

The fall time is computed from the equivalent circuit shown in Fig. 5-13c. The fully charged capacitor voltage must decay through the equivalent

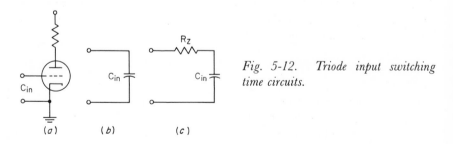

Fig. 5-12. Triode input switching time circuits.

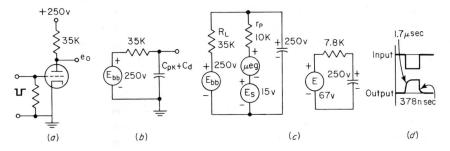

Fig. 5-13.   Triode output switching time circuits.

circuit of the active region. The capacitor is connected to the Thévenin equivalent of the active region (r_p and E_s are determined graphically from the tube's output characteristics and load line). According to Eq. (4-2), the fall time becomes

$$t_f = 2.2\tau_f$$
$$= (2.2)(22)(10^{-12})(7.8)(10^3) = 378 \text{ nsec}$$

The input and output waveshapes are shown in Fig. 5-13d.

5-6   DUAL-TRIODE SQUARING

An improved dual-triode squarer (or clipper) can be made with two triodes, each using cutoff clipping. The circuit is shown in Fig. 5-14. Grid-bias voltage for both stages is developed by the plate currents flowing through R_k. If the input signal goes sufficiently negative, V_1 will be cut off, but a sufficiently large positive swing of the input signal will make the cathode of V_2 positive enough to cut V_2 off. The clipping levels may be adjusted to any desired values by inserting bias voltages of either polarity

Fig. 5-14.   Double clipping with two triodes.

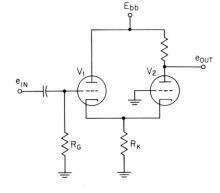

in each of the grid-to-ground leads. By making R_k large enough, V_1 will not draw grid current on large positive input swings, and this circuit will then have little loading effect on the previous stage. This makes the input impedance much higher than that of the diode limiter, or the grid-current limiter, or the saturation type of triode limiter.

Figure 5-15 illustrates a combination of the dual-triode clipper and a conventional two-stage amplifier. It is used in the Heath Model AO-1 audio oscillator, which generates a sine wave or a square wave, depending on the position of the DPDT switch shown in the figure. The input signal is obtained from a sine-wave oscillator adjusted to the desired frequency. If the switch is in the "down" position, the circuit is a normal RC-coupled two-stage amplifier with a feedback resistor from the plate of V_2 to the cathode of V_1; this negative feedback reduces the amplifier's gain but also reduces distortion and improves stability and frequency response. Different values of cathode biasing resistors are required because the second stage is handling signals of higher amplitude than the first. When the

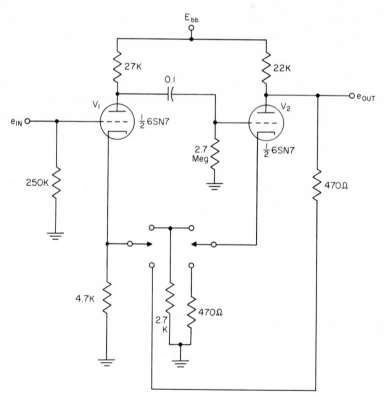

Fig. 5-15. Clipper-amplifier section of the Heath Model AO-1 audio oscillator.

switch is in the "up" position, the negative feedback loop is removed and a common-cathode resistance (4.7 and 2.7 kilohms in parallel) couples the signal from V_1 to V_2. On positive signal peaks V_1 amplifies the signal, and its output is coupled from the plate to the grid of V_2, as well as from its cathode to the cathode of V_2. This combination of signals drives V_2 into cutoff and clips the signal. On negative peaks of the input signal, V_1 is driven into cutoff, and this negative peak is clipped. The result is a good square wave at the plate of V_2.

PROBLEMS

5-1 Assume that a 12AU7 is to operate from a 300-volt d-c supply into a load resistance of 30 kilohms. What is the equivalent-circuit output potential of the two regions of operation, active and cutoff? (Assume $e_g = 0$ volts).

5-2 If the load resistance in Prob. 5-1 is doubled, how is the Thévenin equivalent impedance for the active region influenced?

5-3 What is the "grid base" for the 12AU7 with a 30-kilohm load and a 300-volt d-c supply?

5-4 If the value of load resistance in a triode stage is varied, how does the grid base vary?

5-5 Refer to Prob. 5-1. Assume that a 40-volt negative pulse, whose duration time is 0.1 msec, is applied to the circuit. What is the rise time of the output pulse? (Assume a zero rise time for the input pulse.)

5-6 What is the fall time of the output pulse for the circuit of Prob. 5-5?

5-7 If the load resistance in Prob. 5-5 is increased to 5 kilohms, what are the rise and fall times of the output if the input pulse drives the tube into cutoff in zero time? Assume the duration time of the input pulse to be 500 μsec.

5-8 If a 6SN7 triode is operated as a squaring circuit (Fig. 5-9), with a sine-wave signal (2 kc) whose $E_m = 50$ volts at the input, what are the peak-to-peak output and the rise and fall times of the output if $R_1 = 470$ kilohms, $R_L = 20$ kilohms, and $E_{bb} = 150$ volts? (Assume a distributed capacitance of 50 pf.)

5-9 What is the minimum input switching time for the circuit of Fig. 5-9 if $R_L = 20$ kilohms, $E_{bb} = 150$ volts, $R_1 = 470$ kilohms, $C_{gk} = 4$ pf, $C_{gp} = 3.5$ pf, $\mu = 20$, $r_p = 10$ kilohms?

5-10 What is the maximum a-c frequency which can be squared by the circuit of Prob. 5-9 if E_m is maintained at 50 volts? For an $E_m = 100$ volts? (Assume $E_{co} = -10$ volts.)

5-11   In Prob. 5-8, if R_L is decreased, what change in the output switching time and amplitude will occur?

5-12   If the triode in Prob. 5-11 is replaced by one having a higher μ, will the switching time be increased, decreased, or unchanged?

5-7   TRANSISTORS AS SWITCHES

INTRODUCTION

Analysis of transistor switches is similar to that of the three-element vacuum device. The transistor circuit is divided into three regions of operation: active, saturation, and cutoff. Circuit calculations utilize equivalent circuits, representing the three regions of operation.

Transistor switches are classed in one of two groups: saturating switches and nonsaturating types. The nonsaturating switches must be employed in high-speed switching applications, because of objectionable storage time delay associated with saturating switches. Both types of switches are analyzed in this chapter.

Unlike vacuum tubes, transistors are subject to serious instability with temperature variations. Additional circuitry must be employed in order to overcome the problem. In order to understand the theory of the related compensation circuits, it is important that a student analyze the steady-state characteristics of the transistor device.

STEADY-STATE CHARACTERISTICS

A typical family of collector characteristics is shown in Fig. 5-16b. The circuit associated with these characteristics is shown in Fig. 5-16a. A load line for the circuit is drawn on the characteristic curves. The load line is the graph of the circuit equation:

$$V_{cc} = E_{ce} + I_c R_L \tag{5-5}$$

The operating point of the transistor, for any particular value of base current, will be the intersection of the load line and the particular characteristic curve representing that base current. For example, if V_{bb} is set to 10 volts, the base current will equal 100 μa (the internal base-emitter resistance is negligible compared with the 100-kilohm external resistor). From Fig. 5-16b the collector current is found to be 6.5 ma and the collector voltage is 5.3 volts. Substituting these values into Eq. (5-5), along with the circuit values of V_{cc} and R_L, will allow a check of this graphic solution for the collector voltage and current.

In most of the transistor circuits to be discussed, the transistor will be operating at one of the two extreme ends of the load line and will make rapid transitions between these two states. At one end of the load line the collector voltage is equal to the supply voltage. This is called the *cutoff*

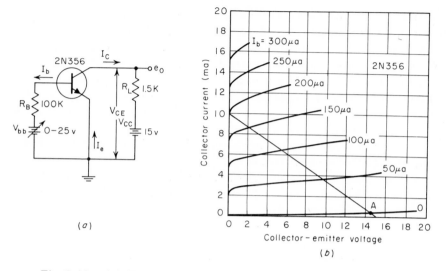

(a)

(b)

Fig. 5-16. (a) Typical transistor amplifier. (b) Graphic representation.

region of operation, and the transistor is said to be *off*. At the other end of
the load line the collector voltage is near zero, and the collector current is
limited only by the load resistor. This is the *saturation region*, and the transistor is *on*. In between these two extremes is the *active region*. In Fig. 5-16,
if V_{bb} is set to zero, the base current is zero and the transistor will be off.
Raising V_{bb} to 20 volts will increase the base current to 200 μa, and the
transistor will be on.

CUTOFF REGION

Figure 5-16*b* shows that when $I_b = 0$, there is still a small collector current, about 0.4 ma. If the collector-base junction of a transistor is reverse-
biased and the emitter connection is left open, as shown in Fig. 5-17*a*, a

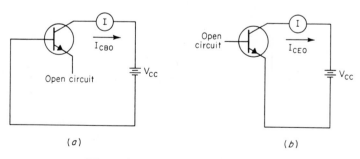

(a)

(b)

Fig. 5-17. Collector leakage currents.

small current will flow due to minority carriers. It is usually of the order of a few microamperes at room temperature, but it increases rapidly with an increase in temperature. For germanium, I_{CBO} doubles for each $10°C$ increase in temperature. For silicon, I_{CBO} triples for each $10°C$ increase in temperature, but the value is usually smaller to start with than than for germanium. At $20°C$, I_{CBO} for silicon is only about one one-thousandth that of germanium. A silicon transistor usually has a much smaller value of I_{CBO} than does a germanium transistor.

If a transistor is connected as shown in Fig. 5-17b, the minority-carrier collector current is called I_{CEO} and is much higher than I_{CBO}.

In a normally biased grounded-emitter circuit, there are several currents flowing, as shown in Fig. 5-18. The emitter current I_e splits up into the base current I_b' and the collector current I_c', so

$$I_e = I_b' + I_c' \tag{5-6}$$

In addition to these currents, the reverse current I_{CBO} is still present at the collector-base junction. This current is in such a direction as to aid I_c' and oppose I_b'. The net base and collector currents are

$$I_b = I_b' - I_{CBO} \tag{5-7}$$

$$I_c = I_c' + I_{CBO} \tag{5-8}$$

Substituting I_b' from Eq. (5-7) and I_c' from Eq. (5-8) into Eq. (5-6) gives

$$I_e = (I_b + I_{CBO}) + (I_c - I_{CBO}) = I_e = I_b + I_c \tag{5-9}$$

which means that the emitter current will equal the sum of the base and collector currents, whether I_{CBO} is considered or not.

From the definition of the emitter-to-collector current gain alpha,

$$\alpha = \frac{I_c'}{I_e} \tag{5-10}$$

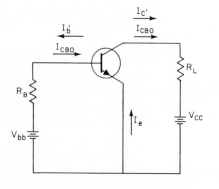

Fig. 5-18. Current paths in a typical transistor circuit.

Substituting I_c' from Eq. (5-10) into Eq. (5-8) gives

$$I_c = \alpha I_e + I_{CBO} \tag{5-11}$$

From Eq. (5-9), $I_e = I_c$ when $I_b = 0$; and substituting this into Eq. (5-11) gives $I_c = \alpha I_c + I_{CBO}$. Solving for I_c gives $I_c = I_{CBO}/(1 - \alpha)$. This value of collector current with zero base current is the I_{CEO} mentioned above and measured with the circuit shown in Fig. 5-17b. Therefore

$$I_{CEO} = \frac{I_{CBO}}{1 - \alpha} \tag{5-12}$$

The base-to-collector current gain beta is related to alpha by

$$\alpha = \frac{\beta}{\beta + 1} \tag{5-13}$$

and substituting for alpha in Eq. (5-12) gives

$$I_{CEO} = (\beta + 1)I_{CBO} \tag{5-14}$$

The 2N356 transistor has a beta of about 30 and an I_{CBO} of about 4 μa at 25°C. From Eq. (5-14), I_{CEO} is found to be 124 μa. At 35°C this would increase to 248 μa; and at 45°C, to 496 μa. This current I_{CEO} is the small collector current shown in Fig. 5-16b for the $I_b = 0$ curve.

It is possible to reduce this value of I_{CEO} by making the base current a small reverse current. If Eqs. (5-9) and (5-11) are combined by eliminating I_e, then $I_c = \alpha(I_b + I_c) + I_{CBO}$; and solving for I_c gives

$$I_c = \frac{\alpha I_b + I_{CBO}}{1 - \alpha} \tag{5-15}$$

If I_b is a reverse current, equal to the value of I_{CBO} at the highest operating temperature, $I_b = I_{CBO}$, and substituting this into Eq. (5-15) gives $I_c = I_{CBO}$, which has been found to be just a few microamperes. At lower temperatures this current will be even less; thus the transistor can be made to act almost like an open circuit or a switch in the OFF position.

SATURATION REGION

In order to better analyze the saturation region of a transistor's operation, the section in Fig. 5-16b where the collector voltage is less than 2 volts is enlarged. This is shown in Fig. 5-19; the load line for the circuit of Fig. 5-16a is still shown. It can be seen that each curve has a *knee* below which the current drops rapidly to zero. The saturation region is that region of operation at which the load line crosses below the knee of the characteristic curve. In Fig. 5-19 the load line crosses the 200-μa curve slightly above the knee, and it crosses the 250-μa curve well below the knee. Therefore, any base current greater than about 220 μa would drive this transistor into the saturation region.

In this region the collector-emitter voltage is low, less than 0.1 volt. Because of the relatively high base current, the base-emitter voltage will be higher than 0.1 volt. Therefore, the base is more positive than the collector and, this being an NPN transistor, the collector-base junction is forward-biased. Of course, the emitter-base junction is also forward-biased, so the transitor will have a low resistance between the collector and the emitter. It can be seen from Fig. 5-19 that for a base current of 250 μa, $V_{ce} = 0.1$ volt and $I_c = 10$ ma. Therefore, the collector-to-emitter resistance is $0.1/0.01 = 10$ ohms. If the base current increases to 300 μa, this resistance drops to less than 8 ohms. This particular transistor is capable of operating in the region of 100-ma collector current and 10-ma base current; this could reduce the resistance to less than 0.5 ohm.

Usually the base current for the ON condition is made two or three times the minimum value needed to just reach saturation. This is done partially to lower the collector-emitter resistance, but more importantly to provide for stability, a margin of safety to take care of variations in the transistor's characteristics due to temperature or manufacturing tolerance.

R_o/R_s RATIO

The cutoff region was established as point A of Fig. 5-16b. The OFF resistance of the device, R_o, can be calculated at this point. With a collector

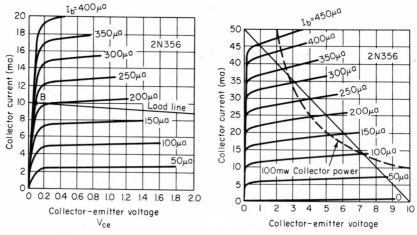

Fig. 5-19. Enlarged collector characteristics.

Fig. 5-20. Collector dissipation curve.

voltage of 14.5 volts and a collector current of about 0.5 ma, $R_o = E_c/I_c = (14.5)(0.5)(10^{-3}) = 2.9$ kilohms.

The ON resistance of the device, R_s, is determined at the saturation point. It was calculated previously at point B in Fig. 5-19 to be 10 ohms.

A figure of merit classifying a transistor as a switching device is identified as the R_o/R_s *ratio*. The 2N356 operating into a 1.5-kilohm load has a figure of merit equal to

$$\frac{R_o}{R_s} = \frac{(2.9)(10^3)}{10} = 290$$

The ideal switch has an R_o/R_s ratio equal to infinity; however, such a value is not possible in a transistor switch. Values between 10^2 and 10^6 are typical. With high R_o/R_s ratios, saturation collector potentials approach zero, and cutoff collector potentials approach the collector supply voltage.

It is apparent that the value of load resistance connected into the circuit influences the R_o/R_s ratio. However, the value of R_L is partially determined by power dissipation, voltage breakdown, and maximum collector current; hence, compromises in the R_o/R_s ratio must be made.

VOLTAGE AND CURRENT MAXIMA

All transistors have certain maximum ratings, and these must be considered when working with switching circuits. The most important of these are collector-emitter voltage, collector current, and collector power dissipation. Switching circuits usually operate with the transistor at either cutoff or saturation and just briefly in the active region, as a transition is taking place. Because of this, the maximum collector-power-dissipation rating is usually of little importance. At saturation the collector voltage is very low, and at cutoff the collector current is very low. During the transition time the voltage and current may be high enough to exceed the maximum power-dissipation rating for a short period of time, but this is usually permissible because transistors are able to withstand power overloads of up to 500 per cent for very short time periods. In Fig. 5-20 the dashed line represents the maximum collector power rating; that is, for any point of operation above the line, the product of I_c and E_{ce} exceeds the 100-ma rating of the transistor. If the transistor were being used in a switching circuit with a 10-volt collector supply and a 200-ohm load resistor, the load line would be as shown in Fig. 5-20. Steady operation at cutoff or saturation would be well below the maximum-power curve. During the transition the maximum power will be exceeded for a small portion of the time; but if this time period is short, compared with the time between transitions, the transistor will not be damaged.

It is important to make sure that the collector supply voltage is less than the maximum allowable collector voltage, and that the collector saturation current is less than the maximum allowable collector current. Additional caution should be observed when using inductive loads, because high-voltage transients can be developed and transistor damage can result.

5-8 TRANSISTOR SQUARING CIRCUIT

Figure 5-21a illustrates a typical squaring circuit employing a transistor as a switch. Figure 5-21b shows the load line plotted on the collector characteristics of the device. The input to the stage is a 20-volt peak-to-peak sine wave at 400 cycles, and the resultant output is a square wave. With no signal applied, the transistor is off and the output is at the collector supply voltage (point A of Fig. 5-21b). When the signal is applied, the negative half of the cycle drives the transistor to saturation, and the output increases to a value near zero (point B). During the positive half of

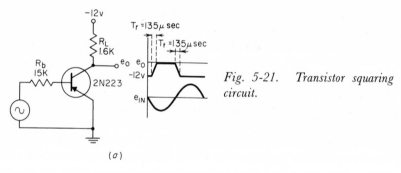

Fig. 5-21. Transistor squaring circuit.

(a)

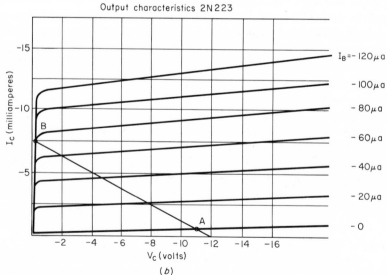

(b)

the input cycle, the input is reverse-biased; hence, the output remains off (point A).

The rise and decay times are determined from the time required for the base current to reach the saturation value. Since the base-emitter resistance is negligible compared with a series R_b of 15 kilohms, the bias current is equal to e_{in}/R_b. Refer to the load line of Fig. 5-21b. Note that the transistor saturates when the base current reaches 80 μa. Therefore, the input voltage required for saturation is the voltage across R_b. The saturation voltage becomes

$$E_{b(sat)} = R_b I_{b(sat)} = (15)(10^{+3})(80)(10^{-6}) = 1.2 \text{ volts}$$

When the input signal reaches -1.2 volts, the switch is saturated and the output rises to approximately -0.2 volt. The rise time (and the fall time) of the output pulse becomes

$$e_{in(sat)} = E_m \sin 2\pi ft$$
$$1.2 = 10 \sin (6.28)(400)t$$
$$0.12 = \sin (6.28)(400)t$$
$$(6.28)(400)t = 6.9° = 0.1205 \text{ rad}$$
$$t = \frac{0.1205}{(6.28)(400)} = 48 \text{ } \mu\text{sec}$$

In the circuit of Fig. 5-21a both the load resistor and the base resistor influence the rise and fall times. The load resistor influences the saturation current required at the base, and the base resistor influences the amount of voltage needed at the input to cause saturation. The rise and fall times of the output wave are also influenced by the frequency of the applied wave. As the input frequency increases, the rise and fall times decrease. However, the transistor can switch no faster than the device is capable of switching.

PROBLEMS

5-13 A 2N398 germanium transistor has beta equal to 60 and $I_{CBO} = 6$ μa at 25°C. Find I_{CBO} and I_{CEO} at 45°C.

5-14 What is the approximate collector ON resistance of the circuit of Fig. 5-22a?

5-15 When no signal is applied to the input of the circuit, what is the quiescent output voltage in the circuit of Fig. 5-22a?

5-16 What is the approximate OFF resistance for the circuit of Fig. 5-22a?

5-17 If resistor R_1 of Fig. 5-22a is increased to 40 kilohms, what is the OFF resistance?

5-18 If resistor R_1 of Fig. 5-22a is 40 kilohms, will the rise time of the

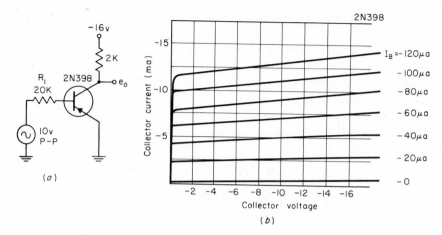

Fig. 5-22. Squaring circuit of Probs. 5-14 through 5-23.

output pulse increase or decrease? At what input voltage will the transistor saturate? (Assume that a 10-volt peak-to-peak signal is applied.)

5-19 If the collector supply in the circuit of Fig. 5-22a is halved, what will be the new peak-to-peak output signal? (Assume that a 10-volt peak-to-peak a-c signal is applied.)

5-20 Refer to Fig. 5-22a. What is the rise time of the output pulse if the applied signal is 400 cps?

5-21 If the value of R_1 in Prob. 5-20 is doubled and a 400-cps signal (a-c) is applied, what is the rise time of the output square wave?

5-22 Refer to the circuit of Fig. 5-22a. If the value of the load resistance is doubled and all the other components are as shown in the figure, what is the rise time of the output square wave if a 400-cycle a-c signal is applied?

5-23 What is the rise time of the output pulse if the frequency of the applied signal at Fig. 5-22a is 1,000 cps a-c?

5-9 TRANSIENT RESPONSE

Assume that a perfect pulse consisting of two step signals is applied to the transistor switch shown in Fig. 5-23. The input and output signals are also shown in the figure. The various time periods involved will be defined along with a brief discussion of the factors involved.

DELAY TIME

This is shown as T_D and is the time from the beginning of the input pulse to the time the output voltage has changed 10 per cent of its total change. Three things cause this delay. First, the collector-emitter capacitance was charged to V_{cc} volts and must discharge through the load resistor. Second, it takes some time for the emitter current carriers to diffuse across the base region. Third, at low emitter current densities, the current gain and frequency response are low.

RISE TIME

This is T_r, the time it takes for the output signal to change in amplitude from 10 to 90 per cent of its highest value. It is caused by the first two factors of the delay time, plus any nonlinear characteristics in the external circuit. It can be reduced by overdriving the transistor into the saturation region, but this can increase the storage time. (This will be explained later.) There is only one accurate means of determining the rise time, and that is through empirical methods. A large number of equations have been developed, and at best they are all approximately correct. The equation (see Seymour Schwartz, "Selected Semiconductor Circuits Handbook," p. 6-5, John Wiley & Sons, Inc., New York, 1960) in use for the common-emitter configuration is

$$T_r = \frac{1}{(1 - \alpha_{FB})\omega_{\alpha_{fb}}} \ln \frac{i_b\alpha_{FB}}{i_b\alpha_{FB} - 0.9i_c(1 - \alpha_{FB})} \tag{5-16}$$

where α_{fb} = normal short-circuit current transfer ratio
$\omega_{\alpha_{fb}}$ = cutoff frequency, rad/sec
i_c = collector saturation current
i_b = base current at saturation

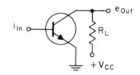

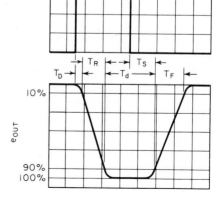

Fig. 5-23.   Transistor switching characteristics.

The equation is useful because it illustrates that the rise time can be held to specifications by controlling the circuit's base and collector currents at saturation.

PULSE TIME, OR PULSE DURATION

This is the length of time the pulse amplitude remains above 90 per cent of its maximum value. It is designated as T_d.

STORAGE TIME

This is the time from the trailing edge of the input pulse to the instant at which the amplitude of the output pulse drops to 90 per cent of its maximum value. It is caused by the time it takes for the minority carriers in the base regions of the transistor to be removed by the collector. The further the transistor is driven into the saturation region during the ON time, the longer it will take to remove these minority carriers during the OFF time. For high-speed switching, this time can be reduced by having the ON state in the active region of the transistor. This increases the collector-emitter resistance and is an unstable condition, but the latter difficulty can be overcome by *collector clamping,* which will be discussed later. Storage time is shown as T_s in Fig. 5-23 and is given as

$$T_s \frac{\omega_{\alpha_{fb}} + \omega_{\alpha_{rb}}}{\omega_{\alpha_{fb}}\omega_{\alpha_{rb}}(1 - \alpha_{FB}\alpha_{RB})} \ln \frac{i_{B_1} - i_{B_2}}{i_{C_1}\left[\left(\dfrac{1 - \alpha_{FB}}{\alpha_{FB}}\right) - i_{B_2}\right]} \tag{5-17}$$

where subscripts 1 and 2 are initial and final values at the time turnoff voltage is applied to the circuit, $\omega_{\alpha_{rb}}$ = reverse common-base cutoff frequency in radians per second, α_{RB} = reverse short-circuit current transfer ratio, and i_B and i_C are base and collector current, respectively.

FALL TIME

The time it takes for the output amplitude to change from 90 per cent of its maximum value to 10 per cent is called fall time and is designated T_f. It is caused by the same factors which effect the rise time. It may be reduced by applying a reverse current at the end of the input pulse. The equation for fall time is given as

$$T_f = \frac{1}{(1 - \alpha_{FB})\omega_{\alpha_{fb}}} \ln \frac{i_{C_1}[\alpha_{FB}i_{B_2}/(1 - \alpha_{FB})]}{0.1i_{C_1} - \alpha_{FB}i_{B_2}/(1 - \alpha_{FB})} \tag{5-18}$$

The sum of the storage time and the fall time is called the *turnoff time* T_{off}. The combination of all these time delays determines the maximum rate at which the circuit can operate.

The total switching time is given as a figure of merit and is

$$T_T = T_{\text{on}} + T_{\text{off}} = T_d + T_r + T_s + T_f$$

This total switching time may seem a serious limitation in the use of transistors in switching circuits; however, even with their deficiencies, transistors more closely resemble the ideal switch than do vacuum tubes. This will be brought out more fully in discussions of particular circuits.

IMPROVING SWITCHING TIME

Equations (5-16) and (5-18) indicate that some control of the rise time and fall time can be effected by controlling the base current. Increasing the forward bias current can reduce the rise time when the transistor is switched to the ON state. Conversely, when the transistor is switched OFF, the fall time can be reduced by applying a large reverse bias current. The switching time of a transistor can be reduced if the driving pulse has a waveshape similar to the one shown in Fig. 5-24a. (The figure shows the output after the ideal pulse is applied at the input.)

The effects of producing a larger-than-normal forward base current can be achieved by connecting a capacitor in parallel with R_b (Fig. 5-24b). During the input transient (negative step) the capacitor bypasses R_b, and a large current flows into the capacitor $[i_c = C(d_e/d_t)]$ through the low-resistance base-emitter junction. Once the capacitor is fully charged, R_b maintains the normal forward bias at the input. The result is a decreased rise time. When the input switches off (positive step), the capacitor discharges through R_b and the input base-emitter junction, providing additional reverse bias current. The result is a decreased fall time. The output in Fig. 5-24b more clearly resembles the ideal pulse at the input.

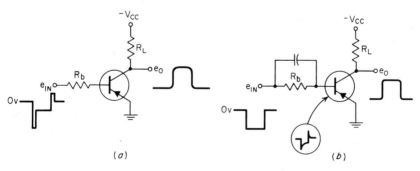

Fig. 5-24. Improved switching time.

The equivalent circuits for the three regions of transistor operation are determined from the graphical linear models. The circuit and characteristics of Fig. 5-16 are used.

CUTOFF-REGION EQUIVALENT CIRCUIT

The equivalent circuit representing the cutoff region for the circuit of Fig. 5-16a is shown in Fig. 5-25a. Note that for cutoff, $I_b = 0$; hence, the βI_b generator represents an approximate zero current source. Since the off resistance $R_o \gg R_L$, the resultant equivalent circuit seen at the output is R_L in series with the collector supply. The equivalent circuit is essentially the load and the collector supply in series.

SATURATION-REGION EQUIVALENT CIRCUIT

The equivalent circuit for the saturation region is shown in Fig. 5-25b. Note that the equivalent circuit consists of a parallel branch of R_s. The value of R_s is generally less than 10 ohms; hence, the final equivalent circuit can be shown as a short circuit.

ACTIVE-REGION EQUIVALENT CIRCUIT

It should be recalled that in establishing the equivalent circuit from the linear model of a vacuum-tube circuit, a compensation potential E_s was employed. In the same manner a compensation current I_o is used in the equivalent circuit of the transistor's active region. Figure 5-26a represents an equivalent circuit of the active region for a circuit similar to that in Fig. 5-16a. Figure 5-26b represents an ideal collector characteristic superimposed on the actual collector characteristic for the 2N337. The parameter β is determined graphically from the relationship

$$\beta = \frac{\Delta I_c}{\Delta I_b}$$

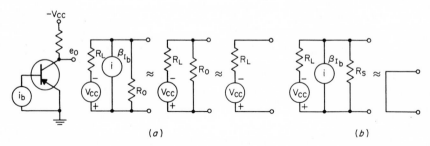

Fig. 5-25.   Transistor equivalent circuits. (a) Cutoff region. (b) Saturation region.

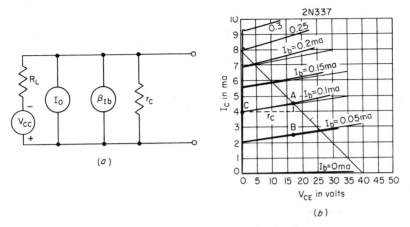

Fig. 5-26. *Transistor equivalent circuit, active region.*

The compensation current I_0 is determined from the relationship

$$I_c = I_o + \beta I_b \tag{5-19}$$

The collector resistance r_c is the reciprocal of the slope of any one of the characteristic curves. The final equivalent circuit can be developed as either a Thévenin or a Norton circuit, depending upon the circuit's application.

EXAMPLE   What is the Thévenin equivalent generator for the active region of a 2N337 with a 5-kilohm load? Assume a collector supply of 40 volts and a base bias of 0.1 ma. ($T_A = 25°\text{C.}$) Beta is determined graphically in Fig. 5-26b (points A and B):

$$\beta = \frac{\Delta I_c}{\Delta I_b} = \frac{(2)(10^{-3})}{(0.05)(10^{-3})} = 40$$

The compensation current is derived from Eq. (5-19):

$$I_c = I_o + \beta I_b$$
$$(4.5)(10^{-3}) = I_o + (40)(0.1)(10^{-3})$$
$$I_o = (0.5)(10^{-3})$$

r_c is determined graphically between points C and A:

$$r_c = \frac{\Delta E_c}{\Delta I_c} = \frac{35}{10^{-3}}$$
$$= 35 \text{ kilohms}$$

The values for β, r_c, and I_o can now be substituted into the equivalent circuit (Fig. 5-27a). In order to develop the Thévenin

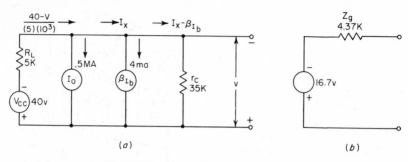

Fig. 5-27. Example of equivalent circuit.

equivalent generator, the open-circuit potential must be determined. This voltage is shown as V in the figure. V is equal to the product of the current $I_x - \beta I_b$ and r_c (35 kilohms):

$$V = (I_x - \beta I_b)r_c$$

However, $I_x = (40 - V)/R_L - I_o$; hence,

$$V = \left(\frac{40 - V}{R_L} - I_o - \beta I_b\right)r_c$$

By substituting the known quantities and solving for V, the Thévenin equivalent voltage becomes 16.7 volts (Fig. 5-27b). The Thévenin equivalent resistance is found by looking into the open-circuit terminals with the current sources removed and the voltage source replaced with a short circuit.

$$Z = 4.37 \text{ kilohms}$$

5-11 NONSATURATING SWITCHES

The main disadvantage of employing saturating transistors as switches is storage delay time. When the transistor is saturated, the collector potential drops below that of the base, and carriers from the collector region are transferred and stored in the base. When the transistor is switched off, time is required to remove these carriers; hence, the storage delay time. The simplest solution to the problem is to maintain the collector at a potential above the base.

In Fig. 4-20 a diode was used as in a clamp circuit. The plate potential on the vacuum tube could not increase above the clamping potential. A similar technique is employed with transistor switches. Figure 5-28 shows a nonsaturating switch utilizing a collector clamp. The collector clamping level is established by the voltage divider, consisting of R_1 and R_2. $E_{c_1} =$

$V_{cc}R_1/(R_1 + R_2)$. With no signal applied to the circuit, the output equals V_{cc}. When a driving pulse is applied at the base, the output rises to the clamp potential E_{c_1}. If diode D_1 and resistors R_1 and R_2 were removed from the circuit, the output would rise to almost zero, as shown by the dotted line. The transistor would saturate.

EXAMPLE   Assume that a 2N337 is to be used as a nonsaturating switch. (Collector characteristics are shown in Fig. 5-26b.) If the collector supply is -30 volts and the circuit is the one shown in Fig. 5-28, what value of R_1 is required if R_2 is to be 5 kilohms and the clamping level is to be -5 volts?

$$E_{c_1} = \frac{V_{cc}R_1}{R_1 + R_2}$$

$$R_1 = \frac{E_{c_1}R_2}{V_{cc} - E_{c_1}}$$

$$= \frac{(5)(5)(10^3)}{30 - 5}$$

$$= \frac{(25)(10^3)}{25} = 1 \text{ kilohm}$$

5-12   TRIODE CLAMPERS

The grid-cathode circuit of a vacuum triode can act like a diode, conducting with positive grid voltages and open with negative. Triodes can therefore be used as d-c restorers or clampers, and the resulting signal can then be amplified along with its d-c component. Of course, the plate cir-

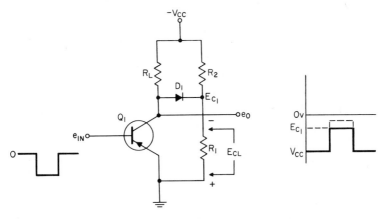

Fig. 5-28.   Clamp circuit used to eliminate storage delay.

cuit of the triode adds another d-c component of voltage, E_b, but this voltage value does not depend upon the amplitude of the input signal. The amplification function of the triode is not altered. The grid of the triode is negative for almost the entire portion of its operation, going positive for a very short portion of each cycle to recharge the capacitor. The d-c voltage added to the incoming signal can be thought of as the bias voltage of the amplifier, but it has the advantage over fixed biasing in that it automatically adjusts to the level of the input signal. This is called *grid-leak biasing*, and is usually used in class C r-f amplifiers. It does distort the waveform slightly and loads down the previous stage.

5-13 SYNCHRONIZED CLAMPING

In all the clamping circuits discussed above, the signal itself controls the time during which the clamping switch is closed. An alternative method is to have a separate *control signal* determine the clamping period. This controlling signal is usually synchronized by the controlled signal voltage, but the points of opening and closing the clamping switch do not have to depend upon a particular amplitude of the controlled signal. These are called *switched* or *synchronized clamps*.

The clamps discussed previously have been able to conduct in only one direction, clamping only when the signal was above a certain level or for a different circuit when the signal dropped below a certain level. These are called *one-way* or *single-side clamps*. When the clamping action does not depend directly on the signal itself, a *two-way* or *double-side clamp* can be designed.

Figure 5-29 shows a triode with its plate and cathode connected in a clamping circuit similar to that of Fig. 4-18a. If E_{cc} is a negative voltage, no clamping action takes place until a positive voltage is applied to the

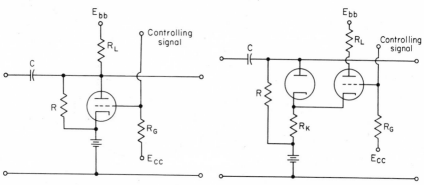

Fig. 5-29. Triode clamping.   *Fig. 5-30. Controlled diode clamp.*

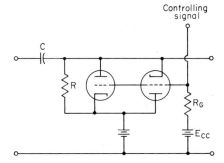

Fig. 5-31. Two-way clamp.

grid. On the other hand, E_{cc} can be positive and clamping will take place at all times unless a negative voltage is applied to the grid. The clamping action is not quite so effective as in a diode clamp because of the higher resistance of the triode.

A controlled diode clamp can be used, as shown in Fig. 5-30. Here the triode is to apply or remove an additional bias voltage (voltage drop across R_k) to the diode. These circuits are still one-way clamps; the grid potential just determines whether or not the tube will conduct when its plate goes positive.

A two-way clamp is shown in Fig. 5-31. Here E_{cc} is made positive. At least one of the two triodes will be conducting no matter what the controlled signal is until a negative voltage is applied to the grids. Then both tubes will be cut off and no clamping action will be present.

PROBLEMS

5-24 If a 2N356 is operated with a collector supply of 8 volts and a load resistance of 5 kilohms, what is the equivalent circuit for the saturated region? For the cutoff region?

5-25 Refer to Prob. 5-24. If the compensation current I_o is 0.1 ma, what is the collector resistance?

5-26 Refer to Prob. 5-25. What is the Thévenin equivalent impedance for the active region?

5-27 Refer to Fig. 5-28. Assume $Q_1 = 2N356$, $R_L = 5$ kilohms, $V_{cc} = 8$ volts, and $R_2 = 1$ kilohm. What value of R_1 will prevent the collector voltage from dropping below 2 volts?

5-28 Refer to Fig. 5-28. If $Q_1 = 2N398$, $R_L = R_2 = R_1 = 1$ kilohm, and $V_{cc} = 16$ volts, what will be the peak-to-peak output if the transistor is driven by a 10-volt p-p square wave? (2N398 characteristics are in Fig. 5-22.)

5-29 Refer to Fig. 5-16a. Assume that V_{bb} is adjusted to 0 volts. What is the equivalent Thévenin circuit seen at the output? If V_{bb} is adjusted to 30 volts, what is the equivalent Thévenin circuit seen at the output?

5-30 Refer to the circuit of Fig. 5-28. Assume the following circuit values: $Q_1 = 2N337$, $R_L = 5$ kilohms, $V_{cc} = 30$ volts, $R_1 = 2$ kilohms, and $R_2 = 6$ kilohms. Assume a negative input pulse whose $t_d = 3$ msec and whose prf is 100 cps. Sketch the output waveshape; label all time and voltage levels.

5-31 Refer to the circuit of Fig. 5-28. Assume the circuit values to be $Q_1 = 2N337$, $R_L = R_1 = R_2 = 1$ kilohm, and $V_{cc} = 20$ volts. If the connections of D_1 are reversed, what is the quiescent output at e_o?

5-32 Assume that the signal of Prob. 5-30 is driving the circuit of Prob. 5-31. Sketch the output waveshape.

CHAPTER 6 BISTABLE MULTIVIBRATORS

Chapter 5 discussed two kinds of transistor switches: saturated and non-saturated. The theory of the saturated switch states that when a driving bias is applied at the input, the output voltage is driven to zero. When the driving bias is removed, the output returns to the collector supply potential. Figure 6-1 illustrates the switch with a driving pulse applied at the input. The circuit is similar to a single-stage common-emitter amplifier where the output is 180° out of phase with the input.

If two such switches are connected so that the output of the first is fed to the input of the second and the output of the second is connected to the input of the first, the circuit becomes a *bistable multivibrator*. It can be identified by many other names: binary, flip-flop, scale-of-two, divide-by-two, and Eccles-Jordan, after the initial developers of the circuit. The circuit is one which exhibits two conditions of stability; hence, the name bistable multivibrator. Figure 6-2 illustrates the direct-coupled version of the bistable multivibrator.

6-1 DIRECT-COUPLED BISTABLE MULTIVIBRATOR

Refer to the circuit of Fig. 6-2. When the collector supply potential (V_{cc}) is applied to the circuit, both transistors begin to conduct.

One will conduct more heavily than the other; assume that this is Q_1. Its collector voltage will drop, dropping the base voltage of Q_2 and causing the collector current of Q_2 to decrease and its voltage to rise. This rise in collector voltage of Q_2 will increase the base voltage of Q_1, which increases the

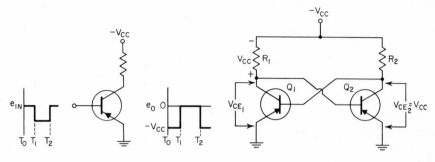

Fig. 6-1. *Transistor as a switch.*   Fig. 6-2. *Direct-coupled bistable multi-vibrator.*

collector current of Q_1 more rapidly. This is a positive-feedback action which drives the circuit very rapidly into its first stable state: Q_1 saturated and Q_2 cut off. Under these conditions the collector-to-emitter resistance of Q_1 is quite small compared with its load resistance R_1. (Refer to the equivalent circuit for a transistor switch under saturated conditions, Sec. 5-7.) The collector voltage of Q_1 is approximately zero. Since this is the input voltage of Q_2, theoretically, there is no bias on Q_2, so it is cut off. The collector-emitter resistance of Q_2 is high compared with its load resistance R_2; therefore, the voltage between its collector and emitter would equal the supply voltage if it were not for the fact that the base-emitter junction of Q_1 is forward-biased. The circuit will remain in this state until some external signal triggers it. Once it is triggered, the conditions reverse. Q_2 is heavily saturated and Q_1 is cut off. The triggering of the circuit can be effected by applying a large negative pulse to the base of transistor Q_2. The input pulse causes Q_2 to saturate, and the collector voltage becomes zero. Since the input of Q_1 is from the collector of Q_2, the bias on Q_2 is removed and switch Q_2 turns off. The actual time required for the regenerative switching action to take place is relatively short—a few microseconds.

The main drawback of the circuit shown in Fig. 6-2 is its triggering requirements. A trigger pulse of relatively large amplitude is required in order to have the circuit change states. Another drawback is the fact that the difference between the on and the off potentials across the transistors is very small—very nearly the same. The circuit is used mostly for current-mode switching, as discussed in Sec. 6-12.

6-2   SATURATED BISTABLE MULTIVIBRATORS

The circuit of Fig. 6-3 represents a modification of the circuit of Fig. 6-2. Note that two resistors have been added in place of the direct-coupling network. The values of these two resistors must be maintained within definite boundaries if the circuit is to perform satisfactorily. For example, if the values are small, the circuit will remain in its stable states and there will be no risk of the circuit being triggered by random noise or dynamic instabilites. However, the magnitude of the input trigger pulse must be very large. If the two resistors are made large, the conditions are reversed. The circuit will require only a small trigger pulse; however, it will be unstable and sensitive to noise or changes in dynamic levels. For every pair of transistors used in this circuit configuration there exists an optimum choice in the values of V_{cc}, the load resistance, and the coupling resistance. It is useful to examine the ON conditions and the OFF conditions for a typical circuit.

ON EQUATION

Refer to the circuit of Fig. 6-3. Assume that Q_1 is on and Q_2 is off and that V_{cc} and R_L have been determined from the collector characteristic curves of the transistor. In deriving the ON equation, it can be assumed that the base-emitter resistance is much smaller than the external circuit resistance. Assume further that when the transistor is off, the collector-emitter resistance is much larger than the external load circuit resistance. I_{co} can be considered to be negligible. With Q_1 on and Q_2 off, the collector current through Q_1 is given as $I_{c_1} = V_{cc}/R_{L_1}$.

$$I_{b_1} = \frac{I_{c_1}}{\alpha_{FE}}$$

$$I_{b_1} = \frac{V_{cc}}{R_{L_1}\alpha_{FE}} \qquad (6\text{-}1)$$

$$I_{R_{b_1}} = I_{b_1} + I_{R_{a_1}} \qquad (6\text{-}2)$$

Since Q_2 is off, $I_{c_2} = 0$; hence,

$$I_{R_{b_1}} = \frac{V_{cc} - V_{b_1}}{R_{b_1} + R_{L_2}} \qquad (6\text{-}3)$$

Fig. 6-3. Basic bistable circuit.

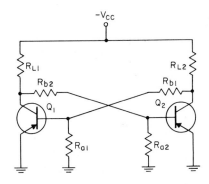

$$I_{R_{a_1}} = \frac{V_{b_1}}{R_{a_1}}$$ (6-4)

Substituting Eqs. (6-1), (6-3), and (6-4) into Eq. (6-2),

$$\frac{V_{cc} - V_{b_1}}{R_{b_1} + R_{L_2}} = \frac{V_{cc}}{R_{L_1}\alpha_{FE}} + \frac{V_{b_1}}{R_{a_1}}$$

If this equation is solved for R_{a_1},

$$R_{a_1} = \frac{R_{L_1} V_{b_1} \alpha_{FE}(R_{L_2} + R_{b_1})}{V_{cc}R_{L_1}\alpha_{FE} - V_{b_1}R_{L_1}\alpha_{FE} - V_{cc}R_{L_2} - V_{cc}R_{b_1}}$$ (6-5)

If the circuit is symmetrical, the subscripts 1 and 2 can be dropped, and Eq. (6-5) becomes

$$R_a = \frac{R_L V_b \alpha_{FE}(R_L + R_b)}{V_{cc}R_L\alpha_{FE} - V_b R_L\alpha_{FE} - V_{cc}R_L - V_{cc}R_b}$$ (6-6)

Since R_L, V_b, α_{FE}, and V_{cc} are constant, the variation of R_a versus R_b can be plotted, and the resultant graph is shown in Fig. 6-4. The ON equation indicates the values of R_a and R_b required in order to maintain transistor Q_1 ON. Note that if the value of R_b is selected as 4 kilohms, the value of R_a required is 3.6 kilohms (point A of Fig. 6-4). Laboratory analysis of the circuit indicates that there is an ON region for Q_1. That is, larger values of R_a are permissible and the transistor will remain ON. This region is shown as the shaded area in Fig. 6-4. For example, if the value of R_b is selected as 4 kilohms, the stability condition would still be satisfied if the value of R_a were 8 kilohms (point B of Fig. 6-4).

OFF EQUATION

Figure 6-5a is a functional schematic showing transistor Q_2 in the OFF state. The voltage $V_{BE} = (I_1 - I_{co})R_{a_2}$ (the I_{co} factor in the OFF state can-

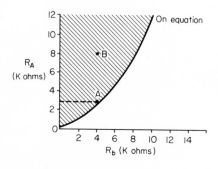

Fig. 6-4. ON equation.

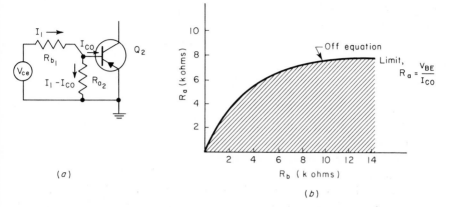

(a)

(b)

Fig. 6-5. OFF *equation.*

not be neglected). The current through $R_{b_1} = (V_{ce} - V_{BE})/R_{b_1}$; therefore V_{BE} becomes

$$V_{BE} = \frac{V_{ce} - V_{BE}}{R_{b_1}} - I_{co}R_{a_1}$$

Solving for R_{a_2},

$$R_{a_2} = \frac{V_{BE}R_{b_1}}{V_{ce} - V_{BE} - I_{co}R_{b_1}} \tag{6-7}$$

If the OFF equation is plotted on a set of coordinates, the resultant function is that shown in Fig. 6-5b. The shaded region indicates the OFF region. For example, if the value of R_a is selected as 4 kilohms, the transistor will remain off for any value of R_b larger than 2 kilohms.

If the ON and OFF equations are plotted on the same set of coordinates (Fig. 6-6), the result is a plot of the optimum stability conditions for a given

Fig. 6-6. ON *and* OFF *equations.*

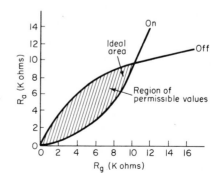

bistable multivibrator. Values of R_a and R_b are selected from the shaded area. The ideal values of R_a and R_b are selected from regions where the maximum R_a and R_b is still within the shaded area. Such a selection will thus ensure maximum stability and a minimum input trigger requirement.

6-3   BISTABLE-MULTIVIBRATOR OPERATIONAL ANALYSIS

The circuit of Fig. 6-7 is similar to the theoretical circuit analyzed in Sec. 6-2. The stability conditions are improved by returning the base resistors to a bias source. The additional bias source overcomes the limitations of thermal runaway dangers associated with transistor switches in the OFF state with no reverse bias.

Shown in Fig. 6-8 is a set of grounded-emitter characteristic curves for the 2N356 NPN transistor with a load line representing the circuit. The two stable states will be with one transistor at cutoff and the other conducting heavily. It will be noted from the characteristic curve that a base current greater than 70 μa will drive the transistor into conduction. The resultant collector current is about 3.2 ma:

$$I_c = \frac{V_{cc}}{R_L} = \frac{15}{(4.7)(10^3)} = 3.2 \text{ ma}$$

A base current of zero would not completely cut off the collector current, but it would be quite low. Assume that Q_1 is at cutoff and that Q_2 is conducting heavily. With Q_1 at cutoff, its base current will be negligible, so its base resistors can be considered to be in series. The collector of Q_2 is at

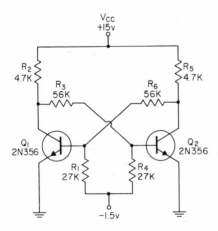

Fig. 6-7.   Biased bistable circuit.

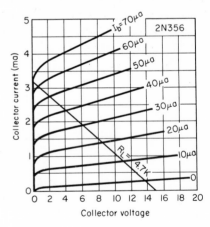

Fig. 6-8.   Output characteristics; 2N356 transistor.

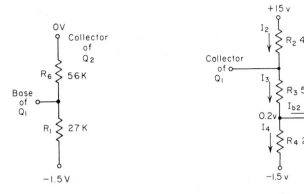

Fig. 6-9. Equivalent schematic of Fig. 6-7.

Fig. 6-10. Equivalent circuit of Fig. 6-7.

about 0 volts, as shown from the load line on the characteristic curve. A partial equivalent circuit is shown in Fig. 6-9. The base voltage of Q_1 is $1.5 + (1.5)(27 \text{ kilohms})/(27 \text{ kilohms} + 56 \text{ kilohms}) = 1$ volt.

With the base of an NPN transistor negative with respect to the emitter, the emitter-base junction is reverse-biased, and very low emitter current will flow.

When a transistor is conducting heavily, the base-to-emitter voltage drop is small, of the order of 0.2 volt. Another partial equivalent circuit is shown in Fig. 6-10. Assuming no collector current in Q_1, $I_2 = I_3 = (15 - 0.2)/(4.7 \text{ kilohms} + 56 \text{ kilohms}) = 244 \ \mu a$; $I_4 = (1.5 + 0.2)/(27 \text{ kilohms}) = 63 \ \mu a$; $I_{b_2} = I_3 - I_4 = 181 \ \mu a$.

As noted earlier, a base current of only 70 μa is needed for saturation. Thus Q_2 is saturated.

Under these conditions the collector voltages are approximately 0 and 15 volts, neglecting the small resistor currents and the collector currents of the cutoff transistor. The amplitude of the output signal can therefore be close to the full supply voltage.

If the bias supply of Fig. 6-7 is removed and the two 27-kilohm resistors are returned to ground, the circuit will operate in the manner outlined above. Refer to Fig. 6-11.

Again, assume that Q_1 is cut off. The collector of Q_2 is at about 0 volts, and the bottom of R_1 is at 0 volts. The base current of Q_1 is practically zero, so the voltage at the base of Q_1 is about zero. The emitter of Q_1 is grounded, so the emitter current of Q_1 is practically zero and Q_1 is at cutoff. In actual practice, the base will be slightly positive with respect to the emitter, so a small current of about 10 to 20 μa will flow, giving a collector current of about the same amount. Compared with the collector current during the conduction state, this current is negligible.

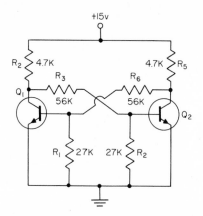

Fig. 6-11. Bistable multivibrator.

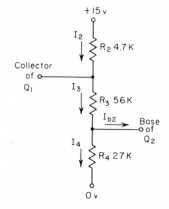

Fig. 6-12. Equivalent circuit.

When the base voltage of Q_2 (in conduction) is about 0.2 volt, the partial equivalent circuit is that shown in Fig. 6-12. $I_2 = I_3 = 244$ μa (as previously calculated). $I_4 = 0.2/27$ kilohms $= 7.41$ μa; $I_{b_2} = I_3 - I_4 = 237$ μa. This again is more than enough base current to keep Q_2 in saturation. The only real difference between the operation of these two circuits is that each transistor is conducting a little more heavily in each stable state.

6-4 VACUUM-TUBE BISTABLE MULTIVIBRATOR

The vacuum-tube version of the bistable multivibrator is shown in Fig. 6-13. This circuit, too, has two stable states of operation. In one stable state, V_1 is at cutoff and V_2 is conducting heavily, with 0 volts on its grid. In the other stable state, conditions are reversed. The first is now conducting while the second is at cutoff. Any other state of operation is unstable, and the circuit will shift rapidly to one of the two stable states. The circuit will remain in a stable condition indefinitely until an external signal causes it to change to the other stable state.

The circuit initially reaches a stable state when it is turned on. No two tubes are exactly identical in their characteristics; hence, there is no danger of the circuit's not establishing a stable state.

Referring to Fig. 6-13, assume that I_{b_1} increases slightly, decreasing e_{b_1}, which also decreases e_{c_2}. When e_{c_2} goes more negative, i_{b_2} decreases, which allows e_{b_2} to increase. This increases e_{c_1} (it goes less negative), which increases i_{b_1} even more. This regenerative effect continues until i_{b_2} reaches zero, and V_2 has then become cut off. V_1 is in clamp; that is, as e_{b_2} increased, e_{c_1} became less negative and then started to go positive. This caused grid current to flow, greatly reducing the grid-cathode resistance to about 1.5 kilohms and clamping the grid to the cathode potential, 0 volts.

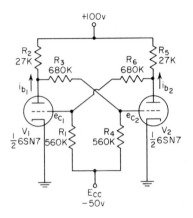

Fig. 6-13.   Vacuum-tube bistable circuit.

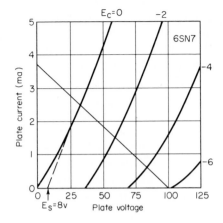

Fig. 6-14.   Plate characteristics; 6SN7 tube.

These limits stop the changing voltages and currents, and the circuit is now in one of its two stable conditions.

Each tube in Fig. 6-13 has a 27-kilohm load resistor and a 100-volt plate power supply. If we draw a load line on the 6SN7GT plate characteristic curve (Fig. 6-14), we find this information: no plate current flows if the grid voltage is more negative than -6 volts; the compensation potential $E_s = 8$ volts and $r_p = 10$ kilohms.

In order to establish that the circuit is in its stable state, the potentials at the grids of each of the tubes must be determined. Assume that V_2 is cut off. The equivalent circuit seen by the grid of V_1 is shown in Fig. 6-15a. The portion of the circuit enclosed by dotted lines is the equivalent circuit of the cutoff region of V_2. The voltage between the grid and the cathode of V_1 is 0 volts because of clamping.

In order to see how this clamping action is accomplished, the Thévenin circuit represented by the circuit to the right of a and b of Fig. 6-15a must

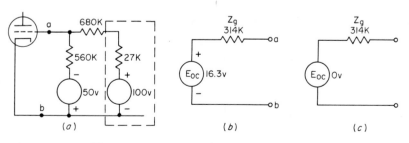

Fig. 6-15.   Equivalent circuits; ON condition.

be determined. The equivalent circuit without V_1 connected is shown in Fig. 6-15b. Note that terminal a is positive with respect to terminal b by 16.3 volts. When V_1 is reconnected into the circuit, grid current flows, thus forward-biasing the input "diode" of the tube. The forward bias of the input clamps the grid to the cathode. The actual equivalent circuit seen by V_1 is shown in Fig. 6-15c.

It must now be established that in fact V_2 is cut off. Figure 6-16a is the equivalent circuit seen by the grid-cathode terminals of V_2. The Thévenin equivalent of Fig. 6-16a is shown in Fig. 6-16b. The voltage between the grid and the cathode of V_2 is -13 volts.

The actual cutoff potential at the grid of V_2 can be determined from the output characteristics shown in Fig. 6-14. Since some current flows through its plate load via the voltage divider R_5, R_6, and R_1, the voltage at the plate of V_2 is not 100 volts. By applying Ohm's law it can be determined that the voltage drop across R_5 is 3.2 volts. The voltage at the plate of V_2 therefore is 96.7 volts. At 94 volts of plate potential, the tube cuts off at -5.8 volts. V_2, therefore, is cut off and the circuit is in the suspected stable state.

The value of the bistable multivibrator is that through various means it can be flipped from one stable state to the other; hence, the name flip-flop. To flip or trigger, either the conducting tube of the circuit may be driven toward cutoff or the nonconducting tube may be made conducting. Once the circuit has been triggered, regeneration causes it to switch from one stable state to the other very rapidly.

If we assume that V_1 is conducting and V_2 is cut off, the circuit could be triggered in any one of the following ways: (a) If the grid of V_2 were shorted to ground, its plate current would flow, dropping its plate voltage and causing e_{c_1} to go negative. This would increase e_{b_2}, which would cause e_{c_2} to try to go positive and would clamp e_{c_2} to cathode potential. (b) Shorting out the grid resistor of V_1 would put -50 volts on the grid, which is sufficient to cut off the plate current. This would cause e_{b_1} to increase,

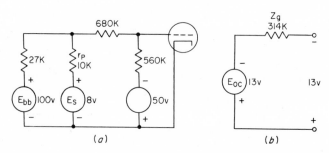

Fig. 6-16. Equivalent circuits; OFF condition.

which would cause e_{c_2} to try to go positive and would clamp the grid of V_2 to its cathode. Its current would increase, its plate voltage would decrease, and the grid voltage e_{c_1} of the other tube would be driven sufficiently negative to cut off its plate current. (c) The same thing could be accomplished by momentarily removing V_1 from its socket. The loss of plate current would cause e_{b_1} to increase as above, and V_1 would be driven to clamp. When V_1 was returned to its socket, its grid voltage would be more negative than the cutoff value. Other methods could also be used, such as shorting the plate load resistor of V_1, opening the plate load resistor of V_2, or opening the grid resistor of V_2.

These methods are not too practical, as they require a physical manipulation. A more practical approach is to introduce a step voltage of the correct polarity and amplitude to reverse the stable states of the tubes.

6-5 TRIGGERING METHODS

From previous discussions it was found that changing the voltage on either the plate or the grid of either tube can trigger the circuit, provided the triggering voltage is of sufficient amplitude and the correct polarity. The amplitude of the signal required for triggering each grid and each plate will now be considered.

If the amplifying action of the tubes is neglected, a signal equal to -6 volts or more will be needed on the grid of the conducting tube to drive it to cutoff. (Note the characteristics of Fig. 6-14.) But these tubes are amplifiers; and as the grid voltage of the conducting tube is made increasingly negative, its plate current decreases, its plate voltage increases, and this causes the grid of the cutoff to become less negative. This grid-to-grid amplifying action will now be calculated.

The gain of either tube, during conduction, can be determined from the load line in Fig. 6-14. A change in grid voltage from 0 to -2 volts changes the plate voltage from 32 to 59 volts. This gives a gain of $(59 - 32)/2 = 13.5$.

Any change in plate voltage of one tube results in a smaller change in the grid voltage of the other tube due to the attenuation in the coupling voltage divider. This attenuation is calculated as

560 kilohms/(560 kilohms + 680 kilohms) = 0.451

The total grid-to-grid voltage gain will be $(0.451)(13.5) = 6.1$. Therefore, to bring the grid voltage of the nonconducting tube from the stable value of -13 volts up to the -6 volts cutoff value requires a negative signal on the grid of the conducting tube equal to $7/6.1 = 1.15$ volts.

If the signal's amplitude exceeds 1.15 volts, the nonconducting tube will begin to conduct, and this tube becomes an amplifier, with a gain of about

6.1 to the other grid. The resulting regenerative circuit will cause the grid voltage of the original conducting tube to be driven more negative than -6 volts, and the grid of the original nonconducting tube will be clamped to the cathode potential. Therefore, a negative signal exceeding 1.15 volts applied to the grid of the conducting tube can flip the circuit.

A positive signal applied to the grid of the tube which is cut off can trigger the circuit. This grid has -13 volts on it, and the cutoff value is -6 volts, so the positive signal will have to exceed 7 volts to bring the tube into conduction. Once the tube starts to conduct, the regenerative action will cause the grid of the conducting tube to go negative and eventually below cutoff, while the grid of the previously cut off tube will be driven to 0 volts, clamped to its cathode potential.

Therefore, the circuit can be triggered with a signal of either 7 or 1.15 volts applied to one of the grids. In general, the circuit will be more sensitive to a negative signal.

Because of the attenuation of 0.451 in the plate-to-grid coupling circuits, higher-amplitude signals are needed at the plate to cause triggering. A positive signal at the plate of the conducting tube would have to have an amplitude of $7/0.451 = 15.5$ volts, so that after attenuation the needed 7 volts would appear at the grid of the cutoff tube. In like manner, a negative signal at the grid of the cutoff tube would have to have an amplitude of $1.15/0.451 = 2.55$ volts.

The triggering signal is usually applied to the grid or plate through a coupling capacitor. This coupling circuit will differentiate the signal, giving a positive pulse if the triggering signal increases and a negative pulse if the signal decreases. If the triggering signal is a rectangular pulse, the output of the coupling circuit will consist of two pulses of opposite polarity, one at the leading edge and the other at the trailing edge of the original pulse.

If a positive pulse with an amplitude greater than 7 volts is applied to the grid of the cutoff tube, the leading edge will flip the circuit, making this tube conduct. The trailing edge now becomes a negative pulse of sufficient amplitude to flip the circuit back again, which is not usually desired. On the other hand, if a negative triggering pulse with an amplitude of 2 volts is applied to the grid of the conducting tube, the leading edge will give a negative pulse of sufficient amplitude to flip the circuit; but the trailing edge will give a positive pulse with a 2-volt amplitude, and this is not sufficient to flip the tube back to conduction. A negative pulse then will provide a single change in stable states, while a positive pulse applied to the grid of the cutoff tube may cause double triggering, which brings the circuit back to its original state.

If a positive pulse of amplitude at least 2 volts is applied to the grid of the conducting tube, the positive leading edge will do nothing more than charge the input coupling capacitor through the low grid-to-cathode resistance. Then the negative trailing edge will give a pulse of sufficient amplitude to flip the circuit.

In the discussion of triggering pulses, it has been assumed that the signals were ideal—that is, with steep leading and trailing edges. If a pulse with a steep leading edge but an exponentially decaying trailing edge were coupled to the multivibrator through a capacitor, the leading edge could trigger the circuit but the trailing edge would not develop a negative pulse with sufficient amplitude to affect the circuit.

The output signal from the bistable multivibrator can be taken from either plate. The signal is a step voltage which varies between two steady d-c values. Usually this signal is passed through a capacitor to a shunt resistor. Such a circuit is a differentiating circuit and produces either a positive or a negative pulse, depending on whether the plate voltage increases or decreases. The difference in the two levels of plate voltage determines the amplitude of the output pulse signal. In our example the two plate levels are 32 and 96 volts, which would give an output pulse amplitude of 64 volts. If the size of the plate load resistor were increased, the plate voltage during conduction would be lower than 32 volts and the pulse would then have a higher amplitude.

6-6 TRANSITION TIME AND RESOLVING TIME

The time it takes for the grid of the conducting tube to reach cutoff is called the *transition time*. The triggering signals are usually pulses of short duration; and to be effective, the duration has to be long enough for the transition to be completed or at least to have the cutoff tube driven into the conduction region, so that the regenerative feedback effect can take over and complete the transition. The transit time of tubes is in the order of nanoseconds (10^{-9} sec), while triggering pulses usually have a duration time of several microseconds, so transit time can be neglected in considering the factors affecting transition time. The main limitation is due to the shunting capacitance between grid and cathode and between plate and cathode.

Suppose V_1 of Fig. 6-13 is conducting and a negative pulse is applied to its grid, driving it toward cutoff. The decrease in plate current will cause plate voltage to rise. Assume that the current is reduced instantaneously from the 2.5-ma value to zero. The partial equivalent circuit is shown in Fig. 6-17, the capacitor C_{pk} representing the shunting capacitance of V_1 between plate and cathode. In the stable state, when the tube is conducting, C_{pk} is charged to 32 volts (the plate voltage of V_1). If the plate current drops instantaneously to zero, the voltage across the capacitance tries to rise from 32 to 96 volts, charging through R_2. If any stray capacitance

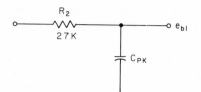

Fig. 6-17. Shunting capacitance involved in switching of V_1.

is neglected, the value of C_{pk} for a 6SN7GT is about 0.7 pf, and the time constant is 0.7 pf times 27 kilohms equals 18.9 nsec or 0.0189 μsec. If it is assumed that the capacitor will complete its charging in five time constants, it will take approximately 0.1 μsec, which is still small compared with a pulse duration time of several microseconds. This will have a minor effect on transition time. The transition time becomes significant when the stray capacitance is at least ten times C_{pk}.

This rise in plate voltage is transmitted through the resistor coupling circuit to the grid of V_2 and is attenuated in the process. There is also a capacitive effect at the grid of each tube. If V_2 is functioning as an amplifier (when plate current is flowing), its input capacitance is much higher than just the grid-cathode capacitance. Because of the Miller effect (Sec. A-9), this capacitance is $C_{gk} + (1 + A_v)C_{gp}$ and will probably be about $2.5 + (1 + 13)(3.5) = 51.5$ pf for a 6SN7GT.

This capacitance has to charge through the 680-kilohm coupling resistor and is effectively shunted by the 560-kilohm grid resistor. This portion of the circuit is shown in Fig. 6-18.

By Thévenin's theorem it can be shown that the capacitor is effectively charging through a resistance equal to the 680- and 560-kilohm resistors in parallel, or 370 kilohms. The time constant is therefore 307 kilohms times 51.5 pf = 15.8 μsec. This is so much longer than the 0.0189-μsec time

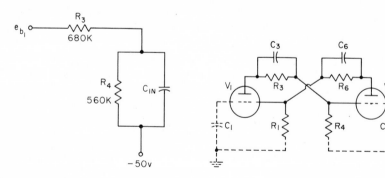

Fig. 6-18. Functional schematic; charging circuit.

Fig. 6-19. Compensating capacitors.

constant in the plate circuit and the 0.001-μsec transit time that the only real problem is in the time required to charge the input capacitance at the grid of the tube.

This problem is identical to that of low-frequency compensation in wideband amplifiers, discussed in Sec. 1-12. In Fig. 6-19 a portion of the circuit is drawn with compensating capacitors C_3 and C_6 shown. C_1 and C_4 represent the effective input capacitances of V_1 and V_2. When $C_3R_3 = C_4R_4$ and $C_6R_6 = C_1R_1$, there is complete compensation, and attenuation is independent of frequency. A sudden change in voltage at the plate of V_1 is transmitted exactly in waveshape, though attenuated. This results in an identical change in voltage at the grid, but of smaller amplitude.

During the time V_2 is not conducting, the voltage gain is zero and the input capacitance is then much lower than the 51.5-pf capacitance previously calculated. The circuit is then greatly overcompensated. The only effect will be to greatly decrease the attenuation, so that a larger percentage of the plate voltage change of V_2 is transferred to the grid of V_1.

These compensating capacitors are called *transpose* or *commutating* capacitors when used in this type of circuit. Their value is somewhere in the order of the input capacitance of the tube, or about 50 pf for a triode. The exact value is not too critical.

A further effect of the commutating capacitors is to make the input capacitance of one grid circuit appear between plate and cathode of the other tube, increasing the time constant at the plate.

Knowing the transition time allows consideration of the pulse duration necessary to flip the circuit, but the time period before the circuit can again be flipped must also be considered. The time required for the circuit to finish its change after the conducting tube has reached cutoff is called the *settling time* or *recovery time*. A combination of the transition time and recovery time is called the *resolving time*, which is the time from the start of a change in stable states until the circuit has reached its new stable state. It is equal to the minimum time that there can be between pulses, and it determines the maximum frequency or pulse repetition rate at which the circuit can operate.

Part of the recovery time is used in charging the shunt capacitances in the circuit to make the necessary changes in grid and plate voltages. This period of time is greatly reduced by the addition of the commutating capacitors, which we have found also decreased the transition time. With these commutating capacitors in the circuit it is found that most of the recovery time is involved in the commutating capacitors themselves charging or discharging to their new voltage levels.

It is found that in a stable state the capacitor between the plate of the conducting tube and the grid of the nonconducting tube will be charged to $32 + 13 = 45$ volts, while the other capacitor will be charged to 96 volts. When the stable state is reversed, each capacitor must change its charge to $96 - 45 = 51$ volts.

Consider now the complete circuit shown in Fig. 6-20. If we assume that V_1 is conducting, C_3 will be charged to 45 volts and C_6 will be charged to 96 volts. When the stable states are reversed, C_3 must charge up to 96 volts. It's charge path is through R_2 and the grid-cathode circuit of V_2, which has negligible resistance. The time constant is 27 kilohms times 50 pf = 1.35 μsec. Capacitor C_6 has to discharge from 96 to 45 volts, and its discharge path consists of R_6 and R_1 in parallel. This time constant is (50 pf) (560 kilohms)(680 kilohms)/(560 kilohms + 680 kilohms) = 15.3 μsec. If the necessary discharge is accomplished in five time constants, it will take approximately 75 μsec for the circuit to reach its stable state after the transition time. This is what was termed the recovery time.

With the commutating capacitors, the transition time has been reduced to a small value, but the resolving time has been greatly increased because of the time it takes for these capacitors to discharge. Has anything been accomplished by reducing the transition time but increasing the recovery time? Remember that minimum pulse width or duration is determined by the transition time, so the main reason for adding the commutating capacitor was to reduce the pulse width needed.

If a positive trigger pulse is applied to the plate of the conducting tube, there is very little attenuation in the pulse which is coupled to the grid of the other tube. This is because when a tube is not conducting, its input

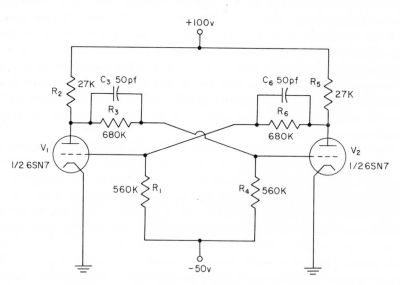

Fig. 6-20.   Flip-flop with compensating capacitors.

capacitance is just its grid-plate capacitance, and therefore its attenuation is very low. The compensating capacitor acts as a temporary short across the coupling resistor, and the result is that the grid-to-grid voltage gain is greatly increased. This means the amplitude of the triggering pulse can be about one-half that needed without the capacitors. Therefore, the increased resolving time, due to the commutating capacitors, is usually more than offset by the reduced pulse width and the pulse amplitude needed for triggering.

The necessity for reducing shunt capacitance at the grid and also at the plate circuit in order to decrease the transition time was pointed out in previous discussions. The trigger source, with its coupling capacitor, will load down the multivibrator circuit, increasing the shunt capacitance and thus the transition time. This effect can be minimized by using a trigger source with high internal impedance or by simulating a high internal impedance by including a large series resistor in the circuit. This, of course, will increase the attenuation effect between the trigger source and the multivibrator circuit, so a higher-amplitude trigger signal will be required, but it will reduce the shunt capacitance and thus decrease the transition time.

As shown earlier, a triggering pulse can just as well be applied to one of the plates of the circuit. If the pulse is applied to the plate of the nonconducting tube, the circuit has a high plate-to-cathode impedance, therefore presenting minimum loading on the trigger source. Thus there will be minimum attenuation in the coupling circuit between the trigger source and the plate of the tube. This requires a negative pulse which transfers to the grid of the conducting tube. The plate voltage of the conducting tube will increase, and this will be transferred to the grid of the nonconducting tube as a positive-going signal which triggers a reversal of stable states.

The problem that the triggering source and the coupling circuit may shunt the multivibrator and increase the transition time, and also the possibility that the trailing edge of the pulse will flip the circuit, could pretty well be eliminated if some means could be found of disconnecting the trigger circuit as soon as the leading edge of the pulse has started the transition. This can be done by means of a switching circuit made up of either a triode triggering tube, a diode tube, or a semiconductor diode.

6-7 CLAMPED BISTABLE CIRCUITS

The preceding paragraphs established the chief limitation of switching time for the vacuum-tube bistable circuits. The resolving time was shown to consist of two parts: the transition time and the recovery time. In the transistorized bistable circuit, the switching time of the circuit has an additional contributing factor when the transistor is saturated: storage time.

The storage of the minority carriers in the base region requires additional time for turning off the device. In addition, changes in temperature influence the levels of the output. The following discussion centers around transistor bistable multivibrators; however, the technique of introducing clamping diodes applies to vacuum-tube circuits as well. Refer to Fig. 6-21.

CONVENTIONAL CLAMPING

The addition of diodes D_1 and D_2 establishes (a) uniform levels of output, (b) decreased switching time, and (c) reliable system performance.

The output levels are established in the following manner. Assume that transistor Q_2 is off and Q_1 is on. With Q_1 on, diode D_1 is off and D_2 is on; the collector current for Q_1 becomes

$$i_c = \frac{V_{cc}}{R_L} + i_{D_2}$$

Diode D_2 clamps the output to ground.

Since transistor Q_2 is off, the impedance between collector and emitter is large; the result is that if E_{R_L} is less negative than V_{cc}, diode D_3 conducts. The voltage at the collector is clamped to E_L. The current through the diode becomes

$$i_{D_3} = \frac{V_{cc} - E_L}{R_L}$$

The current i_{D_2} can be determined from the output characteristics of the transistor, and current i_{D_3} can be determined from the circuit characteristics. Once these currents are identified, the selection of appropriate diodes can be made.

The circuit of Fig. 6-21 does not allow either transistor to saturate; hence, the problems associated with storage time are greatly minimized. The

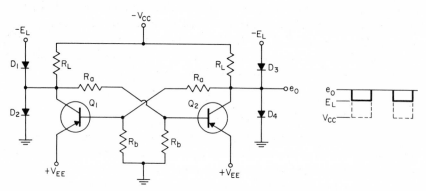

Fig. 6-21. Bistable circuit with clamping.

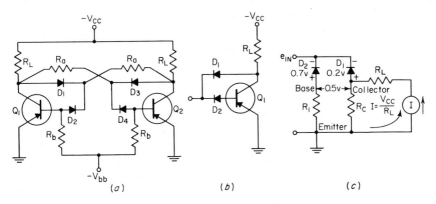

Fig. 6-22. Back clamping.

addition of the diodes also ensures that the output levels will remain uniform between 0 and E_L. Variations in transistor characteristics and temperatures do not change the levels of the output.

It should not be assumed that the addition of clamping diodes eliminates switching-time problems. Some new problems are introduced. Chapter 4 pointed out that diodes themselves have a storage characteristic when forward-biased. Some delay is introduced as a result of diode storage; however, this delay is still much less than the storage time of the transistor. Diode delay can be held to a minimum by maintaining the forward currents through the diode as low as possible.

BACK-CLAMPED CIRCUIT

The most significant drawback of the clamping arrangement of Fig. 6-21 is the need for a separate power supply E_L. The problem can be eliminated by employing *back-clamp* circuitry. Figure 6-22a is a schematic showing the back-clamped bistable circuit. Figure 6-22b and c are functional schematics illustrating the basic theory of operation.

It should be recalled that saturation (which results in the storage of minority carriers in the base) occurs when the collector voltage decreases below the voltage at the base. The back-clamp circuit arrangement maintains the collector 0.5 volt above the base. In order to maintain this condition, diode D_2 must be a silicon type and D_1 a germanium type. When the silicon diode is forward-biased, the voltage knee is 0.7 volt. The knee for the germanium diode is 0.2 volt. Refer to Fig. 6-22c. A negative signal at e_{in} drives the circuit toward saturation. The input voltage is developed across D_2 and the input resistance of the transistor. The silicon diode is forward-biased, and the voltage across it is 0.7 volt. The input voltage is also applied across diode D_1 and the collector resistance. Germanium diode

D_1 is also forward-biased; hence, the voltage drop across it is 0.2 volt. The voltage between the collector and base is 0.5 volt. The collector potential remains 0.5 volt above the base potential; hence there is no storage of carriers.

6-8 STEERING CIRCUITS AND SWITCHING SPEED

Diodes D_2 and D_4 of Fig. 6-22a were identified as part of the back-clamping circuitry. These diodes actually serve a dual function in that they also serve as part of the steering or triggering circuitry.

BASE TRIGGERING

Figure 6-23a is a partial schematic showing the addition of the input trigger circuit. The series of negative input pulses are applied simultaneously to the bases of both transistors. Assume that Q_1 is off and Q_2 is on. Since Q_1 is off, the potential between base and emitter is near zero (the base is slightly positive with respect to its emitter). With Q_2 on, the base is negative with respect to its emitter. When the trigger pulse is applied, a negative pulse is applied to both bases. The input pulse triggers the off transistor, and the circuit switches states.

Figure 6-23b shows one branch of the trigger circuit. A negative input pulse forward-biases D_2 and supplies a differentiated negative pulse at the base, thus driving the transistor on. A negative increment of voltage at the base produces an amplified increment at the base of the on transistor in the same manner as that described for vacuum-tube bistable circuits.

IMPROVED SWITCHING TIME

The basic circuit of Fig. 6-22 provides satisfactory operation when the maximum repetition rate is below 5,000 pps. Modern applications of the bistable circuit demand faster repetition rates. In order to achieve faster

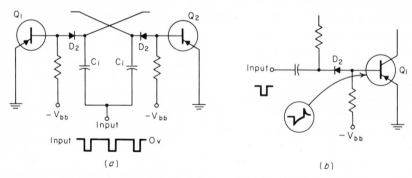

Fig. 6-23. Steering circuits.

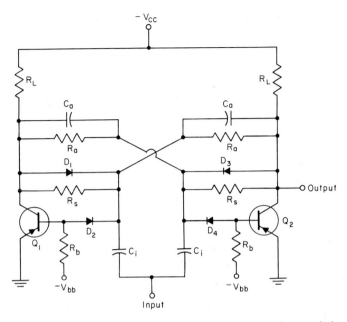

Fig. 6-24. Bistable circuit with improved switching characteristics.

switching rates, a number of modifications to the basic circuit must be employed.

The addition of clamping diodes (discussed in Sec. 6-7) minimizes the problems associated with storage time. Figure 6-24 shows the basic circuit with two additions. Transpose capacitors C_a have been added across coupling resistors R_a. (The theory of speedup capacitors was discussed in Sec. 6-6.) Typical values for C_a range from 10 up to 500 pf.

The addition of R_s is required for the circuit to respond at the maximum repetition rate. R_s actually forms part of the trigger circuit. The time constant of the input capacitance C_i and R_s should be equal to the period of the input repetition rate. For optimum results, the value of R_s should be about three times the value of the load resistance R_L, but not larger than ten times the value of the load.

$$R_s C_i = \frac{1}{\text{prr}}$$

6-9 FOUR-LAYER SEMICONDUCTOR BISTABLE CIRCUIT

A number of special devices have been developed for use as bistable elements. The most popular of these is the four-layer semiconductor, also known by a number of trade names. Thyristor, Binistor, and Trigistor are a few examples. Although these devices are sometimes called controlled rectifiers, the most accurate name is *bistable element.* All the devices have one aspect in common. Once the bistable element is turned on by a trigger pulse, it will remain on even though the trigger pulse is removed. In order to switch the device to the opposite stable state, a second turnoff pulse is required. Figure 6-25 compares a conventional bistable circuit with one using a bistable element.

BASIC THEORY

The basic theory of operation of the various types of bistable elements differs slightly with each type. The fundamental theory can be shown by using the two-transistor analysis. The four-layer unit shown in Fig. 6-26*a* can be illustrated schematically as two separate transistors, one an NPN and the other a PNP (Fig. 6-26*b*). If the voltage at A is positive with respect to point C, the impedance between A and C is high. If a positive pulse is applied at point B, the input of Q_2 is momentarily forward-biased. Q_2 collector current increases, thus forward-biasing Q_1 and increasing its collector current. This increased collector current at Q_1 further forward-biases Q_2, and a regenerative loop gain of unity is quickly established. The two transistors remain on after the input pulse at B is removed. The impedance between A and C drops to a low value. In order to turn the device off, a negative pulse must be applied at B or the positive potential at

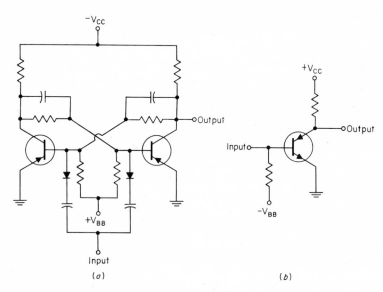

Fig. 6-25. Comparison of a conventional bistable circuit (a) and a four-layer semiconductor bistable element (b).

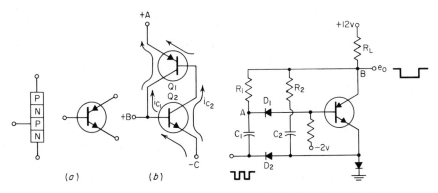

Fig. 6-26. Four-layer semiconductor device.

Fig. 6-27. Bistable element.

A must be removed. The device then switches back to its original stable state.

Figure 6-27 illustrates a practical circuit of a bistable multivibrator. The steering circuit at the input consists of D_1, D_2, R_1, R_2, C_1, and C_2. When the bistable element is off, the voltage at point B is $+12$ volts. C_2 is charged to 12 volts and C_1 has no charge across it. A negative pulse at the input causes D_2 to conduct, and the device turns on. Point B drops from $+12$ to $+1.5$ volts, and A changes to $+1.5$ volts. A second pulse at the input forward-biases D_1, driving the base of the device negative and switching the stability of the unit. The output rises to $+12$ volts.

Bistable devices provide a large degree of simplification; however, they are not readily adaptable for high-speed switching. The maximum repetition is limited to 200 kc and below.

6-10 SCHMITT TRIGGER

The Schmitt trigger is classified as a bistable multivibrator because it has two stable states similar to the circuits just described. The circuit differs slightly in its application. There are two fundamental operating characteristics of the circuit: (a) The period of the output waveshape is the same as the period of the input. (b) The output can be a squared pulse whose duration time varies with the amplitude of the input.

VACUUM-TUBE CIRCUIT

The bistable multivibrator discussed in Sec. 6-4 was identified as plate-coupled; that is, the plate of V_1 is coupled to the grid of V_2, and the plate of V_2 is coupled to the grid of V_1. Each tube is in a grounded-cathode amplifier configuration. It will be remembered that a tube has two other possible circuit configurations as an amplifier: grounded-grid and grounded-plate (cathode-follower). The grounded-cathode circuit has a 180° phase shift which makes the output of the second stage in phase with the input of the first and gives regenerative feedback when the output signal is fed back to the input.

Neither the grounded-grid nor the grounded-plate amplifiers have phase reversal; so if a two-stage amplifier is made of these circuits, the output is also in phase with the input, and regenerative feedback is possible. Assume that a resistor is used for d-c coupling and a grounded-grid amplifier is connected to a grounded-plate amplifier (Fig. 6-28). A direct connection will be made from the output to the input; and because it puts the two cathode resistors in parallel, the two resistors can be replaced by a single resistor. The circuit is shown in Fig. 6-29 and is called a cathode-coupled bistable multivibrator, or sometimes a *Schmitt trigger* after its inventor, O. H. Schmitt.

As the circuit stands, V_1 is cut off and V_2 is conducting. To prove this, assume that V_1 is cut off, the voltage across R_4 equals $(E_{bb})(R_4)/(R_2 + R_3 + R_4)$, and the voltage across R_K will equal the plate current of V_2 times R_K. If the resistor values are such that e_4 is about equal to e_K, and e_K is large enough to cut V_1 off, V_2 will be conducting and V_1 will be cut off. This is a stable state.

In order to apply an input signal, a resistor is inserted between the grid of V_1 and ground; because there is no grid current flowing in this tube, the grid is still at ground potential. A convenient place to take an output signal is at the plate of V_2, if a load resistor is added. The modified circuit is shown in Fig. 6-30.

If the input signal is a d-c voltage that increases from zero in the positive direction, the bias of V_1 will be $e_K - e_{in}$. As soon as this difference

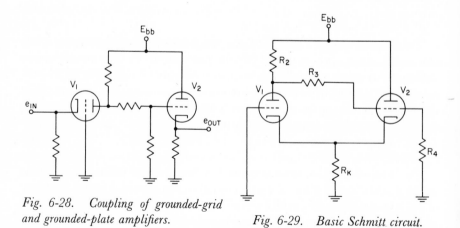

Fig. 6-28. Coupling of grounded-grid and grounded-plate amplifiers.

Fig. 6-29. Basic Schmitt circuit.

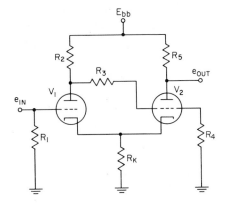

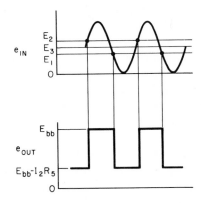

Fig. 6-30. Practical Schmitt circuit.   *Fig. 6-31. Input and output waveshapes for the Schmitt trigger.*

reaches the cutoff value of V_1, conduction begins and the plate voltage drops. This drop in plate voltage is transferred to the grid of V_2, and the plate current of V_2 decreases. This decreases e_K, which causes the bias of V_1 to become less negative, and regenerative action takes place. These changes continue with no further increase in e_{in} until V_2 goes into cutoff and V_1 is conducting heavily. V_2 is cut off because the current through V_1 develops a voltage drop across R_K, and the difference between this voltage and the reduced voltage across R_4 is greater than the cutoff value of V_2.

This new state is maintained as long as e_{in} is high enough to overcome the effect of e_K. If e_{in} is now decreased, the plate current of V_1 decreases and its plate voltage increases, increasing the voltage across R_4. At some point the difference between e_K and e_4 is not sufficient to keep V_2 below cutoff, and plate current starts flowing. This increases e_K, which further increases the negative bias of V_1, and the regenerative action drives V_1 into cutoff and V_2 into high conduction.

This circuit has two possible states, each of which is maintained when the input signal is above or below a certain value. No intermediate states occur; the transition occurs very rapidly.

There is a *hysteresis* or *backlash* involved in this circuit's operation. That is, the input voltage level at which a transition takes place depends on whether the input voltage is increasing or decreasing; when it is increasing, a higher level is required than when it is decreasing.

One application for this circuit is as a squaring circuit. A sine-wave input will give a square-wave output, as shown in Fig. 6-31. Note the two input levels E_1 and E_2 at which a circuit transition takes place. The output signal has just two possible levels. When V_2 is cut off, the output equals E_{bb}; and when V_2 is conducting, the output is $E_{bb} - I_2R_5$.

If a fixed bias voltage equal to E_3 in Fig. 6-31 is applied to the grid of V_1, the circuit can be flipped between its two stable states by alternate positive and negative pulses, and this will act like the plate-coupled multivibrator, with triggering pulses applied to one grid.

Another application of this circuit is as a method of comparing the level of a varying d-c voltage with a fixed reference. The particular state of the circuit indicates whether the input signal is above or below the reference voltage.

TRANSISTOR CIRCUIT

The basic transistorized Schmitt trigger is illustrated in Fig. 6-32. Under quiescent conditions Q_2 is saturated. The emitter current through Q_2 produces a voltage drop across R_4 which holds Q_1 in cutoff. A negative-going signal at e_{in} causes Q_1 to conduct. A regenerative switching action brings Q_2 out of saturation and into the cutoff region. A negative-going signal at the input holds Q_1 in saturation and Q_2 in cutoff until a critical value where the circuit switches. This point is identified as E_1. As the input signal becomes less negative, the circuit returns to its original stable state at a second critical point E_2. There is a difference between E_1 and E_2, since R_1 is larger than R_2. This difference is the *backlash*.

6-11   D-C FLIP-FLOP

The limitation of the basic flip-flop discussed in Sec. 6-1 is the relatively small difference between the on voltage and the off voltage across the transistor. The small increment of voltage makes the circuit virtually unusable as a *voltage-mode* switch. The circuit is used in a *current mode* as a

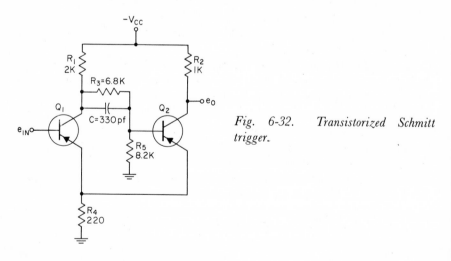

Fig. 6-32. Transistorized Schmitt trigger.

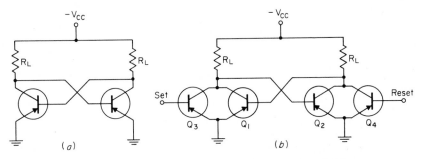

Fig. 6-33. Direct-current flip-flop; current-mode switching.

direct-current transistor logic (DCTL) circuit. Figure 6-33a illustrates the basic circuit. The current-mode circuit utilizes fewer components than the voltage mode. The circuit is used mainly for storage rather than counting (discussed in greater detail in Chap. 10) purposes. When the basic circuit of Fig. 6-33a is to be used for storage purposes, it must be modified to provide a SET input and a CLEAR input. These are also identified as SET and RESET inputs. The modified circuit is illustrated in Fig. 6-33b.

The operation of the circuit will now be discussed. Assume that Q_1 is on and Q_2, Q_3, and Q_4 are off. With Q_1 on, the voltage across it is about -0.2 volt. The voltage at the collector of Q_2 is about -0.3 volt. The circuit remains in this state until it is reset. A negative trigger pulse at the RESET input turns Q_4 on momentarily. The decrease in collector potential at Q_2 is coupled to the base of Q_1, thereby changing the original state from ON to OFF. The circuit is now ready for trigger input at the base (SET) of Q_3, which can either retain the present state of the flip-flop or change it. The storage facility is effected by the identification of the state of the flip-flop.

6-12 CASCADED FLIP-FLOP CIRCUITS

Figure 6-34 shows two flip-flop circuits capacitively coupled through C_2. The relative states of the flip-flops are preset with the RESET button. Momentarily removing the negative bias on the grids of V_2 and V_4 establishes V_1 and V_3 in a cutoff or OFF state and V_2 and V_4 in an ON state. A negative pulse at e_{in} decreases the positive potential at the plate of V_1, and the tube is brought out of cutoff. The circuit flips, with V_2 going to cutoff and V_1 turning on. The negative input pulse produces a positive step at the plate of V_2. The positive step at V_2 is differentiated through C_2 and Z_b, where Z_b represents the impedance seen from the junction of R_2 and R_5. (Figure 6-35 is a functional schematic showing the differentiator circuit.)

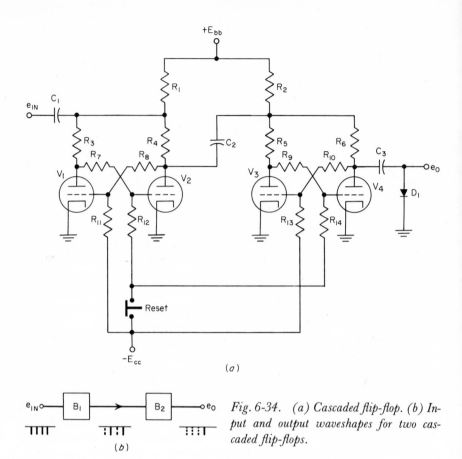

Fig. 6-34. (a) Cascaded flip-flop. (b) Input and output waveshapes for two cascaded flip-flops.

The positive differentiated pulse at the plate of V_3 increases the positive potential at the plate of V_3; hence, the tube remains in cutoff. A second negative pulse at the input, e_{in}, triggers the flip-flop. In this mode V_2 is brought from cutoff. The voltage at the plate of V_2 is a negative step function with the tube going from off to on. The negative step is differentiated through C_2 and R_b and appears as a negative pulse at the plate of V_3. The decreased plate potential at V_3 triggers the flip-flop and turns V_3 on and V_4 off. The resulting voltage at the plate of V_4 is a positive step function. The output at e_o remains at zero since positive pulses clamp e_o to ground.

At this point two negative pulses at the input have produced no output; they have altered the original states of the flip-flops. Thus far in the analysis, V_1 is off and V_2 is on (their original state); and V_3 is on and V_4 is off.

A third pulse at the input triggers the first flip-flop, thus producing a positive differentiated pulse to the second flip-flop. The second flip-flop is uninfluenced by a positive pulse; hence, the output does not change. A fourth negative pulse at the input triggers the first flip-flop again. This time a negative differentiated pulse is coupled to the second flip-flop. The circuit is triggered and a negative differentiated pulse is developed at the output. The two cascaded states required four negative input pulses in order to produce one negative output pulse. The circuit could be considered a divide-by-four circuit. A symbolic diagram is shown in Fig. 6-34b.

Any number of flip-flops can be cascaded in the manner shown in Fig. 6-34a. The division characteristic becomes a factor of 2^n. Figure 6-36 shows four cascaded flip-flops. Since the division factor is 2^4, the circuit is also called a "scale of sixteen." In digital-computer applications, the circuit is also known as a 1-2-4-8 counter.

6-13 CASCADED FLIP-FLOP CIRCUITS WITH FEEDBACK

The counting applications of the cascaded circuits described in Sec. 6-12 are somewhat limited since the counting factor is 2^n. If, however, feedback is incorporated into the basic cascaded circuits, a variety of possibilities result. Figure 6-37 illustrates the most popular of these circuits, the "scale of ten," or the 1-2-2-4 counter.

The circuit is basically a four-stage binary circuit where the step function at the plate of V_5 is differentiated and coupled back to the grid of V_4. A similar feedback leg is developed from the plate of V_7 to the grid of V_6.

The fourth input pulse triggers V_5. The operation for the first four pulses is the same as that described for Fig. 6-34. When V_5 switches on, a negative pulse is coupled back to the grid of V_4, returning V_4 to the OFF condition. If feedback from V_5 to V_4 were not included, V_4 would not be switched back off until the sixth input pulse. The effect is that of skipping ahead two input pulses. On the sixth input pulse the same skipping ahead of two pulses takes place as a result of the feedback from V_7 to V_6.

The feedback loops convert the scale-of-sixteen circuit to a decade counter (division by 10). Application of counter circuits is expanded in later chapters.

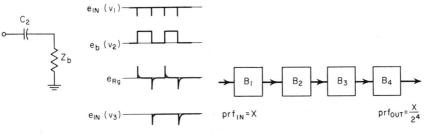

Fig. 6-35. Coupling circuit.   Fig. 6-36. Four cascaded flip-flops.

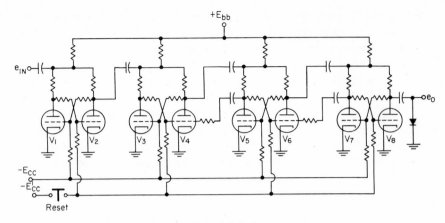

e_{IN}

V_1 V_2 V_3 V_4 V_5 V_6 V_7 V_8

$-E_{CC}$
$-E_{CC}$

e_0

Reset

Fig. 6-37.   1-2-2-4 counter.

PROBLEMS

6-1   Refer to Fig. 6-7. Assume that Q_1 is on and Q_2 is off and $R_2 = R_5 = 6$ kilohms. (*a*) What collector current flows at Q_1? (*b*) What is the quiescent voltage at the collector of Q_2? (*c*) What is the voltage between the base and the emitter of Q_2?

6-2   Refer to Prob. 6-1. (*a*) How much base current at Q_1 is required to saturate the transistor? (*b*) What base current actually flows into Q_1?

6-3   Modify the circuit of Fig. 6-7 to include clamping diodes. Connect these diodes so that the output will switch from -1 to -10 volts.

6-4   If the values of R_3 and R_6 of Fig. 6-7 are increased from 56 to 78 kilohms, what will be the new saturation current at the base of the ON transistor? How does this compare with the value derived in Prob. 6-2?

6-5   Would the circuit of Prob. 6-4 be more or less sensitive to input trigger signals than the circuit of Prob. 6-1?

6-6   How should the values of R_2 and R_5 of Fig. 6-7 be changed in order to make the circuit more sensitive to triggering signals?

6-7   Refer to the circuit of Fig. 6-7. Assume that capacitors are to be used to increase the switching speed. Where should they be connected, and what should their approximate value be?

6-8   Assume that a 2N337 is to be used to design a binary circuit similar to that shown in Fig. 6-21 whose output must switch between -10 and 0 volts. (*a*) What current will flow through R_L if $V_{EE} = +5$ volts, $V_{cc} = 20$ volts, and $R_L = 2$ kilohms when Q_1 is on? (*b*) What is the value of E_L?

6-9 Refer to the circuit of Fig. 6-11. (a) When Q_1 is on and Q_2 is off, what voltage appears between the base and the emitter of Q_2? (b) What voltage appears across R_3? (Assume $Q_1 = Q_2 = $ 2N398.)

6-10 Refer to Prob. 6-9. (a) What base current will saturate Q_1? (b) What base current is flowing at the base of Q_1?

6-11 A bistable multivibrator, using a 6SN7, has a circuit as shown in Fig. 6-13, except with the following circuit values: $R_1 = R_4 = 330$ kilohms, $R_2 = R_5 = 15$ kilohms, $R_3 = R_6 = 470$ kilohms, $E_{bb} = 250$ volts, $E_{cc} = -150$ volts. Assuming that V_1 is cut off and V_2 is conducting, calculate the approximate grid and plate voltages at V_1.

6-12 The switching speed of the circuit of Prob. 6-11 is to be increased. What value of transpose capacitors should be added and across which resistors?

6-13 Refer to the circuit of Fig. 6-32. How do changes in R_5 influence the hysteresis of the circuit?

6-14 Refer to the circuit of Fig. 6-34a. What is the function of D_1?

CHAPTER 7 MONOSTABLE AND

ASTABLE MULTIVIBRATORS

The bistable multivibrator has two stable states of operation and will remain in either state indefinitely until a triggering signal switches it to the other state. The *monostable* multivibrator has just one permanently stable state. A triggering signal will switch it to another, temporarily stable, state; but after a certain time period, it will automatically return to its original state, with no external triggering signal needed for this second transition.

The *astable* (both "a's" pronounced as in ate) multivibrator has no permanently stable state. Even with no external triggering pulses applied, it will periodically shift from one temporarily stable state to the other and then back again. It is, therefore, an oscillator, and can be used as a square-wave generator.

7-1 PLATE-COUPLED MONOSTABLE MULTIVIBRATOR

Compare Fig. 7-1 with the bistable multivibrator of Fig. 6-13. Two changes will be noted. The coupling resistor R_3 of Fig. 6-13 is replaced by a coupling capacitor C_3 in Fig. 7-1. The grid resistor R_4 is returned to ground instead of to a negative voltage as in Fig. 6-13. These changes convert the bistable circuit into a plate-coupled monostable multivibrator.

With proper selection of circuit components and voltages, the circuit will be in a stable condition, with V_1 cut off and V_2 in clamp, or close to this condition. The reason for these conditions is that with zero bias on V_2, it is conducting, and its plate voltage will be considerably lower than the supply voltage. The voltage between E_{cc} and e_{b_2} divides in such a way that e_{c_1} is more negative than the cutoff value, so V_1 is in cutoff.

If a negative signal of sufficient amplitude is applied to the grid of V_2, its plate current will decrease, increasing its plate voltage. This will cause the grid of V_1 to become less negative; and if the cutoff point is reached, V_1 will start to conduct. The plate voltage of V_1 will start to drop. The voltage across C_3 cannot change instantaneously, so the drop in plate voltage of V_1 is transferred as a negative signal to the grid of V_2. This is a regenerative feedback, which continues the action originally started until V_2 is driven to cutoff and V_1 is in clamp.

This is now a temporarily stable condition where C_3 is discharging from its original value. Its discharge path through R_4 is keeping V_2 at cutoff. As soon as the voltage across C_3 has dropped enough so its discharge through R_4 does not develop sufficient bias voltage to keep V_2 at cutoff, V_2 starts to conduct. Its plate voltage drops, driving the grid of V_1 negative and decreasing the plate current of V_1. The plate voltage of V_1 starts to rise, and this increase is transferred to the grid of V_2 as a positive signal, driving V_2 into clamp and decreasing e_{b_2}. This decrease of e_{b_2} decreases e_{c_1} and drives V_1 into cutoff; the circuit has now switched to its original stable state.

Just as in the bistable multivibrator, the transitions take place in very short time periods. An important consideration in this circuit is the time period of the temporarily stable state, that is, when V_1 is conducting and V_2 is cut off. This is dependent on the time constant of C_3 and its discharge path, which is through R_4 and the parallel combination of R_2 and the internal resistance of V_1 while it is conducting. In practice, R_4 is much larger than the internal resistance of V_1, so the discharge time constant of the circuit is about equal to $R_4 C_3$.

A more meaningful analysis of this circuit can be carried out mathematically on an actual circuit with values given. Such a circuit is shown in Fig. 7-2. Again, it can be closely compared with the bistable multivibrator of Fig. 6-13, with just the two changes discussed above. If the stable condition is assumed, V_2 is conducting; and if the small current flow-

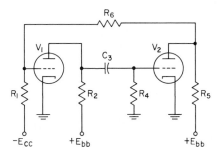

Fig. 7-1.   Conversion to monostable multivibrator.

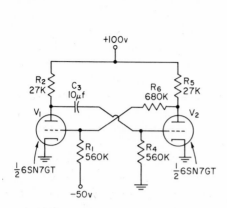

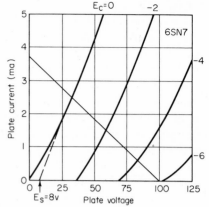

Fig. 7-2. Monostable multivibrator. Fig. 7-3. Load-line characteristic.

ing through R_6 is neglected, e_{b_2} can be found from the load line on the plate characteristic curves shown in Fig. 7-3. It will be noted that because the circuit does not have d-c coupling from the plate of V_1 to the grid of V_2, as was presented in the bistable multivibrator, its grid is not clamped to the cathode; the tube is not operating in the saturation region. In fact, there will even be a slight negative voltage on the grid due to a small Edison-effect grid current flowing, as discussed in Sec. 4-1. Even a current as small as 1 μa would give -0.56 volt bias on V_2. By using this value, a value of 40 volts is obtained for e_{b_2} from Fig. 7-3. A partial equivalent circuit is shown in Fig. 7-4. We find that $e_{c_1} = -50 + (90)(560 \text{ kilohms})/$ (560 kilohms + 680 kilohms) $= -9.4$ volts, which is below the cutoff value of -6 volts. V_1, being cut off, will have a plate voltage of 100 volts.

Assume that a triggering pulse flips the circuit to its temporarily stable state. If it is assumed that V_2 is cut off, the grid and plate voltages of both tubes can be calculated. If there were no grid current flowing in V_1, a partial equivalent circuit would be as shown in Fig. 7-5. We can calculate e_{c_1} as equal to $-50 + (150)(560 \text{ kilohms})/(560 \text{ kilohms} + 680 \text{ kilohms} +$

$e_{b_2}=40\text{v}$

R_6
680K

e_{c_1}

R_1
560K

-50v

Fig. 7-4. Partial equivalent circuit.

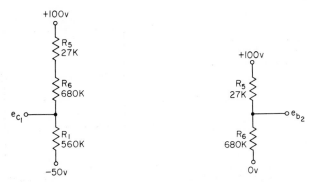

Fig. 7-5.   *Partial equivalent circuit.*   Fig. 7-6.   *Final equivalent circuit.*

27 kilohms) $= 16.4$ volts. Of course, such a positive voltage on the grid of V_1 will clamp the grid to cathode, and the actual partial equivalent circuit is the one shown in Fig. 7-6, e_{c_1} being 0 volts. Then $e_{b_2} = (100)(680$ kilohms$)/(680$ kilohms $+ 27$ kilohms$) = 96.2$ volts.

From Fig. 7-3 it is found that with 0 volts on the grid of V_1, its plate voltage is 32 volts.

To find the grid voltage of V_2, a partial equivalent circuit is drawn which includes the capacitor C_3 with its charge just before the circuit was flipped. The capacitor is connected between the plate of V_1 and the grid of V_2, so its voltage is the difference between e_{b_1} and e_{c_2} during the stable state. This difference is almost 100 volts, and the equivalent circuit is shown in Fig. 7-7. At this instant of time, e_{c_2} is $-100 + 32 = -68$ volts, which means V_2 is definitely cut off.

Now, this is just a temporarily stable state because C_3 immediately begins to discharge. The discharge equivalent circuit is shown in Fig. 7-8,

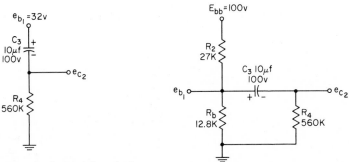

Fig. 7-7.   *Capacitor's partial equivalent circuit.*

Fig. 7-8.   *Discharge equivalent circuit.*

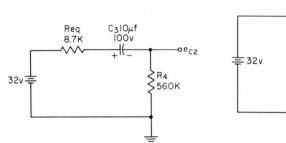 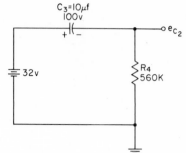

Fig. 7-9. Equivalent Thévenin dis-   Fig. 7-10. Approximate equivalent
charge circuit.   circuit.

where R_b is the d-c plate resistance of V_1 and is calculated as 12.8 kilohms
from the characteristic curves in Fig. 7-3 (with $e_c = 0$, $i_b = 2.5$ ma, and
$e_b = 32$ volts). Thévenin's theorem can simplify the circuit to that shown
in Fig. 7-9. It is seen that R_{eq} is small compared with R_4, and little error
will be introduced if R_{eq} is neglected, as is done in Fig. 7-10. The time constant of this circuit is 560 kilohms times 10 μf = 5.6 sec. As C_3 discharges,
e_{c_2} will become less negative until it finally reaches the cutoff value of -6
volts, and then V_2 will start conducting. From Fig. 7-10, $e_{c_2} = 32 - e_{c_3}$.
For e_{c_2} to equal -6 volts, e_{c_3} will equal 38 volts. Therefore, e_{c_3} has to discharge from 100 to 38 volts. The time required for this to happen can now
be found.

Using Eq. (3-6) with $\Delta e_c = 62$ volts, $E_{R0} = 68$ volts, and $\tau = 5.6$ sec,

$$\Delta e_c = E_{R0}(1 - \epsilon^{-t/\tau})$$

where
$$\tau = R_4 C_3 = (560)(10^3)(10^{-5}) = 5.6 \text{ sec}$$
$$62 = 68(1 - \epsilon^{-t/5.6})$$
$$t = 13.6 \text{ sec}$$

The calculated voltage values for this circuit are shown in Table 7-1.

TABLE 7-1

	V_2 conducting, volts	V_1 conducting, volts
e_{b_1}	100	32
e_{c_1}	-9.4	0
e_{b_2}	40	96.2
e_{c_2}	-0.56	-68 to -6

TABLE 7-2

	V_2 conducting, volts	V_1 conducting, volts
e_{b_1}	100	32
e_{c_1}	−13.9	0
e_{b_2}	30	96.2
e_{c_2}	0.268	−68 to −6

STABILIZATION

It was found from the calculations in Sec. 7-1 that in the stable condition of the circuit, the grid voltage of V_1 was only 3 volts more negative then the cutoff value. This voltage is the difference between E_{cc} and the drop across R_1. Also, it was pointed out that V_2 was not in clamp but, with −0.56 volt on its grid, was in the active region. Both of these conditions lead to instability; that is, small transient signals can trigger this circuit, or, under certain conditions, the circuit could trigger periodically by itself and become free-running.

There are two possible methods of stabilizing the circuit. First, the bias voltage E_{cc} could be made more negative, which would bring V_1 further into the cutoff region. Second, R_4 could be returned to B+ to provide a positive potential on the grid of V_2 and drive it into saturation. The effects of both of these changes will now be considered.

If no change is made in the circuit of Fig. 7-2 except that R_4 is connected to the +100 volts supply instead of to ground, the various voltages can be calculated, and are shown in Table 7-2. (It is assumed that when V_2 is in clamp, its grid-cathode resistance is 1.5 kilohms.) It can be seen from these data that during the stable state V_2 is in clamp; also, this circuit change has caused V_1 to be further into the cutoff region. The effect of this change on the time period of the temporarily stable state will now be determined.

At the start of the temporarily stable state, a partial equivalent circuit is as shown in Fig. 7-11. Compare this circuit with that in Fig. 7-8. The

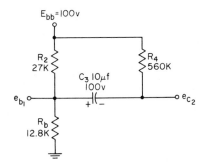

Fig. 7-11. Partial equivalent circuit; positive grid return.

circuit is further reduced to that of Fig. 7-12a to c by applying Thévenin's theorem to V_1 and load. At the first instant that C_3 begins to discharge, the voltage across R_4 becomes 168 volts. However, the polarities of E_{bb} and e_{R_4} are opposite; hence, the voltage between grid and cathode of V_2 is 68 volts. Since the cutoff potential of V_2 is 6 volts, the voltage e_{R_4} must decrease to 106 volts in order to cause V_2 to fire. The increment in capacitor voltage change is 62 volts. If the increment equation [Eq. (3-6)] is applied, the time that V_2 is cut off becomes

$$\Delta e_c = E_{R0}(1 - \epsilon^{-t/\tau})$$
$$62 = 168(1 - \epsilon^{-t/\tau})$$
$$t = 2.58 \text{ sec}$$

Therefore, the circuit change has greatly reduced the time period of the temporarily stable state. This is because in the first circuit the capacitor is trying to discharge from 100 volts down toward 32 volts of the same polarity; in the second circuit it is trying to discharge from 100 volts down through zero and then to 68 volts of the opposite polarity. The actual change allowed is the same in both circuits (from 100 down to 38 volts); but in the second case the actual change is a smaller percentage of the total possible change, so a shorter time is required. The time constant is the same in both circuits.

Positive grid return also improves the accuracy of the OFF time for V_2. Figure 7-12d shows the changing grid voltage on V_2 employing ground-return grids. Note the angle θ at which the grid potential approaches the cutoff potential. A change in one of the circuit parameters, for example, B+, causes the e_{co} to vary to -5.6 volts. The change in OFF time for V_2 is increased by Δt.

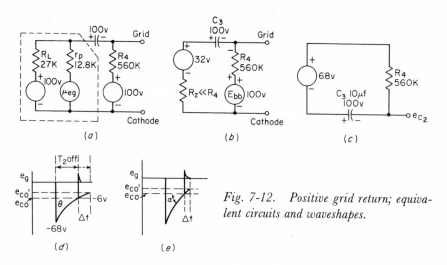

Fig. 7-12. Positive grid return; equivalent circuits and waveshapes.

TABLE 7-3

	V_2 conducting, volts	V_1 conducting, volts
e_{b_1}	100	39
e_{c_1}	-25.8	-0.4
e_{b_2}	40	96.2
e_{c_2}	-0.56	-61 to -6

Figure 7-12e shows the changing grid voltage on V_2 for a circuit employing positive grid return. The grid potential approaches e_{co} at a greater angle (α), thus creating a smaller increment in Δt. Changes in circuit parameters have less influence on the OFF time of V_2.

If R_4 of Fig. 7-2 is now returned to ground but E_{cc} is increased to -80 volts, the calculated voltages are those shown in Table 7-3. The time period for the temporarily stable state is 13 sec. It is seen that the grid of V_1 is very much into the cutoff region during the stable state, but V_2 is not in clamp. The time period is a little shorter than it was for $E_{cc} = -50$ volts, but not nearly so short as with R_4 returned to B+.

The last comparison is with E_{cc} equal to -80 volts and R_4 returned to B+. These changes result in the values shown in Table 7-4. The time period of the temporarily stable state is 2.34 sec. This is the most stable circuit; V_2 is in clamp, and V_1 is well into the cutoff region.

WAVEFORMS

It has been assumed that the transitions from the stable to the temporarily stable state and back again are instantaneous. This is not the case. Figure 7-13 shows how the grid voltage of V_2 and the plate voltage of V_1 vary in the circuit of Fig. 7-2. At time t_1 the circuit is triggered and V_2 is driven to cutoff almost instantaneously, as the 68-volt drop in the plate voltage of V_1 is transferred through C_3 to the grid of V_2. Immediately the capacitor begins to discharge and the grid of V_2 becomes less negative exponentially. At time t_2, this grid voltage has reached the -6-volt cutoff

TABLE 7-4

	V_2 conducting, volts	V_1 conducting, volts
e_{b_1}	100	39
e_{c_1}	-30.3	-0.4
e_{b_2}	30	96.2
e_{c_2}	0.268	-61 to -6

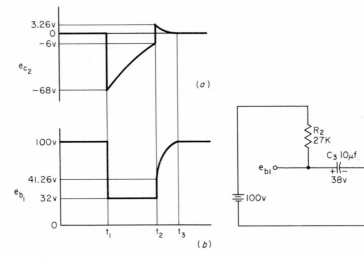

Fig. 7-13. Waveform; monostable multivibrator.

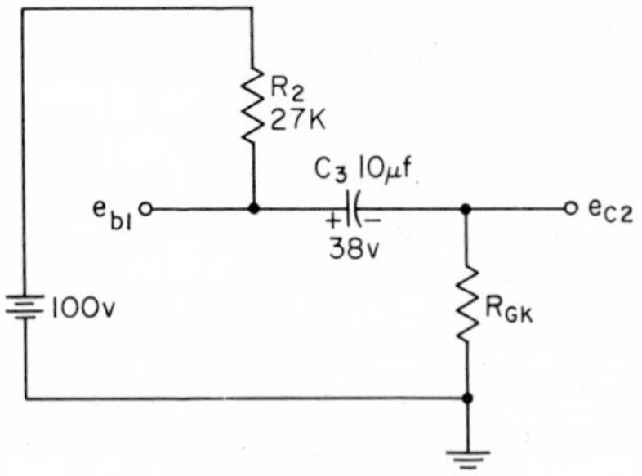

Fig. 7-14. Partial equivalent circuit.

value, and immediately V_2 begins to conduct, while V_1 goes to cutoff. Now, as V_1 goes to cutoff, its plate voltage tries to rise instantaneously to the 100-volt E_{bb} value. Again, this change in plate voltage of V_1 is coupled through C_3 to the grid of V_2. This grid voltage was -6 volts and now is trying to rise to $-6 + 68 = 62$ volts. The two voltages change almost instantaneously until the grid of V_2 goes positive and V_2 goes into clamp. The capacitor's voltage is now 38 volts (the difference between e_{c_2} and e_{b_1} just before time t_2). A partial equivalent circuit at time t_2 is shown in Fig. 7-14. If it is assumed that R_{gk} (the grid-to-cathode resistance of V_2) is 1.5 kilohms, e_{c_2} can be calculated from the series circuit of Fig. 7-14. (V_1 is not conducting.) $e_{c_2} = (100 - 38)(1.5 \text{ kilohms})/(27 \text{ kilohms} + 1.5 \text{ kilohms}) = 3.26$ volts. This is the amount of overshoot in Fig. 7-13a at time t_2. As this same time, e_b will equal $38 + 3.26 = 41.26$ volts.

Grid current is flowing in V_2, and this current is charging C_3. This charging path is the series circuit shown in Fig. 7-14. The charging time constant is $C_3(R_2 + R_{gk}) = (10 \text{ μf})(28.5 \text{ kilohms}) = 0.285$ sec. The charging will continue until C_3 is again charged up to 100 volts. If it takes five time constants for C_3 to completely charge, this will be about 1.4 sec; it is shown as the time between t_2 and t_3 in Fig. 7-13. This is called the *recovery time*, and its value is often of considerable importance in certain circuits.

REDUCING RECOVERY TIME

If the monostable multivibrator is being used where a sequence of triggering pulses is applied, each one shortly after the circuit has returned to its stable state from the previous trigger, it is important that the coupling capacitor recharge completely before each new trigger is applied. Otherwise, voltage conditions will be different for different triggering pulses, and the resulting output waveforms will not have uniform amplitudes and time periods.

It was found that the time required for the coupling capacitor to complete its recharge (recovery time) is dependent upon the time constant $C_3(R_2 + R_{gk})$. Little can be done to reduce R_{gk}, and it is small anyway compared with R_2. Reducing R_2 and/or C_3 will be effective in reducing recovery time.

The ON time is very much dependent on C_3 and R_4; so for a certain time period, if C_3 is reduced, R_4 must be increased. This can result in instability due to positive-ion grid current when there are traces of gas in the tube. Also, a large value of R_4 increases the impedance between grid and ground and makes the circuit more sensitive to unwanted signal pickup. Usually, the upper limit is several megohms.

R_2 can be reduced in resistance, but this will increase the plate current of V_1 and thus its plate power dissipation.

A third and very effective method of reducing the recovery time requires the use of an additional diode and an extra positive-power-supply terminal, as shown in Fig. 7-15. The diode clamps the plate of V_1 to the $+100$-volt terminal when V_1 is at cutoff, but allows the plate voltage to drop below the $+100$-volt value when V_1 is conducting. As V_1 is going from conduction to cutoff, C_3 will be recharging as described in Sec. 7-3, but will now be charging toward 150 volts, so its voltage will rise more rapidly. As it reaches 100 volts, the diode will again clamp the plate of V_1 to the 100-volt terminal, and the capacitor will charge no further. In this case, instead of the recovery time's being five time constants or 1.4 sec, it will just be the time it takes for the capacitor to charge from 38 to 100 volts, with the voltage supply equal to 150 volts.

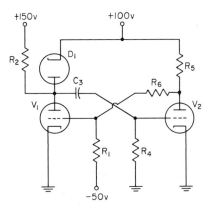

Fig. 7-15. Monostable circuit with plate-catching diode.

With $E_{R0} = 150 - 38 = 112$ volts, $\Delta e_c = 100 - 38 = 62$ volts, and $\tau = 0.285$ in Eq. (3-6),

$$62 = 112(1 - \epsilon^{-t/0.285})$$
$$t = 0.23 \text{ sec}$$

This is much shorter than the 1.4-sec recovery time calculated previously.

This diode is called a *plate-catching diode* because the diode "catches" the plate voltage as it tries to rise above 100 volts.

The overshoot of V_2's grid voltage causes an undershoot in its plate voltage. When the grid goes into the positive region, not only does grid current flow but the plate current is higher than it would be with zero grid voltage. The plate voltage of V_2, of course, drops slightly as its plate current increases. This is shown in Fig. 7-16, where all four voltages are given. Because the voltage at the grid of V_1 is dependent upon the plate voltage of V_2, it too has an undershoot as shown.

COMMERCIAL CIRCUIT

In Fig. 7-17 is shown a circuit of a plate-coupled monostable multivibrator, which is used in the Hewlett-Packard Model 405A automatic d-c digital voltmeter. This complete instrument will be described in more detail in Chap. 13. This particular circuit is called the ramp-gate multivibrator.

V_2, being normally conducting, requires a negative pulse on its grid for triggering. After about 30 msec, the multivibrator returns to its stable

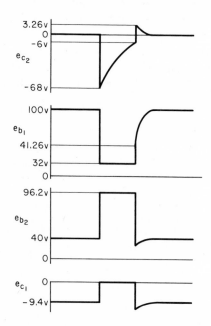

Fig. 7-16. Monostable circuit waveforms.

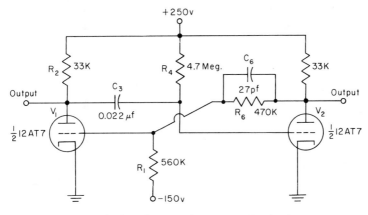

Fig. 7-17. Commercial monostable circuit.

state. Outputs are taken from both plates. Notice that R_4 returns to B+ to clamp V_2 during conduction, and R_1 goes to -150 volts, which biases V_1 to about -36 volts, well below cutoff.

It will be noted that the coupling resistor R_6 is paralleled with a 27-pf capacitor. This is a commutating capacitor and serves a function identical to that of the commutating capacitors in the binary circuits, namely, to reduce transition time.

7-2 CATHODE-COUPLED MONOSTABLE MULTIVIBRATOR

Another type of monostable multivibrator is that shown in Fig. 7-18. Coupling from V_2 to V_1 is by means of the common-cathode resistor R_k, so this circuit is called the *cathode-coupled monostable multivibrator*. Capacitance coupling is still used from the plate of V_1 to the grid of V_2. The grid resistor R_4 of V_2 is returned to its cathode, although it could be returned to $+E_{bb}$, as in the plate-coupled circuit. In either case, V_2 is normally conducting, either in clamp or with a very small negative voltage on its grid with respect to cathode. The high plate current of V_2 flowing through R_k provides enough negative bias on V_1 to keep it at cutoff. Therefore, a stable condition is present.

A triggering signal—for example, a negative pulse on the grid of V_2— will drive V_2 to cutoff. The drop in current through R_k causes the bias voltage of V_1 to decrease and V_1 conducts. The plate voltage of V_1 drops, and this voltage change is transferred to the grid of V_2, keeping it at cutoff, while C_3 is discharging through R_4. When the discharge current through R_4 is no longer high enough to develop the cutoff voltage for V_2, V_2 begins to conduct, increasing the voltage across R_k and cutting off V_1. The stable condition is again present.

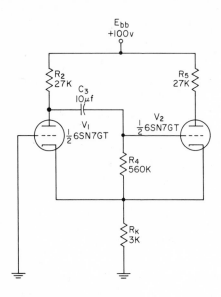

Fig. 7-18.   Cathode-coupled monostable
multivibrator.

If it is assumed that V_2 is conducting, with approximately -0.56 volt between grid and cathode, it can be found from Fig. 7-3 that there is about 40 volts between plate and cathode, and the plate current is 2.2 ma. This current, flowing through R_k, gives a voltage drop of 6.6 volts, which is the grid bias of V_1. This brings V_1 just barely into cutoff, which makes this a stable condition, but not so stable as might be desired. The plate voltage of V_1 is now about 93.4 volts with respect to cathode.

After the circuit is flipped and V_2 is driven to cutoff, the grid and plate voltages of both tubes will be found. An interesting problem presents itself for V_1. Its plate current is dependent upon its bias voltage. Its bias voltage is developed across R_k and is dependent upon the plate current. It looks like a trial-and-error type of problem, but it can be easily and accurately solved in this way. We know that the bias voltage is between 0 and -6 volts. It cannot be positive, because it is developed by plate-current flow through R_k. It cannot be zero, because that would mean no plate current is flowing through R_k. It cannot be more negative than -6 volts, as that bias would develop no plate current. If it were -2 volts, that would mean a plate current of 0.67 ma was flowing [$i = 2/(3)(10^3) = 0.67$ ma]. A dot is placed on the -2-volt curve at 0.67 ma in Fig. 7-3. If the bias were -4 volts, a plate current of 2 volts/3 kilohms $= 1.33$ ma would have to be flowing through R_k. A dot is placed on the -4-volt curve at 1.33 ma. A line is drawn between these two dots, and its intersection with the load line determines the operating point. This gives about 1 ma plate current and -3 volts grid bias. These values are only approximate values, because the load line in Fig. 7-3 assumes a 27-kilohm load resistor, whereas the total resistance in this problem also includes the 3-kilohm cathode resistor. A new load line could be drawn for a 30-kilohm load resistor, but the results would be almost the same as those obtained with the 27-kilohm load line. The plate-to-cathode voltage of V_1 is $100 - (1 \text{ ma})(30 \text{ kilohms}) = 70$ volts. V_2 is not conducting, so its plate-to-cathode voltage is $100 - 3 = 97$ volts.

We find that the plate voltage of V_1 dropped from 93 to 70 volts, a change of 23 volts. This drop is transferred to the grid of V_2 as a -23-volt bias; then, as C_3 begins to discharge, the grid voltage becomes less negative until the -6-volt cutoff point is reached. The time period of the temporarily stable state is now calculated.

C_3 of Fig. 7-18 was charged to 93 volts and now must discharge 17 volts to bring the bias of V_2 up to the -6-volt cutoff value. This discharge path through R_4 and the rest of the circuit is about 580 kilohms, giving a discharge time constant of 5.8 sec. C_3 is trying to discharge from 93 to 76 volts with a source equal to 70 volts. It is found that it takes about 7.8 sec for V_2 to begin to conduct again, after being flipped to cutoff. The plate and grid voltages, with respect to cathode, for this circuit are shown in Table 7-5.

It has been assumed previously that this circuit is triggered by applying a negative pulse to the grid of V_2. An easy way to trigger the circuit experimentally is to momentarily ground the grid of V_2. Its cathode is about 6.6 volts positive with respect to ground, so making the grid at ground potential is equivalent to applying a negative signal to the grid.

Notice that the grid of V_1 is grounded. A resistor could be connected between grid and ground and would not affect the circuit's operation. This, then, provides a very convenient point for triggering, because a triggering circuit coupled into the grid of V_1 will not change the circuit's characteristics through loading.

In the particular circuit under discussion, V_1 is just barely into cutoff. A positive signal of less than 1 volt, applied to the grid of V_1, will flip V_1 into conduction and trigger the circuit. This triggering point provides a distinct advantage of the cathode-coupled multivibrator over the plate-coupled circuit. Triggering of monostable multivibrators will be discussed later in this section.

TABLE 7-5

	V_2 conducting, volts	V_1 conducting, volts
e_{b_1}	93.4	70
e_{c_1}	-6.6	-3
e_{b_2}	40	96
e_{c_2}	10.56	-23 to -6

Another real advantage of the cathode-coupled circuit is that the plate of V_2 is not part of the regenerative feedback loop, and this provides an ideal point from which to obtain the output signal; the output load will not affect the operation of the circuit.

STABILIZATION

It was mentioned earlier that the circuit under consideration was some-what unstable because V_1 was barely into the cutoff region. Also, it can be seen from the voltage values that V_2 is not in clamp but is in the active region of its operation when conducting.

A more stable circuit can be designed by returning R_4 to $+E_{bb}$, as was done with the plate-coupled monostable multivibrator.

Figure 7-19 shows the circuit used in a standard plug-in unit manufactured by Engineered Electronics Company. Capacitor C_3 is externally connected and determines the time duration of the temporarily stable condition. This time duration, in seconds, may be approximated by $0.7C$. If C is in microfarads, the time is in seconds.

In this circuit, the grid of V_1 is biased to about -25 volts during the stable condition, where about -16 volts is the cutoff value of grid voltage. V_2 will be about 0.2 volt positive. Therefore, this is a very stable circuit. There is about a 133-volt difference in the plate voltage of V_2 from conduction to cutoff, and this would normally be the amplitude of the output signal; but in the commercial unit, R_5 consists of a 6.8- and an 18-kilohm voltage divider, which reduces the output amplitude to about 100 volts.

CONTROL OF ON TIME

The cathode-coupled monostable multivibrator is frequently used to delay a signal for a certain amount of time. The incoming signal triggers the circuit; and when it returns to its permanently stable state, the outgoing

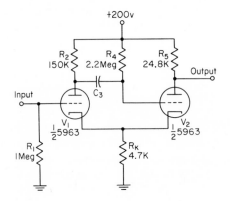

Fig. 7-19. Commercial cathode-coupled monostable multivibrator.

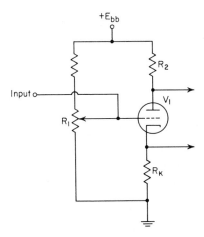

+E_bb

Input

R_2

V_1

R_1

R_K

Fig. 7-20. Delay control of a cathode-coupled monostable multivibrator.

signal is produced, the delay time being the time duration of the temporarily stable state.

It is often desirable to accurately control this delay time. It has been seen how the grid-to-ground circuit of V_1 is isolated from the feedback circuits. The grid can go directly to ground, or there can be a grid resistor across which the triggering pulse can be applied. An adjustable positive d-c voltage can be applied to the grid of V_1, as shown in Fig. 7-20, and it will be found that the conduction time of V_1 will be linearly proportional to this d-c voltage. When the circuit is triggered, the new value of plate voltage for V_1 depends on the grid-to-cathode bias. The more positive this bias voltage, the higher the plate current of V_1, and the further its plate voltage will drop.

It was shown in Sec. 7-6 that e_{b_1} dropped from 93.4 to 70 volts, and this transferred to the grid of V_2 as about -23 volt bias. C_3 was charged to about 93 volts and had to discharge 17 volts to bring the grid voltage of V_2 up to -6 volts. If a positive d-c grid voltage on V_1 caused its plate voltage to drop to 43 volts instead of to 70 volts, the grid of V_2 would be driven to -50 volts. C_3 would have to discharge 44 volts to bring e_{c_2} up to -6 volts. With these voltage values, it takes about 12.3 sec for the ON time period instead of the 7.8 sec calculated previously. Adjusting the bias voltage for V_1 gives a convenient way of controlling the time delay of the circuit.

TRIGGERING

Either the plate-coupled or the cathode-coupled monostable multivibrator may be triggered at any one of a number of places, for example, a positive pulse at the grid of V_1 or a negative pulse at the plate of V_1 or the grid of V_2. In the case of the plate-coupled circuit, a positive pulse at the plate of V_2 will cause triggering; or in the cathode-coupled circuit, a negative pulse at the cathode of V_1.

The advantage of applying the triggering signal to the grid of V_1 in the cathode-coupled multivibrator has been discussed. But if the signal is applied through a coupling capacitor, the grid may draw current, charge the capacitor, and change the bias on this tube, which would change the ON time period.

A preferable method of triggering either circuit would be with a negative pulse applied to the plate of V_1 or the grid of V_2. A smaller-amplitude pulse is required; also, the charging effect of the trigger coupling capacitor is eliminated.

An improvement is possible if the triggering signal is applied through a coupling diode, as discussed in connection with the binary circuit in Chap. 6. The diode disconnects the trigger source after the transition takes place, and keeps it disconnected until the circuit returns to its permanently stable state.

PROBLEMS

7-1 Refer to the circuit of Fig. 7-2. Assume $R_2 = R_5 = 6.7$ kilohms, $C_3 = 0.1$ μf, $R_6 = R_4 = 470$ kilohms, $R_1 = 220$ kilohms, and $V_1 = V_2 = 6SN7$. With no trigger applied: (*a*) What plate current flows through V_2? (*b*) What potential exists between the grid and the cathode of V_2? (*c*) Of V_1? (*d*) What is the charge on C_3?

7-2 Refer to Prob. 7-1. Calculate the time period for the temporarily stable state.

7-3 Indicate how changes in the following circuit values of Prob 7-1 influence the time duration of the temporarily stable state: (*a*) R_2 and R_5 (load resistors); (*b*) C_3; (*c*) R_4; (*d*) the B+ supply; (*e*) the bias supply.

7-4 If R_4 in Prob. 7-1 is connected to the B+ supply instead of to ground, how far into cutoff will V_1 be?

7-5 Refer to Prob. 7-4. Assume that the B+ supply is increased to 250 volts and the circuit components have the following values: $R_2 = R_5 = 15$ kilohms, $C_3 = 0.05$ μf, $R_6 = 680$ kilohms, $R_4 = 560$ kilohms, $R_1 = 330$ kilohms, and $V_1 = V_2 = 6SN7$. (*a*) What will be the time duration of the temporarily stable state? (*b*) What will it be if R_4 is connected to ground instead of to B+?

7-6 Refer to Prob. 7-5. What new value must C_3 be increased or decreased to in order to produce a temporarily stable output time duration of 5 msec (*a*) if R_4 is connected to B+ and (*b*) if R_4 is connected to ground?

7-7 Refer to the circuit of Fig. 7-18. Assume the following circuit values: B+ = 250 volts, $R_2 = R_5 = 20$ kilohms, $C_3 = 0.1$ μf, $R_4 = 470$ kilohms, $R_k = 2$ kilohms, and $V_1 = V_2 = 6SN7$. (a) What is the quiescent voltage drop across R_k? (b) What is the charge on C_3? (c) What is the voltage drop across R_4?

7-8 When the circuit of Prob. 7-7 is triggered and V_1 is conducting and V_2 is cut off, what voltage appears across R_k?

7-9 In the circuit of Prob. 7-7, what is the pulse duration of the output when a trigger pulse is applied at the input?

7-10 If the value of the cathode bias resistor in the circuit of Fig. 7-18 is increased, will the output duration time be increased or decreased?

7-11 Refer to the circuit of Fig. 7-18. Assume that the load resistor of V_1 is increased. (a) Will the output amplitude increase or decrease? (b) Will there be an increase or a decrease in output duration time?

7-12 Can the circuit of Fig. 7-18 be triggered by a 10-kc trigger pulse? If not, explain.

7-13 Refer to the circuit of Fig. 7-18. If the value of resistor R_4 is doubled, how long will the output duration time be?

7-14 Refer to the circuit of Fig. 7-18. If the value of C_1 is doubled, how will the output duration time be affected and by how much?

7-15 If R_4 of Fig. 7-18 is connected to the B+ supply instead of the two cathodes, will the time duration of the temporarily stable state increase or decrease?

7-3 PLATE-COUPLED ASTABLE MULTIVIBRATOR

It was shown how the use of a coupling capacitor instead of a resistor gives the multivibrator of Fig. 6-13 a temporarily stable state during the time it takes for the capacitor to discharge. If both coupling circuits are capacitive, there are no permanently stable states; instead, both are temporary. Such a circuit is the astable multivibrator shown in Fig. 7-21.

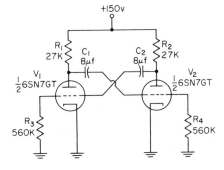

Fig. 7-21. Plate-coupled astable multivibrator.

A load line for a 27-kilohm resistor and a 150-volt plate power supply results in cutoff at about −10 volts. When the grid voltage is zero, the plate voltage is about 47 volts. Therefore, the plate voltage of each tube will vary between 47 and 150 volts.

When a tube is cut off, the capacitor connected to its plate will be charged to 150 volts. When this tube conducts, its plate voltage drops 150 − 47 = 103 volts. This drives the grid of the other tube to −103 volts, cutting off the plate current. This tube will be cut off until the capacitor can discharge from 150 to 57 volts, which will bring the grid of the cutoff tube up to −10 volts, and the tube will start conducting. The discharge equivalent circuit is shown in Fig. 7-22.

It can be seen that $\tau = 4.48$ sec, $E_{R0} = 103$ volts, and $\Delta e_c = 93$ volts. By substituting these values into Eq. (3-6), t is found to equal 10.45 sec. This is the time for each temporarily stable state, and it takes two to make a complete cycle, so this circuit has a total time period of about 21 sec.

Note that when each tube is conducting, its grid voltage is assumed to be zero. Actually, because of a slight grid-current flow through the 560-kilohm resistor, the grid of the conducting tube will be slightly negative. If each 560-kilohm grid resistor is connected to the +150-volt terminal instead of to ground, it will ensure the conducting tube's being driven into the saturation region. The voltages calculated previously are not changed by any significant amount, but the time period is greatly affected.

The new equivalent discharge circuit is shown in Fig. 7-23. The time constant is not changed ($\tau = 4.48$ sec), but now $E_{R0} = 253$ volts and $\Delta e_c = 93$. These values substituted into Eq. (3-6) give $t = 2.06$ sec. Therefore, the total time period for one cycle of operation is 4.12 sec, compared with the 10.45 sec of the previous circuit.

This circuit is symmetrical; each tube is "on" and "off" for equal periods of time. These time periods are controlled for the most part by the coupling capacitors and the grid resistors. If it is desirable to make either one or both of these time periods variable, a variable resistor can be used as a grid resistor.

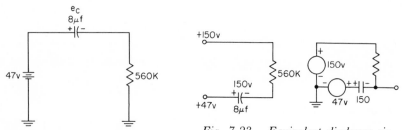

Fig. 7-22. Discharge equivalent circuit.

Fig. 7-23. Equivalent discharge circuit.

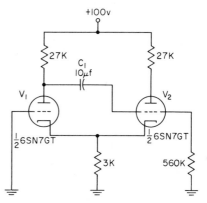

Fig. 7-24. Cathode-coupled astable
multivibrator.

7-4 CATHODE-COUPLED ASTABLE MULTIVIBRATOR

Coupling from one of the astable multivibrator sections to the other can
be through a common-cathode resistor, such as that used for the monostable circuit. This is shown in Fig. 7-24. Notice that the only difference
between this circuit and the monostable circuit shown in Fig. 7-18 is the
connection of the grid resistor of V_2. In the monostable circuit the grid resistor was connected to the cathode, and it was possible for the grid-
cathode voltage of V_2 to be almost zero, keeping V_2 conducting heavily.
Its plate current developed enough bias voltage across the cathode resistor
to keep V_1 permanently at cutoff until a triggering pulse flipped the circuit. Figure 7-24 shows that the grid resistor of V_2 is returned to ground,
which puts the grid at ground potential when V_2 is conducting. V_2's cathode
is positive, because its plate current flows through the cathode resistor;
therefore, the grid of V_2 is negative with respect to its cathode.

The bias voltage developed across the cathode resistor is not high
enough to keep either tube permanently at cutoff. Just as in the monostable circuit, the discharge of the coupling capacitor develops the voltage
necessary to keep one of the tubes at cutoff. The time period during which
the tube is cut off is determined by the time it takes for the capacitor to
discharge enough to bring the grid voltage up to the cutoff value.

When the capacitor has discharged down to the point where the grid
bias of V_2 is just at cutoff, V_2 begins to conduct. As its current increases,
the voltage drop across the cathode resistor increases; and as this is the bias
for V_1, the plate current of V_1 decreases. This raises the plate voltage of
V_1, and this rise in voltage is transferred to V_2 as a rise in grid voltage. This
is a regenerative action and continues until the grid of V_2 goes below the
cutoff value.

The positive grid voltage of V_2 provides a low-resistance path for the
capacitor to charge toward its original voltage. This charge path is through

the grid-cathode tube resistance (about 1.5 kilohms), through the cathode resistor, and through the load resistor of V_1. The time constant of this circuit is only about (1.5 kilohms + 3 kilohms + 27 kilohms)(10 μf) = 0.315 sec, compared with the discharge time constant (560 kilohms)(10 μf) = 5.6 sec.

While V_2 is conducting heavily, V_1 is at cutoff. Its bias voltage is developed across the cathode resistor, and the large charging current and the plate current of V_2 are both flowing through the cathode resistor.

As the capacitor's voltage approaches its original value, its charging current has decreased enough so the bias voltage developed across the cathode resistor is no longer high enough to keep V_1 at cutoff. V_1 starts to conduct, and its drop in plate voltage is again transferred to the grid of V_2, driving it to cutoff.

This circuit does not put out a symmetrical waveform, because of the time difference in the charge and discharge of the capacitor. V_2 is cut off for most of the time and then conducts heavily for a short period of time. If the output signal is taken from the plate of V_2, it can be considered to be a series of negative pulses, as shown in Fig. 7-25.

A common use for this circuit is to develop a sawtooth waveform for the horizontal-sweep signal of a cathode-ray tube. If a capacitor is connected between the plate of V_2 and ground, the output waveform will be greatly modified. The multivibrator can be considered to be a switch which is infinite in resistance when open but when closed has a finite resistance equal to the sum of the d-c plate resistance of V_2 and the resistance of the cathode resistor. This equivalent switch is shown in Fig. 7-26, along with

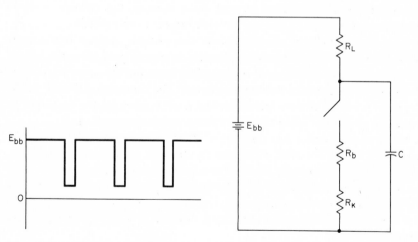

Fig. 7-25. Output waveshape for a cathode-coupled astable multivibrator.

Fig. 7-26. Equivalent circuit of a sawtooth generator.

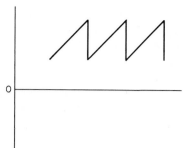

Fig. 7-27. Sawtooth waveform for short discharge RC time constant.

the load resistor of V_2, the extra capacitor which has been added, and the power-supply voltage.

When the switch is open, C charges exponentially through R_L; and whenever the switch is closed, it discharges exponentially through R_b and R_k. If the $R_L C$ time constant is long compared with the time the switch is open, the capacitor will charge to only a small percentage of E_{bb}, and its charge curve will be almost linear. If the $(R_b + R_k)(C)$ time constant is short compared with the time the switch is closed, the capacitor will be as seen in Fig. 7-27, which is the sawtooth waveform needed.

7-5 SYNCHRONIZATION

Even though the free-running multivibrator will continue to oscillate with no external triggering pulses applied, the time periods will not be precise, but will vary with changes in component characteristics and the supply voltage. It is common practice to synchronize the transition times in these circuits with triggering or synchronizing pulses. These pulses are usually timed to cause V_2 to start conducting just before it normally would. Therefore, the circuit must be designed to have a free-running frequency a little less than the frequency of the synchronizing pulses.

A resistor can be added between the grid of V_1 and ground, and then a negative pulse can be applied to the grid. If this pulse occurs when V_1 is conducting, it will be amplified by V_1 and inverted in phase. It will appear at the grid of V_2 as a positive pulse. Figure 7-28 shows the voltage wave-

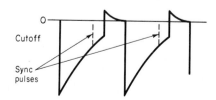

Fig. 7-28. Grid-voltage waveshape; free-running multivibrator.

Cutoff

Sync pulses

form which would appear at the grid of V_2 if the circuit were free-running, with no synchronizing pulses. If a sync pulse were present (shown as a dotted line) just before the circuit would normally flip, the sync pulse would drive V_2 into conduction, and the transition would take place at the desired instant.

If the sync pulses were of the proper amplitude, the circuit could be designed to operate on every other one, on every third, or on every fourth, the other pulses occurring when the grid voltage is negative enough so that the positive sync pulse is not sufficient to drive the tube into the conduction region. In this way the circuit could be used to deliver one pulse for every two, three, or four input pulses; thus it would be a frequency-dividing circuit.

PROBLEMS

7-16 Refer to the circuit of Fig. 7-21. Assume the following circuit values: plate load resistors 15 kilohms each, coupling capacitors 0.5 μf each, grid load resistors 330 kilohms each, and B+ = 150 volts. (a) What grid potential will cut off V_1? (b) What is the oscillating frequency?

7-17 If the coupling capacitors of Prob. 7-16 are reduced to 0.05 μf, what is the new oscillating frequency?

7-18 If the plate load resistors in Prob. 7-16 are reduced, will the oscillating frequency increase, decrease, or remain unchanged?

7-19 Refer to Prob. 7-16 and assume the same circuit values. If B+ is increased to +300 volts, what is the new oscillating frequency?

7-20 Refer to Fig. 7-21. Indicate how the conduction time of V_1 is influenced by increases in the values of the following circuit components: (a) grid load on V_1; (b) grid load on V_2; (c) plate load on V_1; (d) plate load on V_2; (e) coupling capacitor between plate of V_2 and grid of V_1.

7-21 Refer to Prob. 7-16. Assume that the output is taken across V_2. (a) What is the rise time of the output wave? (b) What is the delay time of the output?

7-22 Refer to Prob. 7-21. If the B+ is doubled, what is the new rise time of the output?

7-23 Refer to Prob. 7-21. If the value of the coupling capacitor is decreased, how are the output frequency and rise time influenced?

7-24 Refer to Prob. 7-16. If the two grid resistors are connected to B+ instead of to ground, what is the new oscillating frequency?

7-25 What is the rise time of the output of the circuit in Prob. 7-24?

7-26 Refer to Prob. 7-24. Assume that the output is taken from across V_2. Which coupling capacitor should be changed, and to what value, in order to produce an output whose frequency is 14.3 cps and whose duration time is 4 msec?

7-27 Draw a schematic of a free-running multivibrator similar to the one shown in Fig. 7-21. Assume the circuit values of Prob. 7-24. The output should be clamped to zero and should be a positive-going pulse whose amplitude is clamped to +30 volts.

7-28 Refer to the circuit of Fig. 7-24. If the value of C_1 is decreased, will the new output frequency increase or decrease?

7-29 How do changes in the value of the cathode resistor of Fig. 7-24 influence the output (*a*) frequency, (*b*) rise time, (*c*) amplitude, and (*d*) duration time?

7-6 TRANSISTOR CIRCUITS

A transistorized collector-coupled monostable multivibrator is shown in Fig. 7-29. A comparison with the vacuum-tube equivalent (Fig. 7-17) will show that they are identical except for circuit values.

The transistor circuit can be analyzed by drawing a load line on the characteristic curves (Fig. 7-30). When Q_2 is conducting, its base current is 15 volts/100 kilohms = 150 μa, which is well into the saturation region, and its current is about 3.2 ma. Its collector voltage is zero. The base voltage of Q_1 is equal to $-2 + (2)(27$ kilohms$)/(27$ kilohms $+ 56$ kilohms$) = -1.35$ volts. The negative voltage on the base of an NPN transistor reverse-biases the emitter-base junction, and thus Q_1 is in cutoff, with its collector at 15 volts.

A positive trigger pulse may be applied to either the base of Q_1 or the

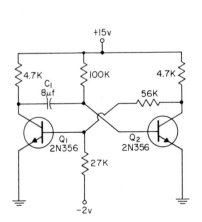

Fig. 7-29. Transistorized monostable multivibrator.

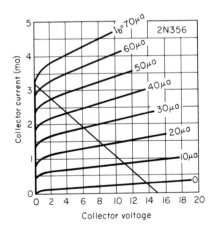

Fig. 7-30. Graphic characteristics for a transistorized monostable multivibrator.

collector of Q_2; or a negative pulse may be applied to the collector of Q_1 or to the base of Q_2. When Q_1 conducts, its collector voltage drops to practically zero, and the capacitor transfers this drop to the base of Q_2, cutting off the collector current. The collector voltage of Q_2 increases; and its value, as well as the base current of Q_1, can be calculated from the partial equivalent circuit shown in Fig. 7-31. $e_{c_2} = 15 - (14.8)$ (4.7 kilohms)/(60.7 kilohms) $= 13.9$ volts. $i_1 = 14.8/60.7$ kilohms $= 244$ μa. $i_2 = 2.2/27$ kilohms $= 82$ μa. $i_{b_1} = i_1 - i_2 = 244$ μa $- 82$ μa $= 162$ μa. Q_1 is definitely in saturation.

The capacitor was originally charged to 15 volts, with the connection to the collector of Q_1 being the positive terminal. Now, the partial equivalent circuit is that shown in Fig. 7-32; the capacitor is trying to discharge to zero and then charge up to 15 volts with the opposite polarity. As soon as the capacitor's voltage drops to zero and reverses polarity, Q_2 will start conducting—its base will go positive. Therefore, the time period of cutoff for Q_2 is the time it takes for the capacitor's voltage to drop to zero. $\tau = 0.8$ sec, $E_{R0} = 30$ volts, and $\Delta e_c = 15$ volts. The time is calculated as 0.555 sec.

This time period may be varied by changing the value of the base resistor of Q_2. By letting this resistor value be R and substituting it into Eq. (3-6) along with the other values of E_{R0}, Δe_c, and C, the time period is found to equal $5.55R$, where R is in megohms and the time comes out in seconds.

A separate negative supply can be eliminated by using emitter biasing. When either transistor is conducting, its emitter current is equal to 3.2 ma. To develop the 2-volt bias needed, the emitter resistor value will be $2/3.2$ ma $= 625$ ohms. Figure 7-33 shows a circuit using this emitter biasing with a 680-ohm resistor. The value of this bias voltage is not too critical.

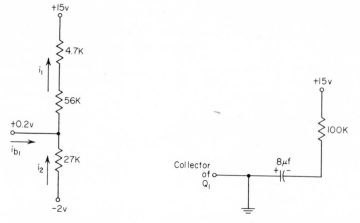

Fig. 7-31. Partial equivalent circuit.   Fig. 7-32. Partial equivalent circuit.

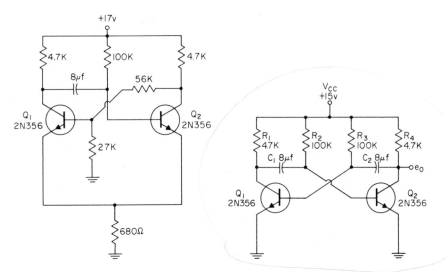

Fig. 7-33. Monostable multivibrator using emitter bias.

Fig. 7-34. Transistorized astable multivibrator.

Note that the power-supply voltage has been increased to 17 volts in order to supply the additional 2-volt drop across the emitter resistor.

By using capacitor coupling for both circuits, and returning both base resistors to the B+ supply terminal, the circuit becomes a free-running, or astable, multivibrator, as shown in Fig. 7-34. The theory of operation is identical with that of the monostable circuit except that now each of the transistors is held in cutoff for a time by the discharge of the coupling capacitor connected to its base. The time period of cutoff has already been calculated, so the total period of oscillation is twice this value, or 1.11 sec.

An interesting example of the small amounts of power required for transistor circuits can be demonstrated with this free-running multivibrator. This circuit will oscillate with a supply voltage of only 0.125 volt. The current draw is only 34 μa, which means only 4.25 μw of power is drawn from the power supply! The output signal has a frequency of about 25 cps and a peak-to-peak amplitude of 60 mv.

PROBLEMS

7-30 Refer to the circuit of Fig. 7-29. Assume that the collector supply voltage is reduced to +14 volts and the load resistances are reduced to 1 kilohm each. (a) What collector current flows through the ON transistor? (b) What is the base-to-emitter potential across the OFF transistor?

7-31　During the temporarily stable state of the circuit of Prob. 7-30, (a) what is the base-emitter voltage across the ON transistor; (b) what is the time period of the temporarily stable state?

7-32　If the coupling capacitor in Prob. 7-31 is reduced to 0.01 μf, what is the time period of the temporarily stable state?

7-33　Refer to Fig. 7-29. If the load resistors are 1 kilohm each, the collector supply is $+14$ volts, and the bias supply is -4 volts, what current is required to saturate the transistors?

7-34　How do changes in the value of the 56-kilohm resistor of Fig. 7-29 influence the (a) time duration of the temporarily stable state, (b) output amplitude, and (c) trigger sensitivity of the circuit?

7-35　If the 2N356 transistors of Fig. 7-29 are replaced with transistors of a higher β, will the circuit be more or less sensitive to trigger pulses?

7-36　Refer to the circuit of Fig. 7-34. Assume the circuit values to be as follows: $R_1 = R_4 = 1$ kilohm, $R_2 = R_3 = 68$ kilohms, $C_1 = C_2 = 0.1$ μf, and the collector supply is 14 volts. What is the frequency of the output square wave?

7-37　Refer to Prob. 7-36. Assume that the value of R_2 is increased to 150 kilohms, the value of C_2 is decreased to 0.05 μf, and the output is taken from the collector of Q_2. (a) What is the output frequency? (b) What is the output duration time?

7-38　If the value of C_1 in Fig. 7-34 is increased, will the saturation be increased, decreased, or unchanged for (a) Q_1 and (b) Q_2?

7-39　How do changes in load resistance on the transistors of Fig. 7-34 influence the output frequency and amplitude?

7-40　Refer to Fig. 7-34. Assume the following circuit conditions: $V_{cc} = 15$ volts, $R_1 = R_4 = 3.3$ kilohms, $C_1 = C_2 = 0.05$ μf, and $Q_1 = Q_2 = 2N356$. What values of base return resistors will produce an output square wave at 1 kc?

CHAPTER 8 BLOCKING OSCILLATORS

A *blocking oscillator* is very similar to the feedback-type oscillator used for the generation of r-f sine waves, where positive feedback is obtained by transformer coupling between the output and input circuits. There are several differences, the most important being that the blocking oscillator is designed so the plate current of a tube, or the collector current of a transistor, is cut off after one half-cycle of oscillation; and this current is cut off or *blocked* for a period of time usually quite long compared with the time period of oscillation. The effect is that the device is on for a short period of time and then off for a much longer period of time.

8-1 BASIC CIRCUIT

The basic circuit is shown in Fig. 8-1. The theory of operation can be explained in this way. If the cathode is heated and is emitting electrons and the plate voltage is applied, current starts immediately to increase from zero. This current cannot increase instantaneously because of the inductance of the primary winding of the transformer through which it is flowing.

As the current through the transformer winding is increased, the resulting magnetic field in the transformer core increases, inducing a voltage in the secondary winding according to $e_s = di_p/dt$. The induced voltage is of such a polarity that it makes the grid positive with respect to the cathode. Regenerative feedback results because the grid's going positive tends to increase the plate current more rapidly, inducing a higher voltage across the

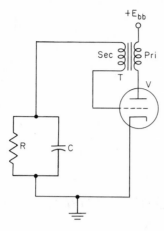

Fig. 8-1. Basic blocking oscillator.

secondary winding of the transformer and thus causing the higher positive grid voltage to increase the plate current even more.

There is a limit to how high the plate current and grid voltage can go. The plate current can increase only when the rate of increase of plate current is itself increasing. This point is important to understand. If the plate current were increasing at a constant rate, a constant value of grid voltage would be produced, but then this constant value of grid voltage would not allow the plate current to increase. The di_p/dt cannot be constant. Even if the grid voltage could in some way continue to increase, the plate current would be limited by Ohm's law; the power-supply voltage, its internal resistance, and the internal resistance of the primary winding of the transformer would limit the current even if the plate resistance of the tube could be reduced to zero.

As the plate current begins to approach this limit, we find that its rate of increase begins to slow down. This causes the secondary voltage to change at a slower rate, which in turn causes the rate of increase of plate current to be even less. Finally, the plate current is increasing at a constant rate, which means that a constant voltage is induced in the secondary winding, and the grid voltage, now being constant, stops the plate current from rising.

As soon as the plate current stops rising at a constant rate, the grid voltage begins to drop; and as the plate current stops increasing, the grid voltage drops to zero. As soon as the grid voltage begins to drop, the plate current begins to decrease, and this decrease in the current through the primary winding of the transformer induces a negative voltage on the grid which decreases the plate current even more rapidly until it finally reaches zero. Since the plate current is no longer changing, there is no longer any voltage induced in the secondary winding of the transformer. It might be expected that the grid voltage will return to zero and the plate current will rise again, but this does not happen in a blocking oscillator.

When the grid was positive, grid current was flowing, which greatly reduced the grid-cathode resistance. Thus, there is a voltage source (the secondary winding of the transformer) and a resistance (the grid-cathode resistance of the tube) in series with a capacitor. (The presence of the resistor R can be neglected for the time being, as it is usually very large compared with the grid-cathode resistance of the tube.) The capacitor will now charge toward the transformer-secondary-winding voltage, and with a time constant equal to the product of the capacitance times the grid-cathode resistance of the tube.

When the plate current drops to zero and the transformer-secondary-winding voltage becomes zero, the tube is biased below cutoff by the capacitor's voltage. The capacitor begins to discharge and, because the grid-cathode circuit is now an open circuit, the only discharge path is through resistor R. As mentioned previously, R usually has a large resistance, so the discharge time constant is relatively long.

As C discharges, its biasing voltage for the tube becomes less and less until finally it is not sufficient to keep the plate current cut off. As soon as plate current begins to increase from zero, a voltage is again induced in the secondary of the transformer. This is a positive voltage on the grid; it opposes the remaining capacitor voltage and again causes the plate current to rise rapidly. The blocking oscillator has thus completed one cycle of its operation and will continue to oscillate in this manner.

When plate current is flowing, the regenerative action in the circuit causes the increase or decrease in plate current to be very rapid. This means that the increase or decrease of current takes a very short time, and a pulse type of signal can be produced.

8-2 WAVEFORMS

Actual component values will now be given for the circuit in Fig. 8-1. Using one-half of a 6SN7GT tube and a transformer with a 1:1 turns ratio, let $R = 100$ kilohms and $C = 0.01$ µf. If E_{bb} is 200 volts, the various waveforms obtained are those shown in Fig. 8-2.

The grid voltage (Fig. 8-2a) increases to 32 volts while the plate current is increasing and then drops rapidly to -225 volts when the plate current drops to zero and the magnetic field of the transformer collapses. Then the grid voltage rises slowly while the capacitor is discharging into the 100-kilohm resistor. When the grid voltage reaches the cutoff value, about -12 volts, the plate current induces a voltage in the secondary of the transformer that drives the grid voltage to $+32$ volts again.

From the supply-voltage value of 200 volts, the plate voltage (Fig. 8-2b)

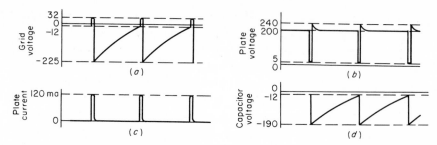

Fig. 8-2. *Waveshapes associated with the blocking oscillator.*

drops rapidly to 5 volts while the plate current is rising. It then rises rapidly while the plate current is dropping. The plate voltage overshoots the original 200-volt level, owing to the collapsing magnetic field; and it reaches a peak of 240 volts before dropping back to the 200-volt level.

The plate current is shown in Fig. 8-2c. It is displayed on the oscilloscope by connecting a 10-ohm resistor in series with the cathode and observing the resulting voltage drop. The waveform shows the current rising rapidly to 120 ma and then dropping rapidly back to zero. The manufacturer of the tube rates it as capable of a maximum plate current of only 20 ma, but oxide-coated cathodes are capable of furnishing currents up to one hundred times the average ratings for a very short time, as long as the *average* current is within the tube's rating.

Figure 8-2d shows how the capacitor's voltage varies. When the grid is positive, the capacitor charges rapidly from 12 to about 190 volts, at which time the grid current is no longer flowing; and then the capacitor discharges more slowly into the 100-kilohm resistor until the 12-volt cutoff value of the tube is reached. Then the tube conducts, the grid goes positive, and the capacitor begins to charge again.

8-3 TRANSFORMER

The characteristics of the blocking oscillator are very much dependent upon the characteristics of the coupling transformer. Desirable characteristics are: (a) high coefficient of couplings; (b) small interwinding capacitance; (c) low Q. The interwinding capacitance forms a resonant circuit with the transformer inductance, and it is at this frequency that the circuit starts to oscillate, completing just one half-cycle before the blocking (plate-current cutoff) occurs.

If the transformer had a high Q, "ringing" would result. That is, the transformer's LC circuit would continue to oscillate for a time, even when plate current was no longer flowing. This can easily be illustrated. The transformer used in the circuit from which the waveforms in Fig. 8-2 were obtained was an ordinary interstage audio transformer. In order to lower the Q sufficiently, a 27-kilohm resistor was connected across the secondary winding. If this resistor is removed, the grid and plate voltage waveforms are those shown in Fig. 8-3.

Compare Fig. 8-3a with Fig. 8-2a; and note that in the higher-Q circuit the grid is driven more negative, but we see that the grid voltage goes through several cycles of oscillation as the capacitor is discharging.

Comparing plate waveforms, we also see several cycles of oscillation taking place; but the most pronounced effect is that without sufficient damping, the plate voltage is allowed to swing up to 320 volts when the plate current stops flowing; this is 60 per cent greater than the supply voltage.

8-4   OUTPUT SIGNALS

Output signals may be taken from any one of a number of points in the circuit of a blocking oscillator. Any one of the four waveforms shown in Fig. 8-2 may be obtained from the corresponding point in the circuit. A voltage representing grid current may be obtained by inserting a small resistor between the parallel RC circuit and ground. This voltage waveform is almost identical in shape to that shown in Fig. 8-2c. The transformer could have a third winding from which the output signal could be obtained. This signal would resemble that shown in Fig. 8-2b in shape, but would not have the 200-volt d-c voltage included; and it would be modified slightly because of transformer leakage and possibly a turns ratio different from 1:1. It could also be inverted in polarity through the transformer.

A blocking oscillator is usually used as a pulse generator, where a very narrow pulse with rapid rise and fall time is desirable. The waveform in Fig. 8-2b represents this desired signal, so the output voltage is usually obtained from the plate or from a third winding on the transformer. The mathematical analysis of the output of a blocking oscillator in terms of component characteristics is very difficult because of the effects of circuit capacitance, transformer leakage, and the tube characteristics at high grid

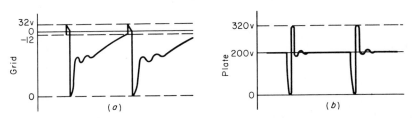

Fig. 8-3.   Grid and plate voltage waveshapes showing ringing characteristics.

voltages and currents. Therefore, such signal values as pulse width, amplitude, rise time, and repetition frequency are determined experimentally, but a qualitative discussion of these relationships will be of some value.

The pulse rise and fall times are determined mainly by the high-frequency response of the transformer, as well as the dynamic grid and plate resistance of the tube.

The pulse duration is greatly affected by the low-frequency response of the transformer, as well as by such factors as the size of C and the tube characteristics.

In discussing pulse amplitude, both voltage and current amplitudes should be considered. When the tube is cut off, the plate voltage is equal to the supply voltage; and when the tube is conducting, it will conduct heavily, cutting the plate voltage down to a very low value. Therefore, the plate-voltage signal amplitude will be somewhere between one-half of E_{bb} to almost equal to E_{bb}. The heavy conduction of the tube will cause quite a large plate current to flow for a very short time. Currents as large as 1 amp or more may flow in small tubes designed for average currents of less than 50 ma, because of the small duty cycle.

The pulse repetition frequency is determined by the time it takes for the capacitor to discharge into its parallel resistor, from its maximum charge value down to the cutoff value of the tube. Therefore, the time constant of R and C is the controlling factor for this frequency. It was noted above that the size of C also has a considerable effect on the pulse duration; so when the value of C is chosen for the correct pulse duration, then R can be adjusted for the desired repetition frequency.

The following values were obtained from the circuit whose waveforms are shown in Fig. 8-2. The amplitude of the voltage pulse at the plate is about 195 volts, very close to the supply voltage of 200 volts. The current pulse has an amplitude of about 120 ma. The pulse repetition frequency was measured as about 350 pps, and the pulse duration (at the 90 per cent points) as about 70 μsec. This gives a ratio of pulse duration to pulse repetition time of about 1 to 40, which is the duty cycle. To make sure that the average current of the tube does not exceed the rated value, multiply the peak current by the duty cycle. This is $(120 \text{ ma})(1/40) = 3$ ma. The maximum average current allowed is 20 ma, so the tube is operating within its rating.

It might be interesting to check the pulse repetition frequency by calculating the time it takes for the capacitor to discharge from its maximum charge value down to the cutoff value of the tube. The discharge of a capacitor when there is no additional voltage applied to the circuit utilizes the equation $e_{co} = E_c \epsilon^{-t/\tau}$. $E_c = 225$ volts and $e_{co} = 12$ volts. The time constant of the circuit is $(100 \text{ kilohms})(0.01 \ \mu\text{f}) = (10^5)(10^{-8}) = 10^{-3}$ sec. Substituting into the equation and solving gives $t = 2.94 \times 10^{-3}$

sec. This is the time period of the pulse repetition frequency. Taking the reciprocal of this value gives the value of the pulse repetition frequency as 340 pps; the measured value from the actual circuit was 350 pps. A good approximation for the pulse repetition frequency for a free-running blocking oscillator is given as

$$f = \frac{0.434}{\tau \log (E_c/e_{co})}$$

where τ = time constant of grid resistor and capacitor
  E_c = peak charge of grid capacitor
  e_{co} = cutoff voltage of tube

8-5 SYNCHRONIZING

The pulse repetition frequency is rather unstable because of slight variations in circuit characteristics. Like the astable multivibrator, the blocking oscillator often is synchronized to some other signal. This is accomplished in a manner very similar to that discussed in Sec. 7-12; a positive pulse applied to the grid of the tube will cause it to start conducting before it would normally. Frequency division can also take place with the blocking oscillator in the manner described in Sec. 7-12.

8-6 MONOSTABLE BLOCKING OSCILLATOR

The blocking-oscillator circuits discussed up to this point are *free-running* or *astable*. That is, they need no external triggering signal to maintain oscillation. If the bottom end of resistor R in Fig. 8-1 is connected to a certain voltage E_{cc} instead of to ground, the repetition frequency of the oscillator will be changed; the capacitor is discharging toward this voltage E_{cc} instead of toward zero. If E_{cc} is negative, and higher in value than the cutoff grid voltage of the tube, the tube will be permanently blocked from conduction until a positive triggering pulse is applied to the grid to start conduction. Then the circuit will go through a half-cycle of oscillation and will be blocked until another triggering pulse is applied. This circuit is called a *monostable blocking oscillator* or sometimes a *blocked oscillator*.

8-7 TRANSISTORIZED CIRCUIT

BASIC CIRCUIT

The circuit diagram of a transistor blocking oscillator, as shown in Fig. 8-4, is almost identical with that of the vacuum-tube circuit. The theory of operation is very similar. When V_{cc} is first applied, there is no

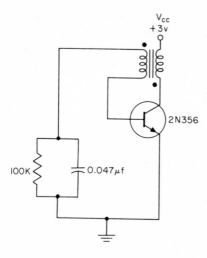

Fig. 8-4. Transistorized blocking oscillator.

base-emitter bias, so the collector current begins to rise and the increase in current through the transformer's primary induces a secondary voltage with such a polarity that the base goes positive. This biases the base-emitter junction in the forward direction and increases collector current even more, which makes the base even more positive. This regenerative action continues until the transistor is driven into saturation. The collector current is no longer rising, so the base voltage stops increasing and begins to decrease because of the collapsing secondary flux. The resulting decrease in collector current induces a secondary voltage which drives the base negative and therefore reverse-biases the base-emitter junction, cutting off the collector current.

When the base-emitter junction was forward-biased, current was flowing and charged up the capacitor. With the junction reverse-biased, the capacitor discharges into the resistor until the base voltage is almost zero and the collector current can begin to rise. The process then repeats itself.

The base and collector voltages vary, as shown in Fig. 8-5. Note the

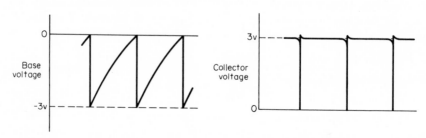

Fig. 8-5. Base and collector waveshapes.

similarity between these and the waveforms for the vacuum-tube circuit (Fig. 8-2). The transistor forms a more perfect switch, so the collector voltage drops to zero when collector current is flowing.

The rapid changes in collector current could cause ringing in the transformer if the Q were very high. It was found necessary to shunt the primary of the transformer with a 1-kilohm resistor to prevent ringing. In the vacuum-tube circuit, a 27-kilohm damping resistor was needed.

It was noted in Fig. 8-3b that without a damping resistor across the transformer the plate voltage increased to about 1.6 times the supply voltage when the magnetic field of the transformer collapsed rapidly. If the 1-kilohm resistor is removed in the transistor circuit, the plate waveform is that shown in Fig. 8-6. Here the collector voltage rises to almost four times the supply voltage. In the vacuum-tube circuit the large back swing is of little concern, but in the transistor circuit it could exceed the maximum allowable reverse collector voltage, and the transistor could be damaged.

In the description of the theory of operation of the transistor blocking oscillator, it was mentioned that the transistor was driven into the saturation region. In Sec. 5-9 it was found that when a transistor is driven into the saturation region, minority carriers are stored in the base region of the transistor, and it takes some time for these to be removed when the transistor is switched off. This can affect the width of the output pulse and may limit the maximum pulse repetition frequency.

A modified circuit is shown in Fig. 8-7. The addition of the two diodes and the split collector-supply voltage will take care of the two troubles mentioned above. Diode D_1 will keep the transistor from going into saturation, and diode D_2 will keep the collector voltage from rising to a high value. The operation of this circuit is described as follows.

When the transistor is cut off, no voltage appears across the primary winding of the transformer, so diode D_2 has no bias across it. The collector voltage is equal to $V_{c_1} + V_{c_2}$; thus the cathode of D_1 is more positive than

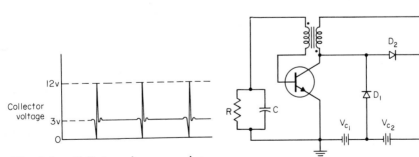

Fig. 8-6. Collector-voltage waveshape showing ringing characteristics.

Fig. 8-7. Modified blocking oscillator.

its anode, so D_1 is reverse-biased. As collector current begins to flow, the collector voltage starts to drop. This makes the cathode D_2 more positive than its anode, and D_2 is reverse-biased, so its presence can be neglected. The collector voltage continues to drop until it tries to drop below a value equal to V_{c_1}. At this time D_1 starts conducting, clamping the collector voltage at V_{c_1} and bypassing the collector current around the primary winding of the transformer. It is at this point that the reversal of secondary voltage takes place and the transistor is kept from going into saturation. The magnetic field of the transformer begins to collapse, causing the primary voltage, and thus the collector voltage, to start rising. Diode D_1 no longer conducts, and the collector voltage continues to rise until it reaches a value equal to V_{c_1} plus V_{c_2}. As it tries to exceed this value, diode D_2 conducts, clamping the collector voltage at a value equal to V_{c_1} plus V_{c_2}, and readily dissipates the remaining energy in the collapsing magnetic field.

A transistorized monostable blocking oscillator may be formed in a manner identical to that of the vacuum-tube circuit, returning the resistor to a negative supply instead of to ground.

COMMON-BASE CIRCUIT

The circuit of Fig. 8-8 illustrates the basic common-base blocking oscillator. Under quiescent conditions V_{cc} reverse-biases the base-emitter junction, holding the transistor off. Only leakage current flows in the collector circuit when the transistor is off. A negative pulse at the input drives the transistor on, thus increasing the current through the primary of the transformer. At this point it should be noted that the difference in the type of transformer used for the common-base circuit compared with the common-emitter circuit is in the polarity indication. The induced voltage of the secondary is such that the current induced in the secondary further forward-biases the transistor. The regenerative feedback drives i_c to saturation. Once saturation occurs, the magnetic flux of the secondary begins to collapse and drives the base-emitter junction toward reverse bias. The result is an output pulse for each pulse at the input.

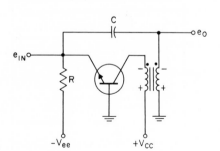

Fig. 8-8. Common-base blocking oscillator.

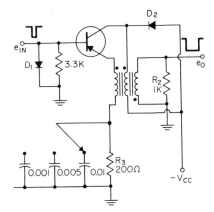

Fig. 8-9. Pulse stretcher.

8-8 PULSE STRETCHER

The circuit of Fig. 8-9 illustrates an application of a transistor blocking oscillator as a pulse stretcher. A given negative pulse of 1 volt amplitude but short duration time can be used to trigger the circuit. The output pulse duration time can be varied by controlling the effects of charge storage.

The emitter RC circuit time constant is varied by switching in different values of C. With values ranging from 0.001 to 0.02 μf, the output pulse width can be varied from 0.6 to 1.5 μsec. Diode D_1 is reverse-biased when the negative input trigger is applied. Once the blocking-oscillator action is initiated, D_1 forward-biases and parallels the input with a low impedance.

8-9 STEP-COUNTER APPLICATION

The blocking oscillator is also employed in conjunction with a conventional step counter. Examine the circuit of Fig. 8-10a. When a series of pulses are applied to the input, the output rises in exponential steps. Assume that a 100-volt positive pulse is applied at the input, diode D_1 is reverse-biased, and diode D_2 is forward-biased. The input voltage e_{in} distributes itself across C_1 and C_2 according to the ratio of their sizes, the greater voltage appearing across the smaller capacitor according to the ratio

$$E_{c_1} = \frac{e_{in}C_2}{C_1 + C_2}$$

At t_1 the input e_{in} drops to zero, and capacitor C_1 discharges through D_1 (Fig. 8-10b). However, C_2 cannot discharge since both D_1 and D_2 are

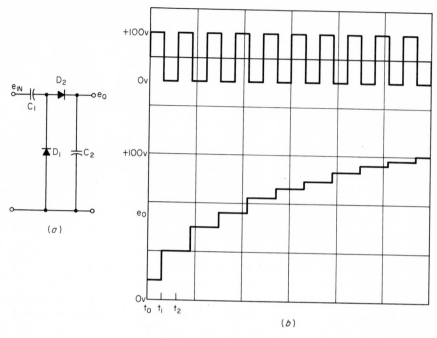

Fig. 8-10. Step counter.

reverse-biased by the voltage across C_2. The potential on C_2 remains. When the second input pulse is applied at t_3, the active voltage in the network is not 100 volts but 100 volts minus the remaining charge on C_2. Hence, the effective voltage once again distributes itself between C_1 and C_2, building up a greater charge on C_2.

EXAMPLE   Assume that $C_1 = 0.01$ μf and $C_2 = 0.09$ μf in the circuit of Fig. 8-10a. If a 100-volt 5kc square wave is applied, what is the voltage across C_2 after three input pulses?

When the first pulse is applied, the voltage across C_2 becomes

$$E_2 = \frac{e_{in}}{C_1 + C_2} = \frac{(100)(0.01)}{0.09 + 0.01} = 10 \text{ volts}$$

When the second pulse is applied, the effective network voltage is 90 volts (10 volts remained on C_2); hence, the additional increase in E_2 is

$$E_2 = \frac{(90)(0.01)}{0.09 + .01} = 9 \text{ volts}$$

Hence the voltage across C_2 is now 19 volts.

When the third pulse is applied, the effective network voltage is 81 volts; hence, the additional buildup on C_2 is

$$E_3 = \frac{(81)(0.01)}{0.09 + 0.01} = 8.1 \text{ volts}$$

The voltage across C_2 at the end of three input pulses is 27.1 volts.

If the output of a step counter is connected to the input of a monostable blocking oscillator, as shown in Fig. 8-11, the blocking oscillator will trigger after a given number of pulses have been stored at C_2. The voltage across C_2 builds up and eventually overcomes the bias cutting off the tube, and the tube conducts. When it does, the grid draws current and C_2 discharges, allowing the output of the step counter to build up again. By varying the amount of bias on V, the circuit can be made to count a preselected number of input pulses.

8-10 CONCLUSIONS

The blocking oscillator can be used in a number of applications. Basically, the circuit is a pulse generator, so any circuit requiring high-amplitude short-duration pulses can be fed from this oscillator circuit. It can be used as a low-impedance switch for quickly discharging a capacitor; one application is a sawtooth generator. By taking the output from a third winding on the transformer, a pulse can be obtained which is isolated from the common-ground connection. A slowly varying signal can trigger a monostable blocking oscillator at a certain voltage level and cause

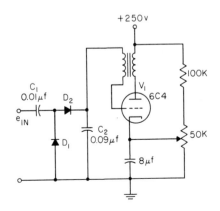

Fig. 8-11. Combined blocking oscillator and step counter.

a sharp pulse to be generated. A weak pulse can be "amplified" by triggering a monostable blocking oscillator, resulting in an output pulse of much higher amplitude. The shape of a pulse can be modified in a similar way. The use of a blocking oscillator as a frequency divider has been discussed in Sec. 8-5.

PROBLEMS

8-1 Refer to Fig. 8-1. If $V = 6SN7$, $E_{bb} = 200$ volts, $R = 200$ kilohms, $C = 0.005$ μf, what is the frequency of oscillation? (Assume that the tube's cutoff voltage is -12 volts and the capacitor charges to 225 volts.)

8-2 In Prob. 8-1, assume that the pulse duration time is 30 μsec. (a) What is the duty cycle? (b) What is the peak current permitted through the tube?

8-3 What determines the pulse width of the output of a blocking oscillator?

8-4 What determines the pulse repetition frequency of an astable blocking oscillator?

8-5 The 6SN7 tube is rated as having a maximum allowable plate current of 20 ma. The waveforms given in Fig. 8-2 show the plate current rising to 120 ma. Will this damage the tube? Explain.

8-6 The supply voltage for the blocking oscillator whose waveforms are shown in Fig. 8-2 is 200 volts. How can the tube's plate voltage rise to 240 volts, as shown in Fig. 8-2b?

8-7 What can be done to reduce the Q of a transformer? Why is this sometimes necessary for a blocking oscillator?

8-8 What effect does the high-frequency response of the transformer have on the pulse waveshape of a blocking oscillator?

8-9 What effect does the low-frequency response of the transformer have on the pulse waveshape?

8-10 If the bottom end of the grid resistor in Fig. 8-1 is connected to a negative bias voltage which is not sufficient to cut off the tube, how will the frequency of oscillation compare with that of the circuit when the grid was connected to ground?

8-11 What is the purpose of each of the diodes in Fig. 8-7?

8-12 In Fig. 8-10a, assume $C_1 = 0.05$ μf and $C_2 = 0.5$ μf. If a 150-volt 2-kc square wave is applied, how many input periods will be required to charge C_2 to 75 volts?

CHAPTER 9 BASIC

SAWTOOTH GENERATORS

One of the most valuable uses of an oscilloscope is to display the waveform of a periodically changing voltage. This is accomplished by having the dot move horizontally across the screen at a constant rate of speed while its vertical deflection is proportional to the voltage variations of the signal being displayed. The resulting pattern shows how the voltage varies with time. The dot movement must be repeated identically over and over to produce a steady pattern. This means that the horizontal deflection plates of the oscilloscope must supply a voltage which is increasing at a constant rate for a certain period of time and then drops to its starting value; then the complete cycle must be repeated.

A graph of such a voltage variation plotted against time is called a *saw-tooth* waveform, and it was discussed in Sec. 1-8. Ideally we should prefer the waveform to have an instantaneous fall time, as shown in Fig. 9-1a, but there is always a finite amount of time required for the voltage to drop to its original value, even if it is short compared with the rise time. We are particularly concerned that the rise of the voltage be as linear as possible,

Fig. 9-1. (a) Ideal sawtooth wave-form. (b) Actual sawtooth waveform.

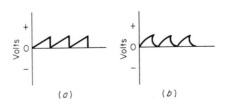

(a) (b)

but the way in which the voltage drops is of no importance as long as the time period is short. An actual sawtooth waveform may appear as shown in Fig. 9-1b.

9-1 BASIC CIRCUIT

It has been found that the simplest way to produce a sawtooth voltage is to allow a capacitor to charge through a large resistance and then to discharge through a small resistance. This means that the charging circuit will have a much longer time constant than the discharge circuit, so the voltage variation has the characteristics of a much shorter fall time than rise time.

A neon bulb has the characteristic of acting like an open circuit until the voltage across it reaches a certain value, called the ionization potential, where the neon gas ionizes and the bulb conducts. Then the potential can be reduced to lower values, and the bulb continues to conduct until the deionization potential is reached and the conduction stops.

If a capacitor and a resistor are connected in series across a d-c voltage source, the capacitor charges at a rate dependent upon the RC time constant. If a neon bulb is connected across the capacitor, as shown in Fig. 9-2, and if the d-c voltage source is higher in value than the ionization potential, the capacitor will charge up until its voltage equals the ionization potential of the neon bulb. Then the bulb will conduct.

What happens next depends on the size of the series resistor and the potential of the d-c voltage source. When the bulb conducts, the capacitor begins to discharge into the bulb resistance, and the capacitor voltage starts dropping. As this voltage drops, the current through the neon bulb also drops. It is desirable to have the capacitor voltage drop below the deionization potential of the neon bulb. This may or may not happen.

Assume that the known factors are the ionization potential E_i of the neon bulb, its deionization potential E_d, and its minimum current while conducting. This current, designated as I_d, will flow just before the bulb deionizes. In order for the bulb to ionize, the supply voltage E_{bb} must be greater than E_i. This may be expressed by $E_{bb} > E_i$. In order for the bulb to deionize, its minimum current I_d flowing through R should drop the

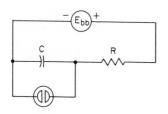

Fig. 9-2.   Neon-bulb sawtooth generator.

voltage across the bulb to a value less than E_d. We can express this statement by $(E_{bb} - I_d R) < E_d$. This last expression can be changed to $E_{bb} < (E_d + I_d R)$. These two conditions—for the bulb to both ionize and deionize—can be combined in the one expression

$$E_i < E_{bb} < (E_d + I_d R)$$

For any particular neon bulb whose values of E_i, E_d, and I_d are known, we can choose a value of R and determine what values of E_{bb} can be used, or vice versa: we can choose a value for E_{bb} and determine what range of values of R may be used.

Whether or not the circuit will oscillate does not depend on the capacitor's size, but the particular capacitance used will help determine the operating frequency.

The frequency of oscillation can be found by determining the time it takes for a capacitor to charge from a lower voltage E_d to a higher voltage E_i, with a supply voltage of E_{bb}. The time period may be calculated from Eq. (3-6):

$$\Delta e_c = E_{R0}(1 - \epsilon^{-t/\tau})$$

Solving for t actually gives the time required for the rise time; but because the fall time will usually be quite short compared with the rise time, the frequency is approximately equal to the reciprocal of the rise time, calculated from Eq. (3-6). The neon-bulb oscillator is a useful source of sawtooth waves at very low frequencies only. The frequency is limited to below 2 kc because of the long ionization and deionization characteristics of neon gas.

In the neon-bulb oscillator of Fig. 9-2, the peak-to-peak amplitude of the output signal is the difference between the ionization and the deionization potentials:

$$E_i - E_d$$

9-2 LINEARITY OF SIGNAL

The importance of the linearity of the sawtooth signal was discussed above. In order for the horizontal movement of the dot on an oscilloscope to represent time, the rise portion of the sawtooth waveform must be linear. It was found in Chap. 3 that the charging rate of a capacitor is not constant but decreases as the capacitor's voltage approaches its maximum value. If the capacitor is allowed to charge for a time equal to 10 per cent or less of one time constant, there is only a small change in its charging rate, and the resulting sawtooth waveform will have a fairly linear rise portion.

One way in which the linearity of the pattern may be evaluated mathematically is to use the following formula:

$$\text{Slope error} = \frac{\text{initial slope} - \text{final slope}}{\text{initial slope}} \tag{9-1}$$

The slope error will now be calculated in a sawtooth waveform produced by an RC circuit where the capacitor is allowed to charge for a period of time equal to one-tenth of a time constant. Equation (3-1) shows how the capacitor voltage varies with time:

$$e_c = E(1 - \epsilon^{-t/\tau})$$

If the time derivative (see Sec. 3-5) of this equation is found, the resulting equation shows how the slope of the curve varies with time.

$$\text{Slope} = \frac{E}{\tau} \epsilon^{-t/\tau} \tag{9-2}$$

Now, when $t = 0$, the initial slope is E/τ. When $t = 0.1\tau$, the slope is equal to $0.905E/\tau$. Substituting these values into Eq. (9-1), we find the slope error to be 0.095.

Another equation for slope error may be derived by solving Eq. (3-1) for $\epsilon^{-t/\tau}$: $\epsilon^{-t/\tau} = E - e_c$. Substituting this into Eq. (9-2) gives slope $= (E/\tau)(E - e_c)$. The initial slope will be $(E/\tau)(E - e_{ci})$, and the final slope is $(E/\tau)(E - e_{cf})$. Substituting these into Eq. (9-1) gives

$$\text{Slope error} = \frac{e_{cf} - e_{ci}}{E - e_{ci}} \tag{9-3}$$

This equation shows that for a certain sawtooth peak-to-peak amplitude, $e_{cf} - e_{ci}$, the larger the supply voltage E, the smaller the slope error.

To summarize:

1. In order for this circuit to oscillate,

$$E_i < E_{bb} < (E_d + I_dR) \tag{9-4}$$

2. The frequency of oscillation is derived from Eq. (3-7) and is

$$f = \frac{0.434}{\tau \, log \, [(E_{bb} - E_d)/(E_{bb} - E_i)]} \tag{9-5}$$

3. The peak-to-peak amplitude is

$$\text{p-p amplitude} = E_i - E_d \tag{9-6}$$

4. Substituting the voltage symbols for the neon-bulb circuit into Eq. (9-3) yields

$$\text{Slope error} = \frac{E_i - E_d}{E_{bb} - E_d} \qquad \textbf{9-7}$$

EXAMPLE Assume that a given neon-bulb oscillator is to produce a sawtooth wave of 1.5 kc. The circuit is shown in Fig. 9-2, where $R = 10$ kilohms, $E_{bb} = 200$ volts, the ionization potential is 70 volts, and the deionization potential is 12 volts. What value of C should be connected in the circuit, and what is the percentage of slope error?

Solving Eq. (9-5) for τ yields

$$\tau = \frac{0.434}{f \log{[(E_{bb} - E_d)/(E_{bb} - E_i)]}}$$

$$= \frac{0.434}{1.5 \times 10^3 \log{(188/130)}} = 1.81 \times 10^{-3}$$

$$C = 0.181 \ \mu f$$

Substituting values into Eq. (9-7) gives

$$\text{Slope error} = \frac{70 - 12}{200 - 12}$$

$$= 30.8\%$$

9-3 THYRATRON OSCILLATOR

The neon-bulb oscillator which has been discussed is not too satisfactory. The characteristics E_d, E_i, and I_d are too erratic, and there is no way in which to change them other than to use a different neon bulb. A free-running oscillator of any kind can be unstable; and in order to ensure a stationary display on the oscilloscope, the horizontal-sweep generator must be synchronized. There is no practical way to synchronize the neon-bulb sawtooth generator.

If a gas triode, a thyratron, is used, the control grid provides a means of synchronizing the frequency with an external signal. The control grid of a thyratron does not control the plate-current flow, as in a vacuum triode, but its potential determines the plate-cathode ionization potential. Once the gas is ionized, the grid loses control and the plate current has to be reduced below a certain value I_d to deionize the gas.

When a hot-cathode type of gas tube is conducting, it offers a low-resistance path between plate and cathode, and there must be an external resistor connected in the plate circuit to limit the plate-current flow. There is also a low-resistance path between grid and cathode when the gas is ionized, so a current-limiting resistor must be inserted into the grid circuit.

To study the characteristics of the thyratron in more detail, consider the circuit shown in Fig. 9-3. With a fixed negative voltage on the grid, E_{bb} is slowly increased from zero. There will be no plate current flowing, so $e_b = E_{bb}$. When e_b reaches voltage E_i, the gas will ionize, plate current will flow, and e_b will drop to a low value, E_d. The current flow will equal $(E_{bb} - E_d)/R_2$. If E_{bb} is now increased or decreased, E_d will remain fairly constant, so i_b will vary. If i_b falls below a certain value I_d, the gas deionizes and conduction stops.

The ionization plate voltage E_i depends on the particular value of e_c, but E_d and I_d do not vary with e_c. Figure 9-4 shows a graph of E_i plotted against e_c for an 884 thyratron. As a rough approximation, $E_i = -8e_c$. Remember that once the gas ionizes, the grid loses control, and the gas can be deionized only by reducing the plate current below the value I_d.

The 884 thyratron has the approximate values $E_d = 16$ volts and $I_d = 1.5$ ma. With this information a sawtooth generator can be designed which has several advantages over the neon-bulb oscillator: (a) the peak-to-peak amplitude may be varied, (b) an output signal of much higher amplitude may be obtained, and (c) synchronization can easily be accomplished.

Some modification must be made in the equation for the sawtooth generator using a thyratron, because of the plate resistor R_2. In order to have oscillation,

$$E_i < E_{bb} < (E_d + I_d R + I_d R_2)$$ 9-8

The resulting frequency will be given by

$$f = \frac{0.434}{RC \log[(E_{bb} - E_d - I_d R_2)/(E_{bb} - E_i)]}$$ 9-9

The peak-to-peak amplitude can be calculated from

$$\text{p-p amplitude} = E_i - E_d - I_d R_2$$ 9-10

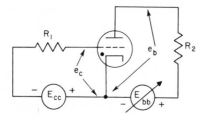

Fig. 9-3.   Thyratron circuit.

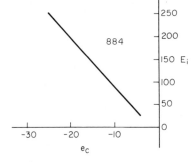

Fig. 9-4. Graph of ionization potential for 884 thyratron.

The slope error is given by

$$\text{Slope error} = \frac{E_i - E_d - I_d R_2}{E_{bb} - E_d - I_d R_2} \qquad \textbf{9-11}$$

Figure 9-5 shows a sawtooth-generator circuit using an 884 thyratron. Its operation will be checked by using the formulas above. From Fig. 9-4, when $e_c = -6$ volts, the gas will ionize when e_b reaches about 38 volts; this is E_i. For an 884, E_d is about 16 volts and I_d about 1.5 ma. $R_2 = 4.7$ kilohms, $R = 1$ megohm, and $C = 0.01$ μf. Equation (9-8) can be used to see whether the circuit will oscillate. $E_{bb} = 250$ volts, which is greater than E_i. $E_d + I_d R + I_d R_2 = 16 + 1,500 + 7 = 1,523$, which is greater than E_{bb}. The circuit will oscillate! The peak-to-peak amplitude can be calculated from Eq. (9-10) and is $38 - 16 - 7 = 15$ volts. The frequency, calculated from Eq. (9-9), is

$$f = \frac{0.434}{10^{-2} \log (227/212)} = \frac{43.4}{0.03} = 1,450$$

The slope error is $15/227 = 0.066$ or 6.6 per cent.

There can be considerable variation in these calculated values and actual measurements which might be made on a circuit, because the data from Fig. 9-4 can vary considerably with different tubes and with the same tube at different temperatures. Therefore, the calculations are only approximate.

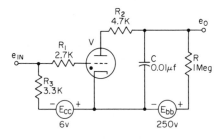

Fig. 9-5. Thyratron sawtooth generator.

Synchronization takes place when positive sync pulses are applied to the grid of the thyratron. If the grid is driven positive just before the gas would normally be ionized, the timing of the positive sync pulse determines the time of the start of the fall in the sawtooth waveform.

For some oscilloscope displays it is desirable to have the sawtooth generator produce a signal only when triggered by a sync signal and to be inoperative when no sync signal is applied. This is called a *driven* or *triggered* sweep generator. It is of value when the waveform being observed occurs at irregular intervals.

9-4   THYRATRON DRIVEN SWEEP GENERATOR

The thyratron sawtooth-generator circuit can be modified into a driven sweep generator. The plate of a diode is connected between the junction of R and C, and its cathode is connected to a positive voltage source whose value is a little less than E_i. The capacitor starts charging toward E_{bb}, but before it can reach a value E_i which would cause the gas in the tube to ionize, the diode starts conducting and clamps e_b to a value below the ionization potential of the thyratron. This point in the circuit's operation is permanent until a positive sync pulse on the grid of the thyratron reduces the value of E_i below the clamped value of e_b, and the tube conducts. The capacitor discharges down to a voltage value of E_d and then begins charging until the diode again conducts and clamps the plate voltage to a value below E_i. Such a driven thyratron sweep generator is shown in Fig. 9-6. The values of R_3 and R_4 are determined by the requirement that $E_{bb}R_3/(R_3 + R_4) < E_i$.

PROBLEMS

9-1   Assume that a neon-bulb sawtooth oscillator is to produce an output frequency of 2.2 kc. (Refer to Fig. 9-2.) If $R = 9.2$ kilohms, $E_{bb} = 220$ volts, the ionization potential is 70 volts, and the deionization potential is 12 volts, what value of C is required?

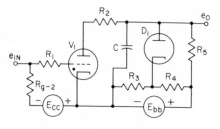

Fig. 9-6.   Thyratron driven sweep generator.

9-2   In the circuit of Prob. 9-1, what is the percentage of slope error? How much increase in R will be required if the frequency is to be halved?

9-3   Refer to the circuit of Prob. 9-1. Construct a table showing how changes in E_{bb}, R, and C influence the output frequency, amplitude, and slope error.

9-4   Refer to the thyratron characteristics of Fig. 9-30. At what potential does the 6D4 thyratron ionize when the grid is maintained at -8 volts?

9-5   What is the peak-to-peak output for the circuit of Fig. 9-5 if the thyraton used is a 6D4, $E_d = 16$ volts, and $I_d = 0.9$ ma?

9-6   What is the frequency output for the circuit of Prob. 9-5?

9-7   Assume that the circuit of Fig. 9-5 has the following values: $R_1 = 100$ kilohms, $V = 6D4$, $R_2 = 400$ kilohms, $R_3 = 390$ kilohms, $C = 0.015$ μf, $R = 1.5$ megohms, $E_{bb} = 200$ volts, and $E_{cc} = -8$ volts. What is the output frequency?

9-8   Refer to Prob. 9-7. What is the slope error of the output?

9-9   In the circuit of Prob. 9-7, if the 6D4 is replaced by an 884 thyratron, will the output frequency change? To what new value?

9-10   Construct a table showing how amplitude at e_o, frequency, and slope error are influenced by E_{cc}, E_{bb}, R_1, R_2, R_3, R, and C.

9-5   VACUUM-TUBE SWEEP CIRCUIT

The thyratron type of sweep circuit has been used for years in oscilloscope and radar indicators, but it has several drawbacks. The time it takes for the gas to ionize and deionize limits the frequency repetition rate to a maximum of about 50 kc. Although this limit can be extended by using hydrogen thyratrons, the range of frequencies is still low. Hydrogen has a faster ionization and deionization time compared with argon or neon. The amplitude of the signal produced by the gas triode is limited by the difference in ionization and deionization potentials of the tube and in the amount of nonlinearity which can be tolerated in the signal.

Both of these limitations can be overcome by the use of high-vacuum tubes. A vacuum tube can be switched from conduction to nonconduction and vice versa in very short time intervals. The signal amplitude for a vacuum-tube sweep circuit can be made almost independent of the tube's characteristics.

HARD-TUBE SAWTOOTH GENERATOR

The circuit of Fig. 9-7a illustrates a sawtooth generator which converts a pulse of given duration to a sawtooth wave of the same duration. The advantage of this circuit is that variations in slope can be controlled through changes in C or R_L while the duration remains slaved to the input

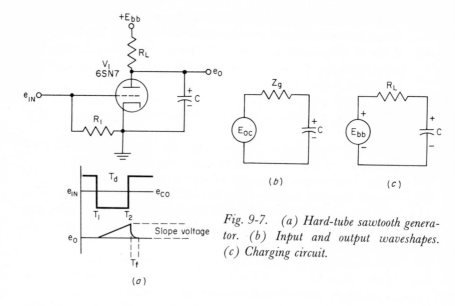

Fig. 9-7. (a) Hard-tube sawtooth generator. (b) Input and output waveshapes. (c) Charging circuit.

pulse. With no signal applied at the grid of the tube, capacitor C charges to the quiescent potential represented by the active region of the tube and load. The equivalent circuit of Fig. 9-7a is shown in Fig. 9-7b. A negative pulse applied at the input of the circuit of Fig. 9-7a drives the tube into cutoff, and capacitor C begins to charge to E_{bb}. The charging circuit is shown in Fig. 9-7c. The capacitor charges over the interval determined by t_d. The amplitude and the percentage of slope error can be determined by using Eqs. (9-6) and (9-7). The fall time t_f is determined by the equivalent circuit of Fig. 9-7b. Refer to Fig. 9-8a. Note that the slopes of the three waves are different; however, the duration times are the same. The variations in slope are effected through changes in C or R_L of Fig. 9-7a. The output duration of the hard-tube sawtooth circuit is always slaved to the input duration time. An application of this characteristic is shown in the scope display of Fig. 9-8b.

EXAMPLE   In the circuit of Fig. 9-7, if $V = 6SN7$, $R = 10$ kilohms, $E_{bb} = 200$ volts, $C = 5$ μf, and the input has an amplitude of -20 volts with a 10-msec t_d, what are the amplitude of the output, the fall time, and the percentage of slope error?

A plot of a 10-kilohm load line on the characteristic of the 6SN7 indicates that the -20-volt pulse at the input is sufficient to cut off the tube (Fig. 9-9). The equivalent circuit for the active region yields the following:

$$E_{oc} = 95 \text{ volts} \qquad Z_g = 4.4 \text{ kilohms}$$

Hence, the capacitor's initial charge is 95 volts (Fig. 9-7b).
When the input pulse is applied, C charges from 95 for 10 msec (Fig. 9-7c).

$$\Delta e_c = E_{R0}(1 - \epsilon^{-t/\tau})$$
$$= 105\,(1 - \epsilon^{-(10)(10^{-3})/(500)(10^{-3})})$$
$$= 105\,(1 - \epsilon^{-1/50})$$
$$= 105\,(1 - 0.98)$$
$$= 105\,(0.02)$$
$$= 2.1 \text{ volts}$$

e_c changes from 95 to 97.1 volts.

The fall time is calculated from the equivalent circuit shown in Fig. 9-7b. The fall time is determined down to the 10 per cent point from the equation

$$t_f = 2.2\tau_1$$
$$= (2.2)(22 \text{ msec}) = 48.4 \text{ msec}$$

where τ_1 is the discharge RC circuit.

The slope error is calculated as follows:

$$\text{Slope error} = \frac{E_{max} - E_{min}}{E_{bb} - E_{min}}$$
$$= \frac{97.1 - 95}{200 - 95}$$
$$= \frac{2.1}{105} = 0.02 = 2\%$$

The preceding example illustrates the chief disadvantage of the hard-tube circuit—the fall time is often longer than the duration time. Some improvement of this problem can be effected by adjusting various circuit components such as E_{bb} and maintaining C as low as practicable.

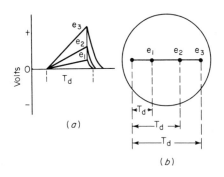

Fig. 9-8. (a) Constant-duration-time varying-amplitude sawtooth waves. (b) Scope display for (a).

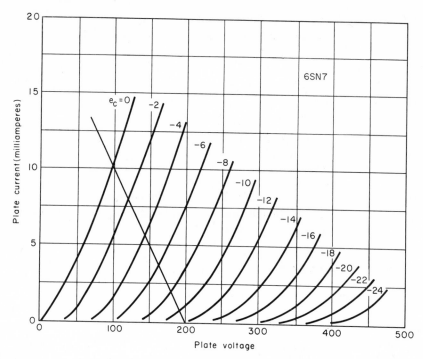

Fig. 9-9. Load line display on 6SN7 characteristics.

SQUARE-WAVE CONVERSION TO SAWTOOTH

Either the multivibrator or the blocking-oscillator type of signal generator may be used for a sweep-generator circuit. It will be remembered that in both of these circuits a vacuum tube is cut off for a time and then conducts heavily for a time. In the blocking oscillator the conduction time is much shorter than the nonconduction time. The multivibrator circuit can also be adjusted so one of the tubes is nonconducting for a much longer period of time than its conduction time period. If a capacitor is allowed to charge through a resistor—usually the plate load resistor of the tube—and then is shorted out when the tube conducts, a sawtooth waveform of capacitor voltage is produced.

The cathode-coupled astable multivibrator discussed in Sec. 7-11 is commonly used as a sawtooth generator. One of the tubes has a plate-voltage variation, as shown in Fig. 7-25; it is cut off for a period of time and then conducts heavily for a short period of time. It was shown in Sec. 7-11 that if a capacitor is connected between the plate of this tube and ground, a sawtooth waveform will be produced. The capacitor starts to charge up through the plate load resistor, and then the tube conducts and discharges the capacitor in a short time period.

A driven sweep generator can make use of the monostable cathode-coupled multivibrator of Sec. 7-6, shown in Fig. 7-18. A capacitor connected between the plate of V_2 and ground will be shorted out until a triggering pulse at the input causes V_2 to start conducting. The capacitor then charges through R_5 for a period of time determined by C_3 and R_4. Then the tube again conducts, discharging the capacitor.

An actual circuit used in the Eico Model 425 oscilloscope is shown in Fig. 9-10. The circuit is simplified somewhat for the sake of clarity. This is a free-running cathode-coupled multivibrator, but it can be synchronized to signals applied to the grid of V_1. This synchronizing signal is coupled through a capacitor, and its amplitude is controlled by the 100-kilohm potentiometer.

The sweep frequency is controlled by the size of C_1 and the adjustment of R_1. The sweep amplitude and linearity are partially affected by the sweep frequency and also by the time constant of R_2 and C_2. Various values of C_1 and C_2 are switched into the circuit for various ranges of sweep frequency; and then R_1 and R_2, which are ganged together, are adjusted for the particular frequency desired.

9-6   TRANSISTORIZED SAWTOOTH CIRCUIT

There are two basic types of synchronized sawtooth generators utilizing transistors: the RC type and the RL type. Figure 9-11a illustrates the RC circuit. Capacitor C charges during the OFF time of the input pulse since Q_1 is in the cutoff region. The equivalent circuit during the charge cycle is shown in Fig. 9-11b. During the interval of the ON time of the input pulse, the transistor is saturated and C discharges. The output sawtooth is synchronized to the input trigger, and a critical time relationship exists between the discharge τ and the duration time of the input pulse. The t_d must be of sufficient duration for C to discharge completely.

Fig. 9-10.   Sawtooth circuit of Eico Model 425 oscilloscope. (Electronic Instrument Co., Inc., Flushing, N.Y.)

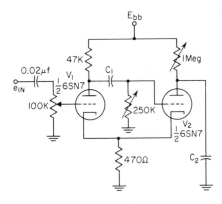

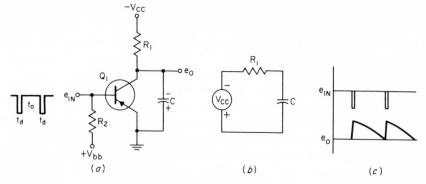

Fig. 9-11. (a) Transistorized sawtooth generator. (b) Equivalent circuit. (c) Output waveshapes.

$t_d = 5\tau_d$, where τ_d is the product of the ON resistance (r_c) of the transistor and C. The output waveshapes are shown in Fig. 9-11c.

An example of the second type of circuit is shown in Fig. 9-12a. This circuit operates in a manner similar to the one described above, except that the output is a linear rise in current which has applications in magnetic-deflection cathode-ray-tube circuitry. The circuit is a modification of traditional pentode circuits. (The pentode's output characteristics are similar to those of the common-emitter transistor.)

The transistor acts as a switch which is turned on when a negative pulse is applied at the base. When the transistor is on, the full collector supply ($-V_{cc}$) is applied across the tank circuit. The current through the inductor rises according to the equation

$$i_r = \frac{E}{r_c}(1 - \epsilon^{-t/\tau})$$

where $\tau = L/r_c$, L is the inductance of the tank, and r_c is the ON resistance

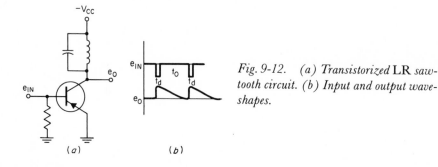

Fig. 9-12. (a) Transistorized LR sawtooth circuit. (b) Input and output waveshapes.

of the transistor. Since r_c is low, the time constant is long; hence, the slope of i becomes the initial slope derived from

$$\frac{di}{dt} = \frac{E_{to}}{L}$$

At the onset of t_d, the transistor turns off. The coil and its parallel capacitor are free to oscillate. Because the tank circuit is critically damped (see Sec. 3-7), a half-cycle returns the current through the inductance to zero. The waveshapes of the input and output are shown in Fig. 9-12b. The relationship between t_d and the choice of L and C is

$$t_d = \pi \sqrt{LC}$$

9-12

In practical applications, inductance L becomes the cathode-ray tube (CRT) deflection coil. The sweep is produced through the linear rise in current through L.

9-7 TRAPEZOIDAL WAVESHAPE GENERATORS

Section 9-6 describes a transistorized current sawtooth circuit. If a vacuum-tube circuit is utilized to generate a sawtooth current through a coil, the waveshape of the voltage must be trapezoidal.

Consider the circuit of Fig. 9-13a. When switch sw is closed, the current through the coil rises exponentially, as shown in Fig. 9-13b. The current reaches a maximum of $I = E/R$. The initial portion of the curve (solid line) of Fig. 9-13b is the most linear. The slope of this linear region is determined by the circuit's resistance, inductance, and applied d-c potential. If the current continued to rise at the initial rate, it would appear as the linear function (dashed line) of Fig. 9-13b. The current, however, reaches a saturation value determined by the applied voltage and the resistance of the circuit.

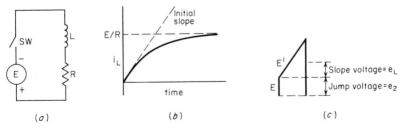

Fig. 9-13. *(a) Direct-current LR circuit. (b) Current function of (a). (c) Applied voltage.*

Assume that the applied voltage E (Fig. 9-13a) is not a step function, but a trapezoidal function, as shown in Fig. 9-13c. If the slope E were equal to the initial-conditions slope of the LR circuit, the current through the inductance would rise linearly, producing the desired linear sweep. A trapezoidal waveshape voltage is identified by two components (Fig. 9-13c). The initial step function is called the *jump* voltage, and the ramp voltage is called the *slope* voltage. The initial slope of i can be determined by differentiating the equation for the instantaneous value of current through the coil:

$$i_L = I - I\epsilon^{-t/\tau}$$

$$\frac{di}{dt} = \frac{I}{\tau} \epsilon^{-t/\tau}$$

By allowing t to equal zero, the slope (di/dt) becomes

$$\text{Slope } E = \frac{+I}{\tau} \tag{9-13}$$

Figure 9-14 illustrates a basic circuit used to produce a trapezoidal voltage waveshape. It is essentially a hard-tube sawtooth circuit with another resistor added in series with C. The jump voltage (step portion) of the output waveform is determined by

$$e_2 = \frac{R_2\,(E_{bb} - E_{co})}{R_1 + R_2} \tag{9-14}$$

The slope voltage (ramp portion) is determined by the same techniques as those employed with hard-tube sawtooth circuits.

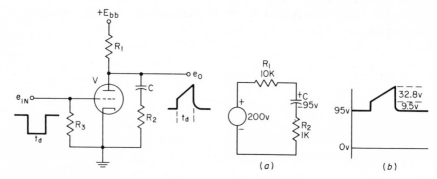

Fig. 9-14. *Trapezoidal waveshape generator.*

Fig. 9-15. *(a) Equivalent circuit for trapezoidal waveshape generator. (b) Waveshape.*

EXAMPLE If the circuit of Fig. 9-7a is converted to a trapezoidal wave-shape generator by the addition of a 1-kilohm resistor in series with C, what are the output jump voltage and the slope voltage? Assume $C = 2$ μf, $R_1 = 10$ kilohms, $R_2 = 1$ kilohm, $E_{bb} = 200$ volts, and the input pulse is -20 volts with $t_d = 10$ msec.

The equivalent circuit for the active region is derived from Fig. 9-9. $E_{oc} = 95$ volts and $Z_g = 4.4$ kilohms, so the capacitor is charged to 95 volts under quiescent conditions. When the input pulse is applied, the tube is cut off, and capacitor C and resistor R_2 see an equivalent circuit as shown in Fig. 9-15a. The jump voltage, according to Eq. (9-14), is 9.55 volts, as illustrated in Fig. 9-15b.

The slope voltage is formed as the voltage across the capacitor builds up and the voltage across the resistor R_2 decays.

$$\text{Slope } E = \Delta e_c - \Delta e_{R_2} \tag{9-15}$$

$$\text{where } \Delta e_c = E_{R0}(1 - \epsilon^{-t/\tau}) \tag{3-6}$$
$$\Delta e_{R_2} = E_{R_2 0}\epsilon^{-t/\tau}$$

In Eq. (9-15) Δe_{R_2} is subtracted from Δe_c because Δe_{R_2} decays as Δe_{c_2} increases.

$$\tau = (11 \times 10^3)(2 \times 10^{-6}) = 22 \text{ msec}$$

$$t = 10 \text{ msec}$$

Substitution in Eq. (3-6) yields

$$\Delta e_c = 105(1 - \epsilon^{-10/22})$$
$$= 105(1 - \epsilon^{-0.455}) = 105(0.37) = 38.8 \text{ volts}$$
$$\Delta e_{R_2} = 9.5\epsilon^{-0.455} = (9.5)(0.63) = 6 \text{ volts}$$

Substitution in Eq. (9-15) yields

$$\text{Slope } E = 32.8 \text{ volts}$$

PROBLEMS

9-11 In the circuit of Fig. 9-7, if $R_L = 15$ kilohms, $C = 0.05$ μf, $R_1 = 470$ kilohms, and $E_{bb} = 150$ volts, what is the amplitude of the output sawtooth signal if a 35-kc negative pulse (0 to -30 volts) is applied? Assume the duration time to be 75 μsec.

9-12 Refer to Prob. 9-11. (a) What is the slope voltage of the output? (b) What is the fall time of the output wave?

9-13 Refer to the circuit of Fig. 9-7. If $R_L = 15$ kilohms, $R_1 = 470$ kilohms, $E_{bb} = 150$ volts, and the input is a 5-kc square wave (0 to -30 volts), what value of C will produce an output sawtooth wave whose slope voltage is 30 volts?

9-14 Refer to Fig. 9-7. Construct a table showing how changes in E_{bb}, R_L, and C influence the output amplitude, linearity, and fall time.

9-15 Assume that a 2N356 is connected in a circuit identical to that of Fig. 9-11. (Supply voltages and input pulse will be of the correct polarity.) Assume the following circuit values: $V_{cc} = 14$ volts, $R_1 = 1$ kilohm, $R_2 = 27$ kilohms, $C = 0.5$ μf, and $V_{bb} = -5$ volts. What is the quiescent output potential?

9-16 Assume that a negative pulse of 20 volts with a 0.005-msec duration time and a period of 0.70 msec is applied to the circuit of Prob. 9-15. (a) What is the slope voltage of the output? (b) What is the peak-to-peak amplitude of the output sawtooth? Sketch the output waveshape.

9-17 If the load resistance in Prob. 9-15 is increased to 3 kilohms, what is the new slope voltage at the output?

9-18 Construct a table for the circuit of Fig. 9-11 and show how changes in E_{cc}, R_1, R_2, C, and E_{bb} influence the output slope voltage and linearity.

9-19 Refer to the circuit of Fig. 9-14. Assume that $V = 6$SN7, $R_1 = 20$ kilohms, $R_2 = 4.7$ kilohms, $R_3 = 470$ kilohms, $C = 0.01$ μf, $E_{bb} = 300$ volts, and when a 0.1-msec negative pulse is applied at the input, V is cut off. (a) What is the value of the jump voltage at the output? (b) What is the value of the slope voltage?

9-20 Refer to Prob. 9-19. If the value of R_2 is decreased, will the new output slope be increased, decreased, or unchanged?

9-21 Does an increase in the duration time of the input pulse influence the jump voltage? If so, how?

9-22 Construct a table showing how changes in the values of R_1, R_2, C, E_{bb}, and t_d (of the input) influence the output amplitude, jump voltage, slope voltage, linearity, and duration time for the circuit of Prob. 9-19.

9-8 MILLER CIRCUITS

The main drawback of all the sawtooth circuits described in the preceding sections is their high percentage of slope error. In all the circuits described, the linearity is improved when a higher supply voltage and a longer time constant are used. Increasing or decreasing the τ or the applied d-c voltage does not change the linearity if the same percentage of the charge curve is used. However, if a fixed increment of time is established, then increasing the charge curve utilizes a smaller percentage of the curve.

A limitation does exist since the size of the supply voltage is limited by the maximum ratings of the device (tube or transistor). The use of feedback in Miller circuits overcomes this limitation by extending the charge curve without increasing the supply potential.

There are three basic circuits which utilize the Miller-effect principle; these are the Miller integrator circuit, the phantastron circuit, and the bootstrap circuit. They are basically all the same circuit, the difference being in how the amplifying device is connected.

Aside from providing linear sawtooth waveforms, the circuits can also be used for pulse-delay purposes. When the basic circuits are incorporated with differentiating and clipping circuits, they can provide accurate delays down to a few microseconds.

PRODUCTION OF A LINEAR SWEEP

Consider the circuit of Fig. 9-16a. When voltage E is applied to the circuit, the voltage (e_c) across the capacitor rises exponentially according to the equation $e_c = E(1 - \epsilon^{-t/\tau})$ (shown graphically in Fig. 9-16b). The most linear portion of the curve occurs just after $t = 0$. The slope of the curve is found by differentiating Eq. (3-1):

$$\frac{de_c}{dt} = \frac{E}{\tau} \epsilon^{-t/\tau}$$

The initial slope can be found by substituting $t = 0$ into the equation:

$$\frac{de_c}{dt} = \frac{E}{\tau} \tag{9-16}$$

If Eq. (9-16) is integrated,

$$e = \frac{Et}{\tau} \tag{9-17}$$

Consider a second circuit, shown in Fig. 9-16c, which is the circuit of Fig. 9-16a with the addition of a second generator. The second generator's

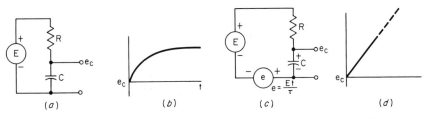

Fig. 9-16. (a) RC circuit. (b) Exponential rise of e_c. (c) RC circuit with compensating slope voltage. (d) Linear rise of e_c.

voltage is one which has a constant rate of change equal to Et/τ from Eq. (9-17). The output of the circuit of Fig. 9-16c will now be a linear rise, as shown in Fig. 9-16d. The slope of the output rise, hence the rate of change of buildup across c, will have a slope equal to E/τ.

THEORETICAL CIRCUIT

Assume that the circuit of Fig. 9-16c is redrawn and three arbitrary points a, b, and c are identified (Fig. 9-17a). If an amplifier is connected to points a, b, c, and its output replaces generator e, the equivalent circuit is that shown in Fig. 9-17b. If the amplifier stage A is assumed to be the three elements of a vacuum tube, then point a represents the grid terminal, b the plate terminal, and c the cathode terminal. This configuration produces the correct polarity for e. Ideally the voltage gain A_0 of the amplifier should be large. The amplifier, therefore, is comparable to a conventional grounded-cathode pentode circuit or a common-emitter transistor circuit.

The circuit can be illustrated by using other configurations as well. Refer to Fig. 9-18a. Note that the position of signal ground has been shifted from point c to point b. Here again the e_0 corresponds to the e of the theoretical circuit. The circuit for A_1 corresponds to a cathode-follower type of circuit, discussed in Chap. 12; hence, the voltage gain A_1 is less than unity. The circuit of Fig. 9-17b is the equivalent circuit for the phantastron and the Miller integrator, while the circuit of Fig. 9-18b is the equivalent circuit for the bootstrap circuit. That the two circuits are the same can be shown by three-terminal network analysis.

Refer to Fig. 9-19. Assume that point a refers to the grid of a tube, b refers to the plate, and c refers to the cathode. For a common-cathode amplifier $A_0 = e_{bc}/e_{ac}$, which is e_0/e_{in}. For the cathode follower $A_1 = e_{cb}/e_{ab} = -e_{bc}/(e_{ac} + e_{cb})$ since, according to Kirchhoff's law, $0 = e_{ac} + e_{cb} - e_{ab}$:

$$A_1 = \frac{-e_{bc}}{e_{ac} + e_{cb}} = \frac{-e_{bc}}{e_{ac} - e_{bc}}$$

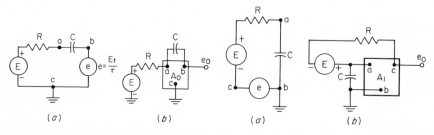

Fig. 9-17. RC *circuit with amplifier.* *Fig. 9-18.* RC *circuit with amplifier* E.

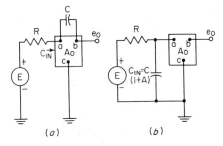

Fig. 9-19.   Three-terminal network.   Fig. 9-20.   Equivalent RC circuit.

Dividing both numerator and denominator by e_{ac} yields

$$A_1 = \frac{-e_{bc}/e_{ac}}{1 - e_{bc}/e_{ac}} = \frac{-A_0}{1 - A_0} = \frac{A_0}{A_0 - 1} \tag{9-18}$$

Hence, from Eq. (9-18), one circuit can be converted to the other by changing the reference point in the circuit.

The Miller equation states that the input capacitance of an amplifier is equal to $C_{in} = C_{gk} + C_{gp}(1 + A)$; however, in both circuits (Figs. 9-17b and 9-18b) capacitor C parallels C_{gp}. If C is many times larger than C_{gp}, then C_{gp} and C_{gk} become negligible. The input capacitance becomes

$$C_{in} = C(1 + A)$$

It must now be established that the output voltage e_o is equal to the initial slope of the charge buildup across C. Refer to the circuit of Fig. 9-20a. Figure 9-20b is an equivalent circuit showing the input capacitance of the stage C_{in}. The gain of the stage is given as $A_0 = e_o/e_{in}$; however, e_{in} is the voltage across C_{in} which equals $e_{c_{in}} = E(1 - \epsilon^{-t/\tau})$, where $\tau = RC(1 + A_0)$. From the gain equation

$$e_o = A_0 E(1 - \epsilon^{-t/RC(1+A_0)})$$

$$\frac{de_o}{dt} = \frac{A_0 E \, \epsilon^{-t/RC(1+A_0)}}{RC(1 + A_0)} \tag{9-19}$$

However, since A_0 is large, $A_0/(1 + A_0)$ is approximately equal to 1. Further, since t is small, Eq. (9-19) reduces to

$$\frac{de_o}{dt} = \frac{E}{RC} \tag{9-20}$$

Solving for e_o gives

$$e_o = \frac{Et}{RC} = \frac{Et}{\tau} \tag{9-21}$$

By referring to Fig. 9-16c, it can be seen that the output voltage of Eq. (9-21) yields the required voltage e for a linear sweep.

The circuit of Fig. 9-21 is a practical circuit of the theoretical circuit shown in Fig. 9-17b. Plate current i_p is cut off as a result of a large negative bias on the suppressor grid. The voltage at the plate is equal to E_{bb}. At quiescent conditions, capacitor C is charged to E_{bb} since the control grid is clamped to the cathode as a result of the positive grid return of R_1. A positive step function applied to the suppressor initiates the rundown at the grid.

Discharge Circuit. The positive gate applied at the suppressor grid causes i_p to increase and the plate voltage to decrease. The voltage waveshapes at the plate, control grid, screen, and suppressor are illustrated in Fig. 9-22. At t_1 the positive step function at the suppressor triggers a regenerative switching. The control grid is driven negative, the screen voltage increases (since space current is diverted from the screen to the plate), and the plate voltage decreases. Grid voltage begins to increase as the input capacitor C_{in} discharges. The increasing control-grid voltage causes a decrease in plate voltage. The equivalent discharge circuit appears in Fig. 9-23a. If a Thévenin equivalent circuit is substituted for the portion of the circuit to the right of points X and Y, the resultant circuit is that shown in Fig. 9-23b. As capacitor C discharges, the voltage across R_1 decreases and hence becomes less negative.

Complete Rundown. The plate-voltage *rundown* (linear decrease) from t_1 to t_2, as shown in Fig. 9-22, results from a given change in e_g. The change in e_g which causes the plate voltage rundown is very small. The grid base for the pentode circuit is given as E_{bb}/A. If A is large, the grid swing required

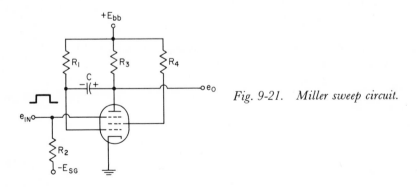

Fig. 9-21. Miller sweep circuit.

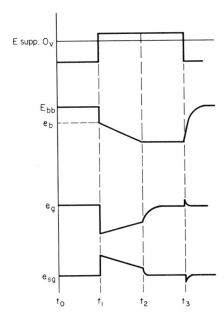

Fig. 9-22.   Voltage waveshapes for Fig. 9-21.

for a *bottoming-out* at the plate is small; it is on the order of 1 or 2 volts. A graphic representation of bottoming-out is seen in Fig. 9-24.

Once the plate voltage has decreased to its least negative value, as a result of bottoming-out, the plate current reaches its maximum value, as shown in Fig. 9-24 (t_2 of Fig. 9-22). Grid voltage continues to increase, thus causing an increase in screen current, since i_p can no longer increase. Capacitor C remains clamped to the plate voltage until the gate potential at the suppressor is removed (point t_3 of Fig. 9-22). When plate current is cut off, capacitor C recharges to E_{bb} and the circuit is returned to quiescence awaiting the next gate pulse, whereupon the cycle is repeated. The linearity of the sawtooth at the plate from t_1 to t_2 is extremely good

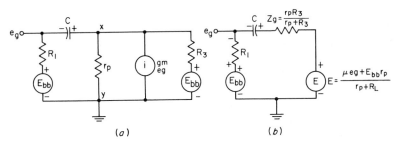

Fig. 9-23.   (a) Discharge circuit. (b) Thévenin equivalent of (a).

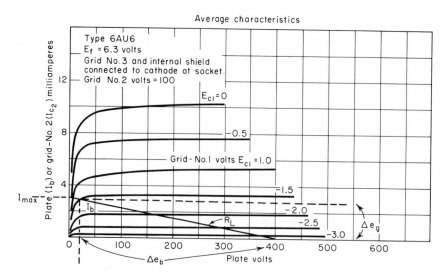

Type 6AU6
E_f = 6.3 volts
Grid No.3 and internal shield
connected to cathode at socket.
Grid No.2 volts = 100

Fig. 9-24.   Bottoming-out.

since only a small percentage of the RC curve is utilized. Two additional factors and the feedback circuit which maintains a constant discharge current must be considered.

1. The time interval from t_1 to t_2 is controllable by varying either R, C, or E_{bb}, hence providing an accurate means of delay.
2. The slope of e_p from t_1 to t_2 is determined by R, C, or E_{bb}, hence providing controllable sweep voltages.

9-9   MILLER RUN-UP CIRCUIT

A variation of the Miller rundown circuit (negative-going sawtooth) is the Miller run-up circuit. The circuit of Fig. 9-25 produces a positive-going sawtooth. It is similar to the circuits used in some time-base oscilloscopes. The RC circuit which determines the slope of the output sweep is R_1 and C_1. Under quiescent conditions C_1 is discharged. With no gate pulse applied at the grid of V_1, the tube is cut off. Diode D_1 clamps the cathode of V_2 to a few volts negative as a result of current through R_2. (The value of R_2 is small.) D_2 clamps the grid of V_3 to the level of the voltage across R_2.

If V_2 conducts, it diverts some of the current flowing through R_2. The voltage drop across R_2 decreases. However, the current through V_2 is determined by the potential between its grid and cathode. This potential in turn is determined by the potential at the grid of V_3, which in turn is also a function of the current through R_2.

Assume that a gate pulse turns V_1 on. The current through R_2 increases as a result of increased plate current through V_1. The drop in plate voltage of V_1 reverse-biases D_1 and D_2. The voltage at the grid of V_3 attempts to decrease. The decrease is opposed, however, through negative feedback; the grid of V_3 going in a negative direction causes the plate to go more positive, thus driving the grid of V_2 more positive, increasing the voltage at the cathode of V_2. The increasing cathode voltage at V_2 is coupled through C_1 to the grid of V_3. The feedback maintains a linear rise in the voltage across C and hence a positive-going sawtooth at the output.

When the gate pulse is removed from the grid of V_1, capacitor C_1 discharges rapidly through R_2 and D_2.

9-10   PHANTASTRON CIRCUIT

The phantastron circuit is essentially a Miller rundown circuit. Where the Miller rundown circuit requires a gate pulse to produce a linear sweep, the phantastron requires a trigger to produce the same output. The circuit is shown in Fig. 9-26a.

In order to follow the circuit discussion, the student should study Fig. 9-27, which gives the plate and screen current characteristics of the

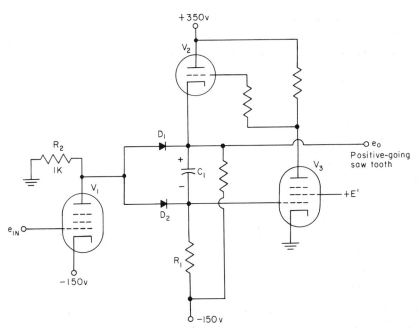

Fig. 9-25.   Miller run-up circuit.

tube connected as a phantastron, as shown in Fig. 9-26a. Note that as the control-grid voltage changes in a negative direction, both plate current and screen current are cut off at a given e_g. As the grid voltage increases, plate current and screen current increase. The plate current, however, reaches a peak and then moves to a second cutoff point. These characteristics are an integral part in the operation of the phantastron.

INITIAL CONDITIONS (t_0 of Fig. 9-26b)

The voltage divider consisting of R_1, R_2, and R_3 establishes the suppressor-grid voltage at $+12$ volts with respect to ground. Screen current flowing through the cathode resistor makes the cathode of the tube $+19$ volts positive with respect to ground. Therefore the suppressor grid is -7 volts with respect to the cathode. The 6AS6 is a special-purpose pentode used in phantastron circuits, and this negative (-7 volts) voltage is sufficient to cut off plate current. A small grid current flows through R_5, clamping the control grid to the cathode.

Because the 1N68 diode is conducting, the plate voltage is clamped to about 100 volts, depending upon the setting of potentiometer R_3.

Capacitor C is charged to the plate potential minus the voltage across the cathode resistor. For this case it is charged 81 volts with the polarity shown.

NEGATIVE INPUT PULSE (t_1 of Fig. 9-26b)

The negative pulse is applied through the diode and capacitor C to the control grid of the tube. The grid momentarily goes negative, causing

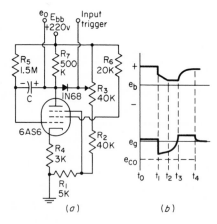 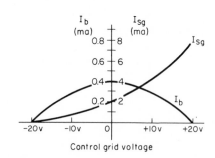

Fig. 9-26. (a) Phantastron circuit. (b) Waveshapes.

Fig. 9-27. Plate and screen characteristics for a pentode connected as a phantastron.

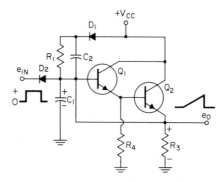

Fig. 9-28. Transistorized bootstrap circuit.

screen current to decrease. The decrease in screen current causes a decrease in the voltage drop across the cathode resistor. When this voltage drops to below 12 volts, the suppressor grid goes positive and plate current begins to flow. The increase in plate current causes the voltage at the plate to decrease, and the diode stops conducting. The drop in plate voltage is coupled to the grid through capacitor C. The subsequent plate rundown is similar to that of the Miller integrator circuit.

SLOPE VOLTAGE (t_1 to t_2 of Fig. 9-26b)

Capacitor C discharges through the 1.5-megohm resistor, keeping the control grid at a negative potential. The operating voltages on this tube are now such as to cause the tube to act as an ordinary pentode amplifier, an amplifier with a high gain A.

SWITCH POINT (t_2 of Fig. 9-26b)

While the capacitor C is discharging, the grid is becoming less negative and the plate voltage is decreasing. Once the plate voltage has bottomed out, the tube no longer acts as an amplifier, and the circuit changes state or reaches a second switch point. Capacitor C cannot discharge to a lower potential than that across the tube. The grid voltage continues to rise, and this rise causes the screen current to increase. This increase in screen current causes a greater voltage drop to exist across the cathode resistor, hence making the suppressor negative and cutting off plate current. At t_3 the grid goes positive with respect to the cathode, and C charges through R_4 to the potential at the plate. The circuit returns to the original stable state.

9-11 TRANSISTOR BOOTSTRAP CIRCUIT

The circuit of Fig. 9-28 is a Miller circuit with its output taken from across the emitter resistor (grounded-collector configuration). This configuration is classified as a *bootstrap circuit*.

QUIESCENT CONDITIONS

With no signal applied at the input, diode D_2 clamps capacitor C_1 to ground. Neither Q_1 nor Q_2 is conducting since the base of Q_1 is also clamped to ground. With no appreciable collector current through Q_1, Q_2 is unbiased and is off.

FEEDBACK CIRCUIT

A positive gate at the input causes C_1 to start charging toward V_{cc}. (Diode D_2 turns off.) The voltage across R_1 would normally drop as C_1 charges. However, an increase in voltage across C_1 increases the bias on Q_1, which in turn increases the collector current at Q_1. The increasing collector current causes increased bias on Q_2, increasing its collector current. The voltage across R_3 begins to increase, and the output increases in a positive direction. This increasing voltage is returned through C_2 to the junction of R_1 and D_1, and keeps the voltage across R_1 from dropping. The resultant feedback produces an almost linear rise in the voltage across R_3 and the output potential.

DISCHARGE CIRCUIT

Once the input gate is removed, diode D_2 becomes forward-biased and C_1 discharges rapidly.

The output sawtooth amplitude is determined by the value of V_{cc} and the duration time of the input gate. The values of R_1, C_1, and V_{cc} determine the slope of the output sawtooth.

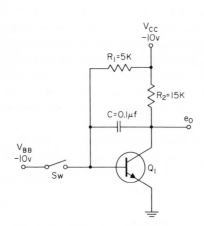
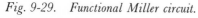

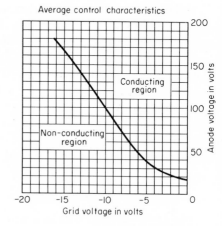

Average control characteristics

Fig. 9-29. Functional Miller circuit.   *Fig. 9-30. 6D4 thyratron characteristics.*

In order for the voltage across R_1 to remain constant, the potential at the junction between R_1 and C_2 must rise above V_{cc}. This cannot occur since the diode switch D_1 disconnects the junction from the supply voltage. In effect, the charging supply voltage is increasing as a result of the increasing charge on the capacitor itself; hence, the name bootstrap circuit.

PROBLEMS

9-23 Refer to the circuit of Fig. 9-29. In this Miller circuit, assume that the switch is in the open position. (a) What is the charge on C? (b) What is the output quiescent voltage level?

9-24 Refer to Prob. 9-23. Assume that the switch is closed. (a) Will the capacitor charge or discharge? (b) What circuit factor influences the time constant of charge or discharge circuit?

9-25 Refer to Prob. 9-23. Will the output waveshape be a positive or a negative ramp? Sketch the output waveshape for a period of 1 msec.

9-26 Assume that the switch in Fig. 9-29 is replaced with a transistor. Redraw the circuit and show how the new transistor will operate as a switch. Under quiescent conditions, will the new transistor remain on or off?

9-27 Refer to Prob. 9-26. Will the circuit modification change the slope of the output wave? If so, how?

9-28 Construct a table for the circuit of Fig. 9-29 and show how changes in E_{cc}, E_{bb}, R_1, C, and R_2 influence the output slope, linearity, and amplitude.

9-29 Refer to the circuit of Fig. 9-26. Construct a table showing how changes in R_4, R_3, R_2, R_5, C, R_7, and E_{bb} influence the output slope and amplitude.

9-30 Refer to the circuit of Fig. 9-21. Construct a table showing how changes in R_1, R_2, R_3, R_4, C, E_{sg}, and E_{bb} influence the output slope.

CHAPTER 10 GATING CIRCUITS

A gating circuit is defined as a circuit which has several inputs and one output. The output signal is obtained only when certain input signals are applied.

There are two main groups of gates: *transmission gates* and *switching* or *logic gates.*

A transmission gate transmits the input signal to the output with no change but only during certain time intervals determined by *control signals* applied to other inputs.

Switching or logic gates have outputs which are pulses or d-c levels but which are not necessarily similar to any of the inputs. Here, also, the time of the occurrence of the output signal is determined by the various input signals.

10-1 LOGIC SIGNAL LEVELS

Logic circuits, including logic gates, operate with two possible signal levels. These signal levels represent the "true" and "false," or ON and OFF, conditions and are usually represented by the *binary numbers* 1 and 0.

Although a complete discussion of number systems is beyond the objectives of this text, the student should understand the importance of the term binary.

The number system in common usage is the decimal (base 10). The 10 fundamental digits are 0, 1, 2, 3, 4, 5, 6, 7, 8, and 9. Additional numbers are developed from the existing digits of the system, for example, 10, 11,

12, 13, 14, 15, 16, 17, 18, 19, 20, and 21. The *octal* number system is made up of eight basic digits: 0, 1, 2, 3, 4, 5, 6, and 7. The binary system utilizes just two digits: 0 and 1. This system is most compatible with many of the circuits discussed in previous chapters. Two different signal levels could be identified as 0 and 1. These two signal levels could be any two different voltage levels. They could be the same polarity or opposite polarities, or one of the levels could even be 0 volts. A variety of pairs of signal levels are in use by different companies. If the most positive level is considered the 1 or "true" signal and the most negative is considered the 0 or "false," it is termed positive logic; the reverse, negative logic. A few examples are: -11 and -3 volts; -10 and 0 volts; -6 and 0 volts; -5 and 0 volts; -3 and 0 volts; and -25 and $+10$ volts.

10-2 DIODE LOGIC GATES

A diode gate consists of two or more inputs with a diode (usually a semiconductor) in series with each input. The two types are shown in Fig. 10-1. Note that they are identical except that the polarities of the diodes and supply voltages are reversed. With the most negative signal a 0 signal and the most positive a 1, Fig. 10-1*a* shows an AND gate and Fig. 10-1*b* shows an OR gate.

An AND gate (sometimes called a *coincidence circuit*) receives its name from the characteristic that a 1 signal appears at the output terminal when a 1 is applied to the first input AND the second input AND to each of the other inputs. If any of the inputs has a 0 applied, the output will also be 0.

The OR gate will give a 1 output if a 1 signal appears at the first input OR the second input OR at any OR all the inputs. As long as at least one of the inputs has a 1 signal, the output will be 1.

These circuits will operate for any two signal levels as long as they are both more negative than the $+E$ of Fig. 10-1*a* and more positive than the $-E$ of Fig. 10-1*b*.

In order to analyze the circuits in more detail, we shall choose a value

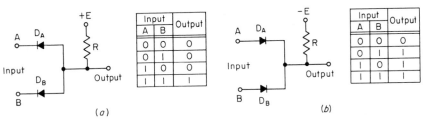

Fig. 10-1.   Diode gates. (a) AND *gate. (b)* OR *gate.*

of 12 volts for E and consider the 1 signal to be $+6$ volts and the 0 signal to be 0 volts.

Assume in Fig. 10-1a that both inputs have 0 volts applied. Both diodes will be forward-biased, making the output 0 volts. If both inputs are at the 6-volt level, both diodes will conduct, applying the 6 volts to the output. If input A is 0 volts and input B is 6 volts, both diodes cannot conduct, as the output could not be both 0 volts and 6 volts at the same time. If diode B conducted, the output would be 6 volts; however, this would also forward-bias diode A, which cannot happen. Therefore, diode A must conduct, making the output 0 volts. The result is reverse bias on diode B ($+6$ volts on the cathode and 0 volts on the plate). The four possible input signals can be summarized in a "truth" table, as shown in Fig. 10-1a. We see that an output of 1 is obtained only when A AND B are both 1.

A similar analysis of the circuit in Fig. 10-1b shows that with both inputs 0, the output is 0; with both inputs 1, the output is 1; and with one input 0 and the other input 1, the diode with the 1 signal ($+6$ volts) applied will be forward-biased, reverse-biasing the other diode and making the output $+6$ volts or 1. The truth table for this circuit shows that an output of 1 is obtained for either A OR B OR both equal to 1.

A careful analysis will show that if the most positive of the two signal levels ($+6$ volts) were taken as the 0 signal and the most negative as the 1 signal, the names of the two circuits would have to be reversed; Fig. 10-1a would be an OR circuit and Fig. 10-1b would be an AND circuit.

As mentioned earlier, these diode gates can have any number of input circuits. The signals applied can be either constant d-c levels, pulses, or a combination. The circuit of Fig. 10-1a will have an output equal to the most negative input signal at any time, and the output of the circuit in Fig. 10-1b will equal the most positive signal at any instant of time. All other diodes will be reverse-biased.

Diode gates have the advantage of simplicity compared with other types of gates. The disadvantage is that no amplification can take place. In fact, there is a signal-power loss through the circuit. After a signal has gone through two or three diode gates, it must be returned to the designated level through signal-amplification stages.

One practical application of diode gates is in converting the output signals of binary counters into decimal signals. It was seen in Chap. 6 that four binary counters with the proper feedback connections could be used to count from 0 to 9, return to 0, and begin again. Table 10-1 shows the ON-OFF state of each of the four binary circuits in a 1-2-2-4 counter. A circuit will now be described which will give an output at any one of 10 terminals, representing the corresponding decimal number.

It was shown in Chap. 6 that an output signal may be obtained from each side of a binary flip-flop. If the binary is ON, one output will be at

TABLE 10-1

Decimal number	Binary stages			
	D	C	B	A
0	0	0	0	0
1	0	0	0	1
2	0	0	1	0
3	0	0	1	1
4	0	1	1	0
5	0	1	1	1
6	1	1	0	0
7	1	1	0	1
8	1	1	1	0
9	1	1	1	1

the 1 level and the other at the 0 level. If the binary is OFF, the signals will be reversed. We shall designate these output signals in the following way: If binary A is on, the output signal corresponding to a 1 level will be called output A and the output signal corresponding to a 0 level will be called output $\overline{A}$. Thus, according to Table 10-1, for decimal number 5 the eight output signals will be: 1-level signals A, B, C, $\overline{D}$; and 0-level signals $\overline{A}$, $\overline{B}$, $\overline{C}$, D. To obtain a single 1-level signal representing this decimal number 5, all that is needed is a four-input AND circuit which is fed signals from outputs A, B, C, and $\overline{D}$ of the binary counter. When the counter is registering the number 5, all inputs of the AND circuit will be at the 1 level, and the output of the AND circuit will be 1. No other combination of signals can give a 1 output from this AND circuit. Nine additional four-input AND circuits will give the outputs corresponding to the other decimal numbers.

This kind of diode gating circuit is called a *matrix* because the circuit diagram is usually drawn with the components arranged neatly in rows and columns, similar to mathematical matrices. The complete circuit for converting the output of the 1-2-2-4 counter into decimal signals is shown in Fig. 10-2.

10-3 TRANSISTOR SWITCHES

In Chap. 5 the simple transistor switch was discussed in detail. If we choose our two signal levels as -10 and 0 volts, four circuit arrangements of the simple switch are possible. Two of these are inverting switches and two do not invert. Two of these circuits make use of PNP transistors, and the other two use NPN. All four are designed for operation with a single -12-volt supply voltage. These four circuits, together with their input-output characteristics, are shown in Fig. 10-3.

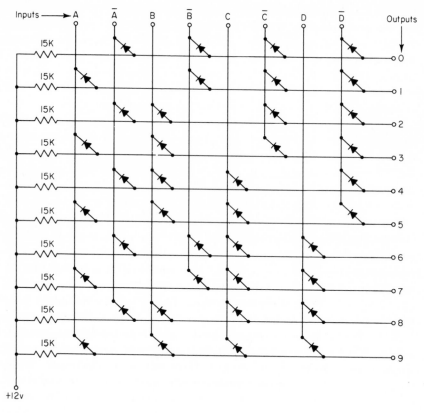

Fig. 10-2.   Diode matrix.

In Fig. 10-3*a* an input of −10 volts gives a base current of about 10 volts/68 kilohms = 147 μa, which drives the transistor into saturation and gives an output of 0 volts. When the input is 0 volts, the base current is 0 and the transistor is cut off; the output is equal to the supply voltage, −12 volts. If the circuit is feeding a load of about 10 kilohms, the output will drop to −10 volts and therefore be at the desired signal level. This circuit inverts the output and is therefore called an *inverter*. The output signal is *not* the same as the input signal, so this circuit is often called a NOT circuit.

The circuit shown in Fig. 10-3*b* has the load resistor in the emitter circuit and is often called an *emitter follower,* because the emitter voltage "follows" the input signal as it changes from one level to the other. (The use of the emitter follower as an amplifier will be discussed in detail in Chap. 12.) When the input signal is −10 volts, the transistor will be forward-biased. It is incorrect to assume that a base current of

10 volts/2.2 kilohms = 4,550 μa would flow, which would definitely drive the transistor into saturation, giving an output of −12 volts. Further analysis shows that the emitter voltage could not be more negative than the base voltage (−10 voltage), as this situation would reverse-bias the transistor. Actually, the voltage drop across the load resistor is slightly less than 10 volts, so that the resulting base-emitter voltage gives a base current of about 15 μa and an emitter current of a little less than 1 ma.

An NPN transistor can be used by reversing the power-supply connections as shown in Fig. 10-3c and d. The positive terminal of the power supply is still kept grounded. The circuit of Fig. 10-3c is an inverter like that of Fig. 10-3a, but it should be noted that with an input of −10 volts, a base current of only 2 volts/68 kilohms = 29.4 μa will flow, which does not drive the transistor to cutoff, but keeps it in the active region, with a collector voltage about 8 volts positive with respect to the emitter, or −4 volts output with respect to ground. Therefore, this circuit would be unusable because of the change in signal level. An input of 0 volts will give a base current of 12 volts/68 kilohms = 177 μa. The transistor is driven into saturation, and the output level will be −12 volts.

The circuit of Fig. 10-3d is also an emitter follower. The output signal will follow the input signal just as it did in the circuit of Fig. 10-3b.

It is seen that circuit a can be used for an inverter and circuits b and d can be used as emitter-follower amplifiers. One may wonder at first about the need for the circuits of b and d, as the outputs are identical with the inputs. The circuits provide isolation between the load and the source. They have the characteristics of high input resistance and low output resistance. Therefore, they represent a light load on the driving source

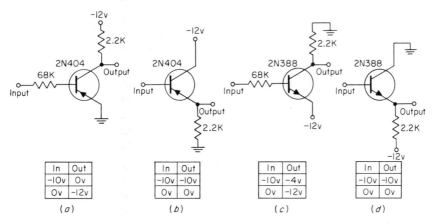

Fig. 10-3. Transistor switches. (a) NOT *circuit. (b) Emitter follower. (c) Inverter circuit. (d) Emitter follower.*

while they are capable of furnishing considerable current to any following loads. Though not considered voltage amplifiers, they are current or power amplifiers.

10-4 DIODE-TRANSISTOR LOGIC GATES

One class of commonly used logic gates is made up of the diode AND or OR gates discussed in Sec. 10-2, followed by either an inverter or an emitter follower, both of which were discussed in Sec. 10-3. These gates are sometimes called *diode-transistor logic* gates, or DTL gates. They also have been called *hybrid* logic gates because they are made up of two types of circuits. It is, of course, possible to use several levels of diode gates and then put in an amplifier wherever needed. If an amplifier is added to the output of every diode gate, a basic building block results which has a good output for driving other circuits, and equipment design problems are minimized.

Figure 10-4 shows diode OR and AND circuits, each followed by an emitter follower. The signal characteristics of each are shown.

It should be noted that the NPN switch of Fig. 10-3d could just as well be used as an emitter follower in the circuits of Fig. 10-4 but would have no particular advantage.

In Fig. 10-5 each of the diode gates is followed by an inverter or NOT circuit. Again, the signal characteristics are shown. It will be noted that the 0-level output is actually − 12 volts instead of the − 10 volts desired. If a load of about 10 kilohms is connected to either output, the level will drop to − 10 volts. In Fig. 10-5a, if both inputs are 0 level, the output is 1. If either or both inputs are 1, the output is 0. This circuit is a NOT-OR circuit, more commonly called a NOR circuit.

In Fig. 10-5b, if both inputs are 0, the output is 1. If only one of the inputs is 1, the output is still 1. If both A and B inputs are at the 1 level,

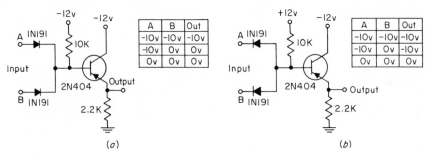

Fig. 10-4. Hybrid circuits.

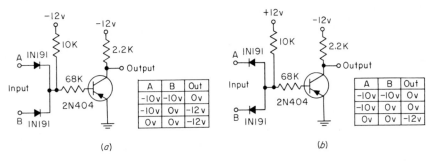

Fig. 10-5. (a) NOR circuit. (b) NAND circuit.

the output is 0. This circuit could then be called a NOT-AND circuit; the name is generally shortened to NAND.

10-5 DIRECTLY COUPLED TRANSISTOR LOGIC GATES

The circuits of Sec. 10-3 were called switches and then were referred to in Sec. 10-4 as current or power amplifiers. It is possible for these same switches to be used to perform logic gating without the use of diodes.

Frequently an introduction to logic gates makes use of simplified explanations involving mechanical switches. Two mechanical switches in series represent an AND circuit. As shown in Fig. 10-6a, both switch A AND switch B have to be closed for the lamp to light. In Fig. 10-6b either switch A OR switch B OR both may be closed to light the lamp.

In the same way, transistor switches may be connected in series or in parallel for logic gates.

Referring back to Fig. 10-3, note that the switch in Fig. 10-3c was not good because the 1 signal level output was −4 volts instead of 0 volts. It can also be shown that the circuit of Fig. 10-3b gives poor results when used in series or in parallel with another like switch. This leaves the circuit of Fig. 10-3a for an inverting switch and the circuit of Fig. 10-3d for a non-inverting switch. These switches can be connected in series for AND gates and in parallel for OR gates.

Fig. 10-6. (a) Mechanical AND circuit. (b) Mechanical OR circuit.

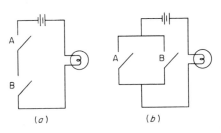

Figure 10-7 shows the noninverting switch used in series for an AND circuit and in parallel for the OR circuit. Only when an input is 0 volts will the switch close and make the emitter (output) at the collector potential. If either switch of Fig. 10-7*a* is open, the whole circuit is open, so it takes both inputs at the 1 level to give a 1 level output, an AND circuit. In the circuit of Fig. 10-7*b*, either input having a 1 signal will clamp the emitter to the collector and give a 1 output, an OR circuit.

The inverting switch is used in the series and parallel circuits of Fig. 10-8. In Fig. 10-8*a*, as long as either one of the inputs is at the 1 level (0 volts), we have an open circuit and the output will be at the 0 level (-12 volts). This results in an OR gate with an inverted output, a NOR circuit. In Fig. 10-8*b*, if either input is at the 0 level (-10 volts), conduction takes place and the output is clamped to ground, giving a 1 output. This, then, is an AND circuit with an inverted output, or a NAND gate. Because these transistors are directly coupled together, the circuits are called directly coupled transistor logic gates, or DCTL gates.

10-6 RESISTOR-TRANSISTOR LOGIC GATES

It is possible to simplify logic gates somewhat by using resistors to perform the logic function. Consider the simple circuit shown in Fig. 10-9. It can easily be shown that when both inputs are at -10 volts the current flow I is 294 μa. If one input is -10 volts and the other is 0 volts, the current drops to 147 μa. If both inputs are 0 volts, the current is zero. Our various combinations of input-signal levels have produced various levels of current flow. Now, if current flow can be converted to output voltage levels, the possibility of a logic gate results.

A transistor switch is operated by current flow. The inverting switch of Fig. 10-3*a* requires a base current of at least 100 μa to close, that is, for the transistor to be driven into saturation. The current flow from the

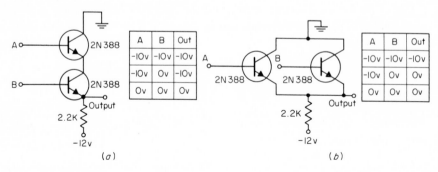

Fig. 10-7. (a) Transistor AND circuit. (b) Transistor OR circuit.

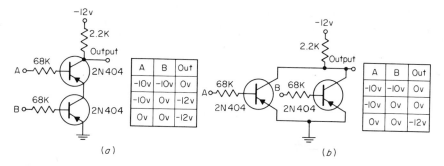

Fig. 10-8.   Inverting switches.

simple resistor circuit of Fig. 10-9 may be used to open and close the inverter switch. The result is the circuit shown in Fig. 10-10, along with its input-output characteristics. (As before, a load of 10 kilohms will drop the −12-volt output signal to the desired −10 volts.) We note that as long as either input is −10 volts, enough base current flows to drive the transistor to saturation, and the collector (output terminal) is essentially grounded. This circuit has the same input-output characteristics as those shown in Fig. 10-8b and is thus called a NAND gate. It can be seen that one less transistor is used; otherwise the components are identical. These are called resistor-transistor logic gates or RTL.

There is no way of forming a NOR circuit from current summing resistors, using the signal levels which have been adopted for the discussion up to this point. If signal levels are redefined as 0 volts representing a 0 logic level and −10 volts representing a 1 logic level, the circuit of Fig. 10-10 becomes a NOR gate.

If a similar circuit is constructed using an NPN transistor and a +12 volt supply, signal levels of 0 and +10 volts can be used to form a NOR gate or a NAND gate. Such a circuit is shown in Fig. 10-11. Its input-output

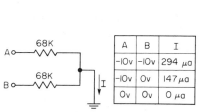

Fig. 10-9.   Resistor logic circuit.

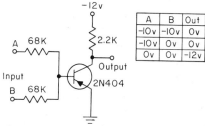

Fig. 10-10.   Resistor logic circuit and transistor switch.

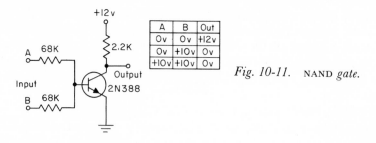

A	B	Out
0v	0v	+12v
0v	+10v	0v
+10v	+10v	0v

Fig. 10-11. NAND *gate.*

characteristics are such that if the most positive signal is the 1 level, it is a NOR gate, and if the most positive signal is the 0 level, the circuit becomes a NAND gate. This is just the opposite relationship present in the gate circuit of Fig. 10-10.

10-7 CIRCUIT IMPROVEMENTS

In all the gating circuits discussed to this point, only the essential components have been included. In Chap. 5, many refinements of the basic transistor switch were discussed. These included (*a*) various clamping circuits to maintain signal levels; (*b*) clamping circuits and the addition of speed-up capacitors to increase switching time. Many transistor logic circuits make use of these circuit improvements.

10-8 USES OF NOR AND NAND GATES

An interesting characteristic of the NOR and NAND gates is that either one may be used to form all the basic building blocks of a digital computer. That is, the AND and OR gates, the inverter, and all three types of multivibrators may be formed from just a combination of NOR gates or from NAND gates. It takes one NOR or NAND for an inverter; two for a multivibrator; two NORs for an OR; two NANDs for an AND; three NORs for an AND; and three NANDs for an OR.

Consider the NOR gate, shown in block-diagram form in Fig. 10-12*a* along with its input-output characteristics. If one input is connected permanently to a 0-level signal, the output will always be the reverse of the other input signal. These are the characteristics of an inverter; the block diagram is shown in Fig. 10-12*b* with its input and output characteristics.

The two NOR gates shown in Fig. 10-12*c* are connected in such a way that the circuit has the characteristics of an OR gate. If both inputs are 0, the output of the first NOR is 1. The second NOR has inputs of 1 and 0 and thus an output of 0. If the first NOR has inputs of 0 and 1, its output will be 0. The inputs of the second NOR will both be 0, so the output will be

1. If both inputs to the first NOR are 1, its output will be 0. The second NOR will have both inputs 0 and thus an output of 1. Another way of considering this circuit is that the output of the first NOR is inverted by the second NOR connected as an inverter. A NOR circuit is just an OR circuit with its output inverted, so inverting it again results in just an OR gate.

The three NOR gates in Fig. 10-12d form an AND gate. Each input is inverted, and then the two signals drive a NOR gate. A step-by-step analysis will show that a 1 output occurs only when both inputs are 1.

Two NOR gates can be connected to form a RESET-SET flip-flop. Such a connection is shown in Fig. 10-12e. The SET and RESET terminals are considered to be at the 0 level and switched temporarily to the 1 level for setting or resetting the flip-flop.

Assume the output to be at the 0 level. Both inputs to the left NOR will be 0, and its output will be 1. The inputs to the right NOR will be 1 and 0, so it will give the 0 output which was assumed.

If a 1 signal is applied to the R input, nothing will happen because the output of the right NOR is 0, whether one or both inputs are 1. Therefore, a RESET signal has no effect when the flip-flop is already turned off (output 0).

If a 1 signal is applied temporarily to the S input, the left NOR gate will give an output of 0. The right NOR gate, now having both inputs equal to 0, will give a 1 output. This 1 signal is applied to the input of the left NOR gate and thus holds its output at 0 after the SET input signal has returned to 0. The flip-flop has now been turned on with a pulse applied to the SET input.

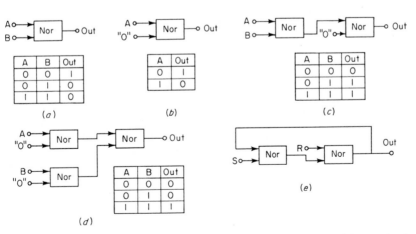

Fig. 10-12. Computer building blocks. (a) and (b) NOR gates. (c) OR circuit. (d) AND gate. (e) Flip-flop.

In the ON condition a 1 signal applied to the SET input has no effect, because the output of the left NOR will be 0 with either one or both inputs at the 1 level. If the RESET input should temporarily be changed to a 1 level, the right NOR will give a 0 output. This makes both inputs to the left NOR 0, and its 1 output will hold the right NOR with a 0 output, even after the RESET signal has returned to the 0 level.

By inserting a capacitor in the coupling lead between the two NORs, a monostable multivibrator is formed. A capacitor in each of the coupling leads will form an astable or free-running multivibrator. Thus, even a signal source and a delay circuit can be formed from the NOR gate.

10-9 APPLICATIONS OF LOGIC GATES

Logic gates are used in the arithmetic portion of a digital computer as well as in certain other digital-type equipment. Only a few examples of their uses will be discussed here.

Most of a digital computer's arithmetic operations are performed by addition or subtraction. Some of its basic circuits, then, are adders and subtracters. Some of these will be shown as examples of uses of logic gates.

A half-adder is a circuit with two inputs and two outputs. It adds two single-order binary digits and gives a sum and a carry. Call the two numbers X and Y and the sum S and the carry C. Either number can be 0 or 1, and the sum or carry can each be 0 or 1. In binary arithmetic:

$$
\begin{array}{cccc}
0 & 0 & 1 & 1 \\
0 & 1 & 0 & 1 \\
\hline
0 & 1 & 1 & 10
\end{array}
$$

These relationships are shown in Table 10-2 (called a truth table).

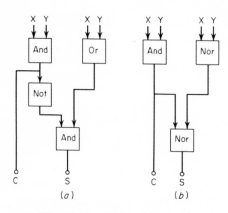

TABLE 10-2

X	Y	S	C
0	0	0	0
0	1	1	0
1	0	1	0
1	1	0	1

Fig. 10-13. Half-adder circuit.

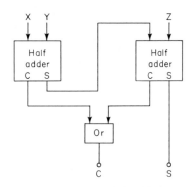

TABLE 10-3

X	Y	Z	S	C
0	0	0	0	0
0	0	1	1	0
0	1	0	1	0
1	0	0	1	0
0	1	1	0	1
1	1	0	0	1
1	0	1	0	1
1	1	1	1	1

Fig. 10-14. Full adder.

Figure 10-13 shows block diagrams of two ways in which a half-adder may be built. Both circuits have the characteristics represented in Table 10-2.

A full adder combines three input signals to give two outputs. It adds together three single-order binary digits to give a sum and a carry. The possible combinations are:

$$
\begin{array}{cccccccc}
0 & 0 & 1 & 0 & 1 & 0 & 1 & 1 \\
0 & 0 & 0 & 1 & 1 & 1 & 0 & 1 \\
0 & 1 & 0 & 0 & 0 & 1 & 1 & 1 \\
\hline
0 & 1 & 1 & 1 & 10 & 10 & 10 & 11 \\
\end{array}
$$

These relationships are shown in Table 10-3, and Fig. 10-14 shows how two half-adders and an OR gate can be combined to form the full adder.

These adder circuits are normally used to add two binary numbers. The half-adder is used for the first-order digits, and the full adder for each of the other orders. The third input of each full adder is from the carry output of the previous order.

The characteristics of a half-subtracter are shown in Table 10-4, with X the minuend, Y the subtrahend, D the difference, and B a digit borrowed from a previous order. Three variations of the circuit are shown in Fig. 10-15.

A full subtracter has three inputs and two outputs. Its characteristics are shown in Table 10-5. X is a minuend, Y a subtrahend, Z represents a digit borrowed from this order for a following order, D represents the difference, and B represents a digit borrowed from a previous order which is needed for this order.

Two full-subtracter circuits are shown in Fig. 10-16; that in Fig. 10-16b uses a half-adder in combination with a half-subtracter and an OR circuit.

As with the adder circuits, these subtracter circuits are used to subtract

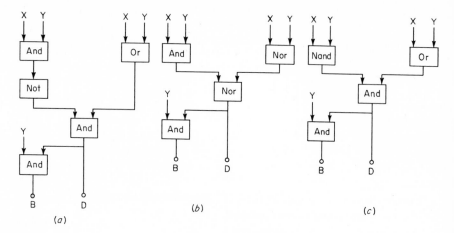

Fig. 10-15.   Half-subtracter.

one binary number from another. The half-subtracter is used for the first-order number, where there is no borrow required for a following order. All the other orders require full subtracters.

These circuits are called *parallel* adding and subtracting circuits because all orders are combined at the same time. A *serial* adder or subtracter is one in which only one order at a time is combined. The two binary numbers are stored in *shift registers;* and after the end digits are combined by adding or subtracting, both numbers are shifted over one space, and again the end numbers are combined. This process is continued until all orders have been combined. This is a slower process, but less equipment is required.

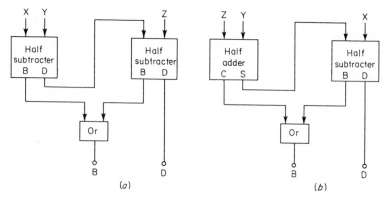

Fig. 10-16.   Full subtracters.

TABLE 10-5

TABLE 10-4

X	Y	D	B
0	0	0	0
1	0	1	0
0	1	1	1
1	1	0	0

X	Y	Z	D	B
0	0	0	0	0
1	0	0	1	0
0	1	0	1	1
1	1	0	0	0
0	0	1	1	1
1	0	1	0	0
0	1	1	0	1
1	1	1	1	1

Further discussion of applications of logic gates will be found in Chap. 13, where complete systems are discussed.

10-10 DIODE TRANSMISSION GATES

A transmission gate was defined as a device which transmits the input signal to the output, with no change in the signal; but the transmission takes place only during certain time intervals which are determined by a control signal.

Figure 10-17 shows a simplified series diode transmission gate, capable of passing an a-c signal. The control signal, in this case, is determined by the polarity of voltage applied to the anode of the diode.

The gate operates in this way. The capacitor charges up to a voltage equal to the average value of the input signal in series with the control voltage. Then the capacitor's voltage is in series with the input signal, and this varying voltage is applied to the diode and load resistor in series. When this combination voltage forward-biases the diode, conduction takes place and the gate passes the signal. If the combination voltage reverse-biases the diode, no conduction takes place.

For the gate to completely block the input signal, the control voltage must be present and must be greater than the peak positive input signal

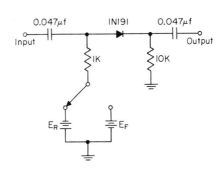

Fig. 10-17. Diode transmission gate.

minus the average input signal. For example, assume that the input signal consists of a series of short-duration pulses with peak value of 8 volts and that the voltage is zero between pulses. If the average d-c input voltage is 2 volts, the control voltage E_R must be greater than 8 volts $-$ 2 volts $=$ 6 volts. Assume $E_R = 7$ volts; the capacitor would charge up to 9 volts with the negative toward the plate of the diode. This 9 volts in series with the input signal would never allow the diode to become forward-biased, so the signal would be blocked.

In order to allow transmission of the input signal the E_F control voltage must be present and must be larger than the peak negative input signal plus the average input signal. In this example the peak negative signal is zero, so E_F must be greater than $0 + 2$ volts. If E_F is made 3 volts, the capacitor would charge up to 1 volt (E_F and the average d-c input signal in series opposing) with the positive toward the plate of the diode. This 1-volt capacitor in series with the input biased signal would never allow the diode to become reverse-biased, so the signal would be transmitted to the output terminal.

The gate will work satisfactorily for a symmetrical periodic waveform if E_R and E_F are equal and greater in value than the peak value of the input, the average value of the input signal being zero.

Several input signals can be simultaneously controlled and mixed together in the circuit shown in Fig. 10-18. Complete control is possible if E_R and E_F are large enough to fulfill the requirements stated above, for both input signals.

The control signal can come from any one of a variety of sources. It may even be the result of a combination of several sources applied simultaneously. These several sources could be applied to a logic AND gate or an OR gate, and the output signal could control the transmission gate. If the

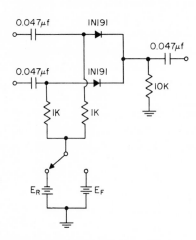

Fig. 10-18. Multiple-input transmission gate.

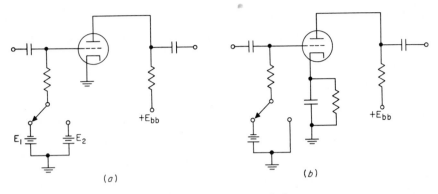

Fig. 10-19. Triode transmission gates.

AND control gate were used, all the input control signals would have to be on for the transmission gate to pass the signal. If an OR gate were used, at least one of the control signals being on would allow conduction through the transmission gate.

The advantages of the diode transmission gate are its simplicity, the short time delay in a transmitted signal, and the fact that no power is drawn by the gate during the OFF or blocked state.

Two disadvantages of this type of gate are as follows: first, there is inter-action between the control-voltage source and the signal being transmitted through the gate; second, because the input coupling capacitor has to change its charge each time the gate is opened or closed, there is a time delay in this switching action. Therefore, this kind of gate is of value only when the transmitted signal occurs after the gate is fully open and ceases before the gate is fully closed.

10-11 TRIODE TRANSMISSION GATES

A vacuum-tube amplifier stage may be switched back and forth between two grid-bias levels: one for proper operation as an amplifier, and the other far enough below cutoff so the input signal will not be able to cause any plate-current flow. Such a circuit is shown in Fig. 10-19a. E_1 and E_2 should be the correct values to establish the conditions stated above.

In the circuit of Fig. 10-19b, one of the bias batteries has been eliminated by resorting to cathode biasing. Of course, in actual use, a control-signal voltage could come from any one of a number of sources.

A transistorized transmission gate is shown in Fig. 10-20. This particular circuit is an emitter follower, which will pass the input signal without amplification or phase inversion. A common-emitter amplifier could have been used, which would amplify and invert the signal when the gate is open. The operation of the gate is self-evident; with positive control voltage applied to the base, the base-emitter junction is reverse-biased and no conduction takes place. With the control signal at ground potential, the base emitter has the correct bias for proper operation as an emitter follower.

The two triode gates just considered have the same disadvantages as the diode gates discussed in Sec. 10-10. There is coupling between the signal input circuit and the control-signal input; that is, the control signal could be coupled into the signal source. There is also delay in turning the gate on and off because the coupling capacitor has to charge and discharge.

The delay in gate operation can be eliminated in the triode or diode circuits by replacing the coupling capacitor with a coupling resistor. This arrangement attenuates the input signal but renders the gate fast-acting.

Figure 10-21a shows the output waveform when a sine-wave signal is applied at the input of the gate of Fig. 10-20, and a square wave is used as the control signal. When the gate is turned on, the output signal builds up gradually; when the gate is turned off, the signal drops at the same rate. If the coupling capacitor is replaced by a 15-kilohm resistor, the output waveform is as shown in Fig. 10-21b; the gate opens and closes rapidly.

10-12 PENTODE TRANSMISSION GATES

The coupling between the signal and control inputs, experienced with diode and triode gates, can be eliminated by using a special pentode whose suppressor grid can be used as a second control grid. The circuit is shown in Fig. 10-22. The third grid can be driven negative to cut off current flow

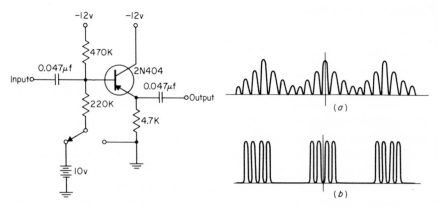

Fig. 10-20. Transistorized transmission gate.

Fig. 10-21. Transmission-gate waveforms.

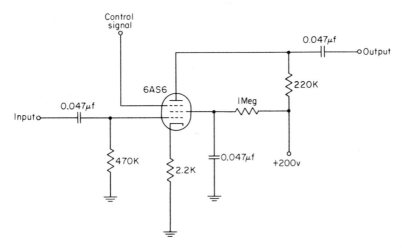

Fig. 10-22. Pentode transmission gate.

and close the gate, or can go to 0 volts and open the gate. Again, the input coupling capacitor could be replaced by a coupling resistor.

10-13 APPLICATIONS OF TRANSMISSION GATES

One common use for a transmission gate is in a counter, where a control signal will open a gate and allow a counter circuit to count pulses from an oscillator for a certain period of time, and then the gate is closed again and the number of cycles counted appears on an indicator.

Other uses for transmission gates will be discussed in Chap. 13.

PROBLEMS

10-1 What is the fundamental difference between a *transmission gate* and a *logic gate?*

10-2 The number 12 in the decimal system is represented by what number in (*a*) the octal system; (*b*) the binary system?

10-3 The number 1101 in the binary system represents what number in (*a*) the octal system; (*b*) the decimal system?

10-4 What is the advantage of using the binary number system rather than the decimal system in digital computing circuits?

10-5 What is meant by *negative logic?*

10-6 How can an AND gate be converted to an OR gate?

10-7   In Fig. 10-1a, if the A input is +6 volts and the B input is 0 volts, why will diode B conduct but diode A not?

10-8   In Fig. 10-1b, if A input is +6 volts and B input is 0 volts, which diode will conduct? Why will the other diode not conduct?

10-9   If, in the diode matrix of Fig. 10-2, the diode connected between the B input and the 7 output is permanently open, what decimal output number(s) will be affected, and in what way?

10-10 What is the answer to Prob. 10-9 if the diode is permanently shorted?

10-11 Refer to the inverter circuit in Fig. 10-3a. What would be the output voltage with 0 volts input if the circuit were feeding into a 6.8-kilohm load?

10-12 What is the principal function of the NOT circuit?

10-13 How does a NOR circuit differ from a NOT circuit?

10-14 Explain the operation of a NAND circuit.

10-15 If the transistor in Fig. 10-10 takes at least 50 μa of base current for saturation, and if its base current should not exceed 2 ma, what is the maximum number of input circuits that can be used if the signal levels are -10 volts and 0 volts?

10-16 Refer to Prob. 10-15. (a) What are the largest input resistors which can be used in place of the 68-kilohm resistors? (b) What is the maximum number of input circuits which can be used with these larger input resistors?

10-17 Draw a schematic diagram of the half-adder shown in Fig. 10-13b, using only five of the NOR circuits shown in Fig. 10-11.

10-18 If both inputs to the half-adder of Prob. 10-17 are 0, which of the five transistors are conducting?

10-19 If one of the inputs of Prob. 10-17 is 0 and the other is 1, which of the five transistors are conducting?

10-20 If the C output of Fig. 10-13a is neglected, the rest of the circuit is called an EXCLUSIVE OR circuit. Make a truth table for this circuit.

10-21 Assume that the input signal to the circuit of Fig. 10-17 is a square wave which varies between -2 and $+5$ volts. Find the minimum values which E_R and E_F can be.

CHAPTER 11 DELAY CIRCUITS

In many pulse circuit applications, it is necessary to delay a signal by a certain amount of time. If the signal is rather complex and it is necessary to keep the same waveshape, this may present quite a problem. Usually, the signal is a pulse, and the exact waveshape does not have to be preserved.

Delay circuits may be classed in two main groups: electronic circuits and electromagnetic lines. Electromagnetic delay lines will be discussed first, and then some of the electronic circuits discussed in previous chapters will be considered in regard to their abilities to delay signals.

11-1 ELECTROMAGNETIC DELAY LINES

Transmission lines, which are usually thought of in their ability to transfer electrical energy from one point to another, have an inherent characteristic of time delay associated with them. That is, it takes a finite amount of time for the electrical energy to travel from the input terminals of the line to the output. This characteristic can be of value when it is desired to delay a signal a finite length of time.

Not only can an actual line be used for this purpose, but a line can be simulated by the use of networks of inductances, resistances, and capacitances. The actual line is called a *distributed-parameter line,* because the inductive, resistive, and capacitive characteristics are distributed uniformly along its length. The line which is simulated by inductors, resistors, and capacitors is called a *lumped-parameter line.* Each type has its individual advantages and disadvantages and will be discussed in detail.

231

Theory. In order to understand how a transmission line can be used to delay a signal, an equivalent circuit must be derived. This equivalent circuit can represent a small section of the line, and then the entire line can be represented by a number of these sections.

There are four properties of a line which can be represented by individual components. In a two-conductor line each conductor has finite resistance. This line resistance can be represented by a series resistor in each side of the line (Fig. 11-1*a*). Any conductor has a certain amount of self-inductance due to the changing magnetic field around the conductor cutting the conductor itself and inducing a counter emf. This self-inductance can also be represented by a series inductor in each side of the line.

Because the line is composed of two conductors separated by an insulator, there is capacitance between the conductors. In the equivalent circuit, the capacitance effect is shown by shunt capacitors.

No insulator is perfect; there will always be some leakage. We represent this high resistance between conductors as a shunt conductance.

The complete equivalent circuit is shown in Fig. 11-1*a*. This cannot exactly represent the actual line, because the actual line is uniformly constructed and reacts identically to energy going either way. In Fig. 11-1*a* this would not be true. A modification will give an equivalent circuit which will react identically to energy going in either direction. At the same time the circuit can be simplified.

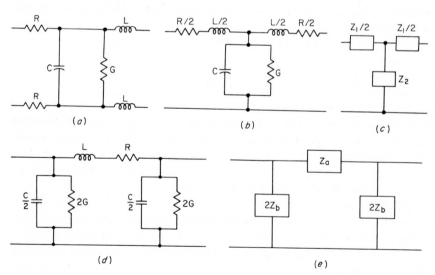

Fig. 11-1. (*a*) *LCR properties of a two-wire line.* (*b*) *Balanced equivalent circuit.* (*c*) *Line impedances.* (*d*) *and* (*e*) *π-type equivalent circuits.*

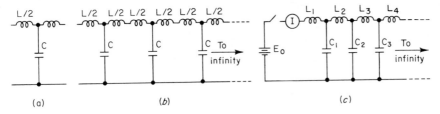

Fig. 11-2. *(a) Ideal T section. (b) Infinitely long line. (c) Applied voltage to infinitely long line.*

The series resistances in the two conductors can be combined into just one side of the line, and the series inductors can be combined in like manner. The series resistance can then be divided in half and the halves located on both sides of the shunt components. If the same thing is done with the series inductances, the result is the balanced equivalent circuit of Fig. 11-1b, which represents the same circuit to energy coming from either direction. Note that the R represents the total series resistance of the two conductors for each section of line, so in splitting this resistance, each resulting resistance is labeled $R/2$. The same thing holds true for the total series inductance per line section.

If each series portion of the line and the shunt portion are represented by impedances, the line can be simplified to that shown in Fig. 11-1c.

These circuits are called T sections. Another equivalent circuit, a π section, could also represent a section of the transmission line. This type of circuit is shown with representative components in Fig. 11-1d and with impedances in Fig. 11-1e.

The equivalent circuits contain both resistance and reactance. Reactance will store energy and return it to the circuit, while resistance dissipates the energy in the form of heat. Now let us consider a lossless line, one with no series resistance or shunt conductance. Though this assumption is theoretical, in practice the ideal can be approximated. The equivalent T section is shown in Fig. 11-2a. If an infinitely long line is being considered, it can be represented by an infinite number of sections combined as shown in Fig. 11-2b.

If a voltage E_0 is applied to one end of the line (Fig. 11-2c), C_1 starts to charge through L_1. Its charge is not instantaneous, for the current increase is opposed by L_1.

As the voltage across C_1 begins to build up, it becomes the "source" voltage to start charging C_2 through L_2. Again, as C_2 starts charging, it becomes the source for charging C_3. This becomes a continuous process, as there are always more capacitors to be charged further along the line. The result is that there is a constant current flow I_0 through the ammeter; the transmission line is acting as a fixed resistor with value equal to E_0/I_0.

This resistance is called the *characteristic resistance* or, more generally, the *characteristic impedance* of the line, and is given the symbol Z_0. It is dependent only upon the inductance and capacitance of the line.

Time-delay Characteristics. When a voltage is suddenly applied to the input terminals of the infinite transmission line, each succeeding capacitor along the line begins to charge up at a little later time than the previous one. Therefore, the voltage change at the input terminals results in a similar voltage change at a point some distance from the input terminals at a later time. This voltage change is conducted down the line at a constant rate which is dependent only on the inductance and capacitance of the line.

Referring again to a single T section of the ideal line (Fig. 11-2a), we see that the charge on the capacitor is equal to

$$Q = CE_0 \tag{11-1}$$

The electric charge which has left the battery to charge the capacitor is equal to

$$Q = I_0 T \tag{11-2}$$

The charge which has left the battery is the same as the charge which is stored in the capacitor, so equating these two charges gives

$$I_0 T = CE_0 \tag{11-3}$$

As the capacitor starts to charge to E_0 from 0 volts, the potential difference across the coil is E_0. This voltage drop across the coil is due to the coil's inductance and the fact that the current through it is changing. The relationship is given by

$$E_0 = L \frac{di}{dt} \tag{11-4}$$

The total change in current, from zero to I_0, is just equal to I_0, and if the time for this change is defined as T, Eq. (11-4) becomes

$$E_0 = L \frac{I_0}{T} \tag{11-5}$$

which can be rewritten as

$$\frac{E_0}{I_0} = \frac{L}{T} \tag{11-6}$$

Equation (11-3) can also be rewritten as

$$\frac{E_0}{I_0} = \frac{T}{C} \tag{11-7}$$

Two important equations can now be obtained from Eqs. (11-6) and (11-7). The characteristic impedance of a transmission line was defined as E_0/I_0; therefore Eq. (11-6) becomes

$$Z_0 = \frac{L}{T} \tag{11-8}$$

and Eq. (11-7) becomes

$$Z_0 = \frac{T}{C} \tag{11-9}$$

Multiplying these two equations together and then taking the square root of each side yields

$$Z_0 = \sqrt{\frac{L}{C}} \qquad \boxed{\textbf{11-10}}$$

which gives the characteristic impedance of a transmission line in terms of the line's inductance and capacitance.

Equating the Z_0 of Eq. (11-8) to the Z_0 of Eq. (11-9), we have

$$\frac{L}{T} = \frac{T}{C}$$

and solving for T, we have

$$T = \sqrt{LC} \qquad \boxed{\textbf{11-11}}$$

which shows us that the time for charging the capacitor depends on the inductance and the capacitance. This time T can be defined as the time it takes for the energy to travel along one section of transmission line composed of L and C where a section is defined as a fixed length.

EXAMPLE 1   It is found that a 100-ft section of transmission line has an inductance of 0.5 mh and a capacitance of 800 pf. Find (a) Z_0 and (b) the time required for a pulse of energy to travel the length of the line.

SOLUTION: (a) Substituting the given values for L and C into Eq. (11-10) yields

$$Z_0 = \sqrt{\frac{5 \times 10^{-4}}{8 \times 10^{-10}}} = \sqrt{62.5 \times 10^4} = 790 \text{ ohms}$$

(b) Substituting for L and C in Eq. (11-11) gives

$$Z_0 = \sqrt{5 \times 10^{-4} \times 8 \times 10^{-10}} = \sqrt{40 \times 10^{-14}}$$
$$= 0.632 \ \mu\text{sec}$$

EXAMPLE 2   How long a section of the transmission line in Example 1 would be needed for a time delay of 3 μsec from the input to the output terminals?

SOLUTION: It was found that the line had a delay of 0.632 μsec per 100 ft; hence by dividing the desired 3-μsec delay by the delay per 100 ft, the answer becomes

$$\frac{3 \mu\text{sec}}{0.632 \mu\text{sec}/100 \text{ ft}} = \frac{(3)(100)}{0.632} \text{ ft} = 475 \text{ ft}$$

It has been assumed that the transmission lines under discussion are infinite in length and thus that once a pulse of energy is started at one end, it travels continuously in one direction. For a finite length of line the energy would reach the end and the discontinuity would cause the energy to be reflected and to start back in the other direction. This is undesirable when a transmission line is to be used as a delay line, so either the line has to be infinite in length, which is an impossibility, or some other solution to the problem must be found.

If the first few sections of the line were removed, the remaining line would still have the same Z_0, as it would still be infinite in length and have the same inductance and capacitance per section. Now if, instead of the infinite line's being connected back to the first few sections which were removed, a resistance equal to Z_0 is connected to the output terminals of the first few sections, the input characteristics would be the same. That is, whether the first few sections terminate in the rest of the infinite line or in a resistance equal to Z_0, a voltage source connected to the input of the first sections of the line would result in the same current flow. Thus, the line would appear to be infinite in length, and no reflected energy would appear.

The L and C of a transmission line are both functions of the geometry of the cross section of the line. For example, a two-wire transmission line, made up of wires with diameter d, which are separated by a distance of D (measured between wire centers), will have an inductance in microhenrys per meter of length given by

$$L = 0.921 \log \frac{2D}{d}$$

11-12

and a capacitance in picofarads per meter of length given by

$$C = \frac{12.06K}{\log 2D/d}$$

11-13

where K is the relative dielectric constant. $K = 1$ for air.

Substituting these two equations into Eq. (11-10) gives

$$Z_0 = \sqrt{\frac{L}{C}} = \sqrt{\frac{9.21 \times 10^{-7} \log{(2D/d)}}{1.206 \times 10^{-11} \times K/\log{(2D/d)}}}$$

$$Z_0 = \sqrt{\frac{7.64 \times 10^4}{K}} \log{\frac{2D}{d}} = \frac{276}{\sqrt{K}} \log{\frac{2D}{d}} \qquad \textbf{11-14}$$

Substituting Eqs. (11-12) and (11-13) into Eq. (11-11) yields

$$T = \sqrt{LC} = \sqrt{\left(9.21 \times 10^{-7} \log{\frac{2D}{d}}\right)\left[1.206 \times 10^{-11} \times \frac{K}{\log{(2D/d)}}\right]}$$

$$= \sqrt{9.21 \times 10^{-7} \times 1.206 \times 10^{-11}K} = \sqrt{11.1 \times 10^{-18}K}$$

$$T = 3.33 \times 10^{-9} \sqrt{K} \text{ sec/m} \qquad \textbf{11-15}$$

Notice that the time delay is independent of the diameter of the wires and the spacing between them. In fact, the time delay depends only upon the magnetic permeability and the dielectric constant of the insulating material between the conductors, as shown by the following equation where μ is the magnetic permeability and ϵ is the absolute dielectric constant:

$$T = \sqrt{\mu\epsilon} \qquad (11\text{-}16)$$

For air, $\mu = 4\pi \times 10^{-7}$ henry/m and $\epsilon = 1/(36\pi \times 10^9$ farads/m). Substituting these values into Eq. (11-16) gives the same result as that obtained from Eq. (11-15):

$$T = \sqrt{\frac{4\pi \times 10^{-7}}{36\pi \times 10^9}} = \sqrt{\frac{1}{9} \times 10^{-16}} = \frac{1}{3} \times 10^{-8} = 3.33 \times 10^{-9} \text{ sec/m}$$

The reciprocal of this value is $1/(3.33 \times 10^{-9})$ m/sec $= 3 \times 10^8$ m/sec, the velocity with which electromagnetic waves travel through free space.

For a coaxial transmission line with inner conductor of diameter d, outer conductor with diameter D, and the insulating material with dielectric constant K,

$$L = 0.46 \log{\frac{D}{d}} \qquad \mu h/m$$

$$C = \frac{24.1K}{\log{(D/d)}} \qquad pf/m$$

It can be shown that the characteristic impedance is

$$Z_0 = \frac{138}{\sqrt{K}} \log{\frac{D}{d}}$$

and the time delay is

$$T = 3.33 \times 10^{-9} \sqrt{K} \text{ sec/m}$$

which is the same as for the two-wire transmission line.

The lines which have been discussed are of practical use for short time delays only. For example, to obtain a time delay of only 1 μsec would require an air dielectric line to be almost 1,000 ft long!

The low-loss dielectrics commonly used, such as Teflon, polystyrene, or polyethylene, have relative dielectric constants of about 2.3, which would only decrease the length of the 1-μsec delay line to about 650 ft.

These lengths are impractical. The time delay may be increased in any one or a combination of ways. If the inner conductor is replaced by a continuous coil of wire in the form of a helix, the inductance is greatly increased and therefore the time delay is increased to the order of 0.15 μsec/m. The characteristic impedance is also increased by about the same amount.

Another method of further increasing the inductance is by winding the helical coil on a magnetic core. This can bring the delay up to around 0.25 μsec/m.

An increase in the diameter of the coil without an increase in the outer conductor's diameter could increase both L and C and thus the time delay. A typical value would be about 2 μsec/m, which would require about 20 in. for a 1-μsec delay line, compared with the 650 ft for the straight wire line.

Experimental lines with time delays up to 30 μsec/m have been built, but they have poor rise time and more distortion than the types which have been discussed.

For longer time delays than can be obtained with the distributed-parameter transmission lines, lumped-parameter lines are used.

11-2   LUMPED-PARAMETER DELAY LINES

In developing the theory of transmission lines, the line was represented with equivalent circuits containing inductors and capacitors. Not only does this procedure work theoretically in order to simplify calculations, but it is possible to actually construct networks of inductors and capacitors which will have characteristics very similar to the actual lines they represent.

These so-called *lumped-parameter* delay lines can be used to obtain much longer delay periods than are practical with distributed-parameter lines, and there is usually less attenuation in signal level. These lumped-parameter lines frequently distort the signal to a greater degree. The more sections present in a lumped line, the closer it approaches the distributed-parameter type of line in its characteristics.

CONSTANT-k LINE

The first of these delay lines to be considered is that shown in Fig. 11-2a. This circuit was considered in detail in Sec. 11-1, and equations for its characteristic impedance and delay time were derived. It will also be seen that this delay line is a low-pass filter. That is, it will pass sine waves with frequencies from zero up to a cutoff frequency f_c. This cutoff frequency can be calculated from the equation

$$f_c = \frac{1}{\pi \sqrt{LC}}$$

11-17

If the frequencies of all signals being transmitted through the delay line are much less than the cutoff frequency, the equations derived in Sec. 11-1 hold for this T section of line.

$$Z_0 = \sqrt{\frac{L}{C}}$$

(11-10)

$$T = \sqrt{LC}$$

(11-11)

The important characteristics of a delay line are the characteristic impedance Z_0, the total delay time t_d, and the rise time t_r of the output voltage when an ideal step is applied at the input. Both t_d and t_r are related to the delay per section, t_s. This delay per section can be calculated approximately from Eq. (11-11). (The value depends to a certain extent on the internal impedance of the source generator.)

Some of the theory concerning lumped delay lines is rather involved, but the following equations may be of some value (see Jacob Millman and Herbert Taub, "Pulse and Digital Circuits," Chap. 10, McGraw-Hill Book Company).

If we assume that a delay line with n sections is matched to its characteristic impedance Z_0 at both ends of the line, and if all frequency components of the applied signal are small compared with the cutoff frequency f_c, Eqs. (11-18) to (11-21) apply. The delay time per section is

$$t_s = 1.07 \sqrt{LC}$$

11-18

The rise time per section is

$$t_{r_1} = 1.13 \sqrt{LC}$$

11-19

The total delay time is

$$t_d = nt_s$$

11-20

The rise time after n sections is

$$t_r = n^{1/3}t_r$$

11-21

This particular type of delay line is called a constant-k section because the product of the impedances of the two components L and C is a constant, independent of frequency. $Z_1 = L$, $Z_2 = 1/C$, so $Z_1Z_2 = L/C = k$.

m-DERIVED LINE

Figure 11-3a shows a delay line with the shunt part containing a series inductor in addition to the capacitor. The theory of this line is beyond the scope of this book (see Millman and Taub, Chap. 10). For various values of m the delay line will have various characteristics. For $m = 1.27$ the variation in t_s with frequency is a minimum. If $m = 1$, it can easily be shown that this line becomes the constant-k line; the shunt inductor is equal to zero, the capacitor equals C, and each of the series inductors is equal to $L/2$.

A close look at the shunt inductor will show that for values of m greater than 1, it will be a negative inductance. This, of course, is impossible, but such an effect is possible if the shunt inductor is removed and magnetic coupling is present between the two series inductors. This circuit is shown in Fig. 11-3b. The following equations can be useful in comparing the two circuits in Fig. 11-3. If it is assumed that m is to be the optimum value of 1.27, the coefficient of coupling K in Fig. 11-3b is 0.237. The delay time per second is

$$t_s = 1.57 \sqrt{L_1 C_1}$$

11-22

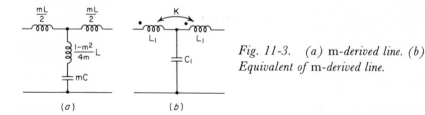

Fig. 11-3. (a) m-derived line. (b) Equivalent of m-derived line.

The rise time per second is

$$t_{r_1} = 1.51 \sqrt{L_1 C_1}$$ 11-23

The total delay time is

$$t_d = n t_s$$ 11-20

The rise time after n sections is

$$t_r = n^{1/3} t_{r_1}$$ 11-21

The main advantages of the m-derived line over the constant-k line are the following: First, about 16 per cent fewer sections are required for the same ratio of delay to rise time. Second, the peak overshoot is only about 4 per cent compared with about 8 per cent for the constant-k line. A disadvantage is that with the m-derived line an initial undershoot of about 12 per cent appears in the output compared with none for the constant-k.

It was mentioned that more distortion is present when lumped-parameter delay lines are used. Quite often ringing is present. Usually, this type of distortion is of little importance because the absence or presence of a pulse is the important factor. If ringing is going to affect the operation of the following circuit, the delay time can be designed with a cutoff frequency much higher than the bandpass characteristics of the following circuit. Because the ringing frequency is near the cutoff frequency of the delay line, the ringing will be eliminated in the following circuit.

11-3 ELECTRONIC DELAY CIRCUITS

Several of the electronic circuits discussed in previous chapters may be used effectively in delaying a pulse. These circuits operate on the principle of being in a stable state until triggered by a pulse. Then they shift to an unstable state for a period of time determined usually by the time constant of an RC circuit. After this period of time, the circuit returns again to its stable state until triggered again by another pulse.

If some means is provided to have a pulse generated at the time the circuit returns to its stable state, a time-delay circuit results. The output pulse is not necessarily an exact reproduction of the input pulse. Its amplitude and width are dependent upon the circuit producing it and not on the amplitude and width of the input pulse. Usually this is of little importance. The important factor is the accuracy of the time interval between the leading edge of the input pulse and the leading edge of the output pulse.

Often it is desirable to be able to vary this time interval. This can be done by varying the resistance in the RC circuit or sometimes by varying the operating characteristics of the tube or transistor in the circuit.

MONOSTABLE MULTIVIBRATOR

The monostable multivibrator discussed in Chap. 7 remains in its temporarily stable state while the coupling capacitor discharges through the grid or base resistor. The tube or transistor begins to conduct again, once C has discharged to a critical potential. By varying this discharge resistor, the time period of the temporarily stable state can be controlled.

The circuit can be triggered by either a positive-going or a negative-going pulse, depending on which tube or transistor the pulse is applied to, and also depending on which electrode the pulse is applied to. The output pulse can be either a positive-going or a negative-going pulse, depending on which tube or transistor the pulse is taken from. Thus, the pulse can be inverted, as well as delayed. If a sharp trigger pulse is desired, the output square wave can be differentiated and clipped to retain a pulse of the desired polarity.

BLOCKING OSCILLATOR

In Chap. 8, the monostable blocking oscillator was discussed. In this circuit the tube or transistor is biased to be in the cutoff state until a triggering pulse starts conduction. The circuit goes through one half-cycle of oscillation and then is cut off again. A time delay between the occurrence of the original triggering pulse and the time the circuit returns to its original stable state is dependent on the resonant frequency of the tank circuit, and control of this delay time is less convenient than for the monostable multivibrator. For the transistor circuit the degree of saturation can be controlled, thus providing a control over storage time (Sec. 8-8).

PHANTASTRON

The phantastron, discussed in Chap. 9, makes an ideal time-delay circuit, as the delay time is directly proportional to one of the applied d-c voltages. This makes remote control of the delay time possible through unshielded cables, since there is no signal present in the control circuit.

Normally, the initial value of the plate voltage will determine the delay time. If this voltage is controlled, the time period between the application of the triggering pulse and the completion of the cycle of operation will also be controlled, thus causing a variation in the delay time.

PROBLEMS

11-1 Assume that a 100-ft section of transmission line has an inductance of 250 μh and a capacitance of 500 pf. (a) What is the characteristic impedance of the line? (b) What time period is required for a pulse to travel the length of the section?

11-2 Assume that a 100-ft section of transmission line has an inductance of 120 μh and a capacitance of 500 pf. (a) What is the characteristic impedance? (b) What time is required for a wave to travel 35 ft along the line?

11-3 Refer to Prob. 11-1. What length of line would be required to produce a 0.5-μsec delay?

11-4 A two-wire open transmission line utilizes 20-gauge wire (diameter = 0.032 in.) and is separated between centers 0.8 in. (a) What is the inductance of 3 m of line? (b) What is the capacitance? (c) What is the characteristic impedance?

11-5 (a) What spacing of 20-gauge wire is required to produce an open transmission line whose impedance is 300 ohms? (b) If the line is 5 m long, what is the time delay?

11-6 Assume that a constant-k delay line has an inductance of 100 μh and a capacitance of 250 pf per section. (a) What is the cutoff frequency? (b) What is the surge impedance?

11-7 Refer to Prob. 11-6. What are the rise and delay times per section?

11-8 An m-derived line has an inductance of 250 μh and a capacitance of 5,200 pf per section. (a) Three sections of this line will produce what delay? (b) What will be the rise time after three sections?

11-9 Theoretically, what is the smallest characteristic impedance a two-wire open transmission line could have?

11-10 Theoretically, what is the smallest inductance (in microhenrys per meter) a two-wire transmission could have?

11-11 Theoretically, what is the largest capacitance (in picofarads per meter) a two-wire open transmission line could have?

11-12 If a two-wire open transmission line has a capacitance of 7.5 pf/m, find its inductance in microhenrys per meter.

11-13 Find the dielectric constant of the transmission line of Prob. 11-1.

11-14 Find the dielectric constant of the transmission line of Prob. 11-2.

11-15 Measurements on a 40-m length of coaxial cable show a 319-pf total capacitance and a delay of 0.36 μsec. Find (a) the dielectric constant of the insulating material and (b) the total inductance.

11-16 An m-derived transmission line is found to have a total rise time of 5 μsec and a total delay time of 19 μsec. How many sections does it have?

CHAPTER 12 *SPECIAL-PURPOSE CIRCUITS*

There are a number of circuits which are of value in pulse and switching operations, which do not easily fall into one of the major categories covered up to this point. These are grouped together in this chapter for convenience. They include circuits used to compare two voltage levels for equality; circuits used to amplify any difference between two input signals; amplifiers that have particular characteristics which are of great value in certain applications; and high-gain d-c amplifiers, which can be used to perform mathematical calculations by connecting the proper feedback networks between output and input.

12-1 VOLTAGE COMPARATORS

In Chap. 10, transmission gates were discussed which have the characteristics of passing a signal part of the time and rejecting the signal the rest of the time. The "open" and "closed" time intervals are determined by a separate *control* signal.

In Chaps. 4 and 5, clipper circuits were considered. These pass a signal when it has an amplitude above or below a certain voltage level but reject the signal for all other voltage levels.

The circuits considered here are actuated when the signal voltage reaches a certain reference level, but these are not gating or clipping circuits; that is, they do not pass or reject the input signal; they mark in some way the exact instant at which the signal voltage reaches the fixed reference voltage.

They compare the varying signal voltage with the reference voltage and thus are called *voltage comparators*. Usually an output signal, either a pulse or a step signal, marks the coincidence of the signal level with the reference level.

PICKOFF DIODE

One of the clippers discussed in Chap. 4 was the biased series clipper shown in Fig. 12-1a. This has the characteristic that only input signals with amplitudes higher than $+E_1$ volts will appear at the output. All other signal levels will be blocked by the reverse biasing on the diode. If we assume that a ramp signal is applied to the input, as shown in Fig. 12-1b, the output (Fig. 12-1c) is a constant E_1 volts until the ramp signal reaches a value equal to E_1 volts; then the diode conducts and the input signal appears at the output.

This circuit was previously called a clipper, and it was important that the portion of the waveform passed by the diode was not distorted. The exact time t_1 at which the diode began conducting was of secondary importance.

Now this circuit will be considered as a voltage comparator, and of primary concern is the time at which the input signal voltage reaches the reference level E_1. The shape of the output waveform is of secondary importance. A diode used for this purpose is called a *pickoff diode*.

The characteristics of a semiconductor diode (see Fig. 4-3b) are such that there is not an abrupt "break" in the diode's characteristic curve between conduction and nonconduction. This means that the time at which the diode begins conducting is not so exactly defined as we might like. There is a small range of uncertainty ΔE in the value of input signal which will cause a change in output signal. This results in a corresponding time uncertainty Δt during which interval the t_1 occurs.

Figure 12-2 shows three ramp signals, A, B, and C, each with a different slope. If the same small voltage uncertainty (which is a property of the

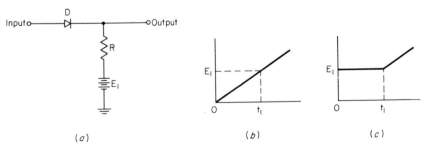

Fig. 12-1. Clipper used as a voltage comparator.

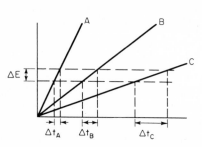

Fig. 12-2. Three ramp signals illustrating small voltage uncertainty.

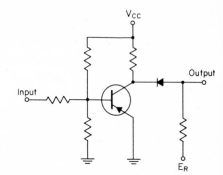

Fig. 12-3. Comparator with amplifier.

diode circuit being used) is assumed, the ramp signal with the greatest slope is found to give the smallest time uncertainty. Therefore, to decrease the time uncertainty, and thus increase the accuracy with which the input signal's amplitude can be compared with the reference voltage, the slope of the input signal needs to be increased. This is done by amplifying the signal before applying it to the diode circuit. Such a circuit is shown in Fig. 12-3.

TRIODE COMPARATOR

Using a diode in a voltage-comparator circuit causes a loading effect on the previous stage. A triode vacuum tube, biased negatively, presents a very light load and therefore has advantages.

Triode clippers were discussed in Chap. 5. It was shown that clipping could take place at cutoff, at the point where grid current starts to flow, or at plate-current saturation (where plate current is limited by the plate load resistor). Only the first, cutoff limiting, operates with negative grid voltage and therefore presents a light load to the previous stage.

A tube operating at cutoff and used as a voltage comparator can have the reference voltage in series with the signal or applied to the cathode. Using a cathode voltage as reference may be more convenient, but another problem arises. The value of cutoff voltage depends on the plate voltage. Changing the reference cathode voltage changes the effective plate voltage (between cathode and plate) and thus changes the cutoff voltage needed. Thus, a change in the reference voltage does not result in an equal required change in the input signal for voltage comparison. A signal applied to a voltage comparator which has this effect is called a *common-mode signal,* and the resulting error in the comparator's operation is called the *common-mode effect.*

The common-mode effect can be greatly reduced by using a cathode follower to apply the reference voltage to the cathode of the comparator. Such a circuit is shown in Fig. 12-4a. The two cathode resistors can just as well be replaced by a single resistor, giving the circuit shown in Fig. 12-4b. This circuit is called a *difference amplifier* or *differential amplifier*.

The output voltage of this circuit is proportional to the *difference* between the two inputs. Any signal common to both inputs is canceled out because it changes the grid and cathode voltages of V_2 by the same amount, leaving the net grid-cathode potential the same.

A transistorized version of the difference amplifier is shown in Fig. 12-5. One difference shown is a load resistor and output signal available from each transistor. Either one or both outputs could be used. They will be equal but of opposite polarity. They might be used to drive a following difference amplifier.

The rejection of the common-mode signal in a difference amplifier is due to the common cathode or emitter resistor. The larger this resistor, the better the rejection. It is obviously impractical to use too large a resistor, say 5 or 10 megohms, because of the increased value of supply voltage needed. A large cathode or emitter resistor can be simulated by a d-c amplifier with current feedback. Such a circuit is shown in Fig. 12-6.

Common-mode rejection can also be improved by balancing any slight difference in the characteristics of the two tubes or transistors by adjusting the operating voltages to slightly unequal values. Sometimes even the shunt capacitances are balanced for common-mode rejection of rapidly changing signals.

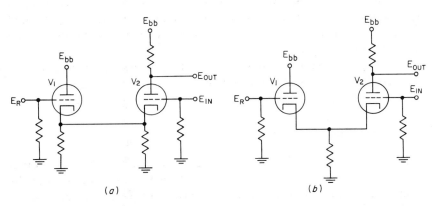

Fig. 12-4. Difference amplifiers.

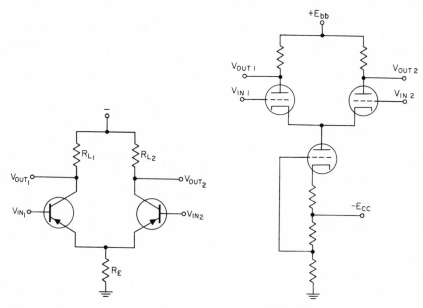

Fig. 12-5.   Transistorized difference amplifier.

Fig. 12-6.   Difference amplifier with an amplifier as cathode resistor.

The application of difference amplifiers as voltage comparators is obvious. A reference voltage can be applied as one of the input signals, and the voltage to be compared can be applied to the other input. The output will be proportional to the difference. The circuit can be adjusted, for example, so that if the varying input signal is below the reference, operation is below cutoff; but as soon as the signals are equal, conduction starts and a large change in output signal takes place. This output signal can be differentiated, resulting in a pulse occurring at the instant the two input signals are equal.

Any degree of sensitivity in comparing two voltages is possible, by just increasing the number of stages of difference amplifiers.

12-2   CATHODE FOLLOWER

The circuit shown in Fig. 12-7 has negative feedback with all the output signal fed back to the input. As the input signal drives the grid in the positive direction, the plate current increases and the voltage drop across R_K increases. As the cathode is positive with respect to ground, the output voltage is going in the positive direction. This means that the output signal at the cathode is in phase with the input signal at the grid, and the cathode voltage "follows" the input voltage; hence, the name *cathode follower*.

Because of the 100 per cent negative feedback, this circuit has the advantage of low distortion, but it has the one disadvantage of low gain. In fact, by letting beta equal minus one in Eq. (A-57) (see Appendix Sec. A-12) we find the voltage gain is equal to $A/(1 + A)$, where A is the gain the tube would have with no feedback; this shows that the gain of the circuit is less than 1. If, for example, the circuit has a gain of 24 without feedback, its gain would be 0.96 with feedback.

An equation for voltage gain in terms of the circuit and tube constants can be calculated from Eq. (A-57) and the fundamental equation for gain of an amplifier:

$$A = \frac{\mu R_L}{r_p + R_L} \tag{12-1}$$

Letting $R_L = R_K$ and $\beta = -1$, and substituting these values and Eq. (12-1) into Eq. (A-57), gives

$$A_f = \frac{\mu R_K/(r_p + R_K)}{1 + \mu R_K/(r_p + R_K)} = \frac{\mu R_K}{r_p + R_K + \mu R_K}$$

$$A_f = \frac{\mu R_K}{r_p + (1 + \mu)R_K} \qquad \textbf{12-2}$$

Dividing numerator and denominator by r_p gives

$$A_f = \frac{\mu R_K/r_p}{1 + (1 + \mu)(R_K)/r_p}$$

and if $1 + \mu \approx \mu$,

$$A_f = \frac{g_m R_K}{1 + g_m R_K} \qquad \textbf{12-3}$$

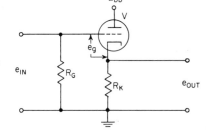

Fig. 12-7. Cathode follower.

Without feedback the output impedance of this circuit would be the internal plate resistance r_p in parallel with R_K:

$$Z = \frac{r_p R_K}{r_p + R_K} \tag{12-4}$$

Letting $R_L = R_K$ and $\beta = -1$, and substituting Eqs. (12-1) and (12-4) into Eq. (A-59), gives

$$Z_f = \frac{r_p R_K/(r_p + R_K)}{1 + \mu R_K/(r_p + R_K)} = \frac{r_p R_K}{r_p + R_K + \mu R_K}$$

$$Z_f = \frac{r_p R_K}{r_p + (1 + \mu)R_K} \tag{12-5}$$

Dividing numerator and denominator by r_p gives

$$Z_f = \frac{R_K}{1 + (1 + \mu)(R_K)/r_p}$$

and if $(1 + \mu) \approx \mu$,

$$Z_f = \frac{R_K}{1 + g_m R_K} \tag{12-6}$$

If Eqs. (12-3) and (12-6) are combined,

$$A_f = g_m Z_f \tag{12-7}$$

An interesting phase of the analysis of the cathode-follower circuit is that it acts like a conventional grounded-cathode amplifier using a tube with amplification factor equal to $\mu/(1 + \mu)$ and internal plate resistance equal to $r_p/(1 + \mu)$.

One advantage of the cathode follower over the conventional amplifier is the reduced input capacitance. Section A-9 gives the input capacitance of a conventional amplifier as

$$C_{in} = C_{gk} + (1 + A)C_{gp}$$

This is due to the fact that the output signal plus the input signal appears across the grid-plate capacitance, and the resulting current is drawn from the input-signal source. An additional input current is due to the input signal's appearing across the grid-cathode capacitance.

In the cathode follower, the plate is at ground potential as far as the signal is concerned, so only the input signal appears across the grid-plate capacitance, and the input minus the output signal appears across the grid-cathode capacitance. The resulting expression for the input capacitance (Sec. A-11) is

$$C_{in} = C_{gp} + (1 - A_f)C_{gk} \qquad \text{A-53}$$

This means that whereas the input capacitance of the conventional amplifier with a voltage gain of 20 might be around 100 pf, the input capacitance of a cathode follower with a voltage gain of 0.9 might be about 5 pf. Of course, there is also the input resistance, which is equal to the grid resistor R_G in Fig. 12-7.

A graphic treatment of the cathode-follower circuit is shown in Fig. 12-8. If E_{bb} is assumed to be 300 volts and R_K to be 20 kilohms, a load line is plotted in exactly the same manner as that for conventional tubes. The grid-voltage characteristics must now be reinterpreted. From Fig. 12-7 the equation for e_{in} becomes

$$e_{in} = e_g + e_{out} \qquad (12\text{-}8)$$

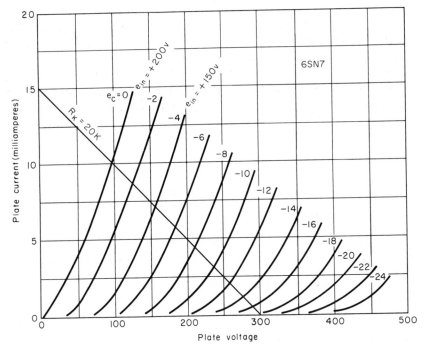

Fig. 12-8. Graphic analysis of cathode follower.

Since $e_{out} = i_p R_K$, Eq. (12-8) can be restated as

$$e_{in} = e_g + i_p R_K \qquad (12\text{-}9)$$

The zero-volt grid characteristic of Fig. 12-8 can now be restated to be the e_{in} characteristic of $+200$ volts. This value can be determined in the following manner. With $e_g = 0$, a plate current of 10 ma flows. By substituting the known values of $e_g = 0$, $i_p = 10$ ma, and $R_K = 20$ kilohms into Eq. (12-9), the value of e_{in} to cause this condition is 200 volts. By a similar process another input e_{in} characteristic can be determined from a different grid-voltage characteristic. Assume that $e_g = -4$ is chosen. When $e_g = -4$ volts, a plate current of 7.2 ma flows. Substituting the known values into Eq. (12-9) results in an input voltage of $+150$ volts. The entire input characteristic can be developed by using Eq. (12-9). It is apparent that when $e_g = -18$ volts no plate current flows; hence, $e_{in} = e_g$.

The characteristics of Fig. 12-8 yield two important facts. The gain of the stage can be calculated graphically by dividing an increment of e_{in} into an increment of e_b (the voltage ordinate). The maximum swing of the input signal without distortion extends from cutoff (-18 volts) to where e_g is 0 volts and e_{in} is $+200$ volts.

The cathode resistor in a cathode follower is usually selected by considering impedance-matching requirements, and may be a higher value than would normally be needed for cathode biasing. Too high a cathode bias voltage will mean that the amplitude of the input signal will be limited; the negative swing of the input signal will drive the tube into cutoff. The bias voltage may be reduced but the load resistance kept the same by using a circuit like that shown in Fig. 12-9. The voltage gain can still be calculated from Eqs. (12-2) and (12-3), where $R_K = R_1 + R_2$. The bias

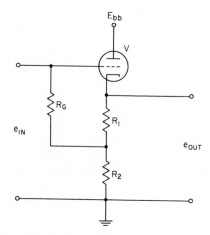

Fig. 12-9. Modified cathode follower.

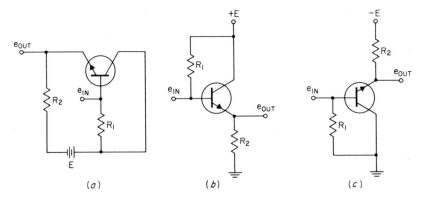

Fig. 12-10. Emitter-follower circuits.

voltage is the plate current times just R_1. This circuit change will also modify the input resistance to (Sec. A-10)

$$R_{in} = \frac{R_G}{1 - A_f R_2/(R_1 + R_2)}$$

12-10

It might be thought that the cathode follower has little value because the voltage gain is less than 1. One of the most advantageous characteristics of this circuit is the step-down impedance ratio. The input impedance is on the order of several hundred thousand ohms, while the output impedance is only a few hundred ohms. This impedance ratio of about a thousand means that even though the voltage gain is less than 1, the power gain and current gain can be around a thousand.

The high input resistance and very low input capacitance make this an ideal coupling device to minimize loading effects. All the advantages of negative feedback make the cathode follower preferable to a transformer for step-down impedance matching.

A similar transistor circuit is shown in Fig. 12-10*a*. This is the grounded-collector circuit, also known as the emitter follower. The emitter-base junction is forward-biased with R_1, R_2, and E in series across the junction. The voltage drop across R_1 is the collector-base voltage, which is the correct polarity to reverse-bias this junction.

Because of the forward biasing of the emitter-base junction, the voltage drop across this junction is small, a few tenths of a volt. Therefore, the base and emitter are at almost the same potential; and if the base voltage is varied by an input signal, the emitter voltage will "follow" the base voltage and will be the output signal. Either side of the battery can be grounded, and these two circuit arrangements are shown in Fig. 12-10*b* and *c*. As with the cathode follower, the voltage gain is less than 1, power gain and current gain are high, there is no phase reversal through the circuit, the input impedance is high, and the output impedance is low.

12-3 GROUNDED-GRID AMPLIFIER

The input signal to an amplifier tube is applied between grid and cathode. Usually the cathode is grounded and the signal is applied to the grid. The grid could be grounded and the signal applied to the cathode. This type of circuit, called a *grounded-grid amplifier,* has some especially desirable characteristics when used as an r-f amplifier.

The grounded-grid amplifier is also used for impedance-matching purposes; here the input impedance is low and the output impedance is high. A typical circuit is shown in Fig. 12-11. The circuit provides a gain greater than unity and has some reduced distortion characteristics due to the unbypassed cathode resistor.

If a cathode follower drives a grounded-grid amplifier, the output of one stage is at its cathode and the input of the following stage is at its cathode. If both amplifiers are designed to have the same value of cathode biasing, the two cathodes can be connected together, and direct coupling results. The two cathode resistors can be replaced by a single equivalent resistor. The circuit (Fig. 12-12) has slightly less voltage gain than a single, conventional amplifier stage, but it has other desirable characteristics. There is no phase shift from input to output. There is a self-balancing feature, because both plate currents flow through the common-cathode resistor. If the current of V_1 should increase, because of some change in the tube's characteristics, the cathode of V_2 would go more positive, decreasing the current of V_2 and thus decreasing the amount of change in voltage across

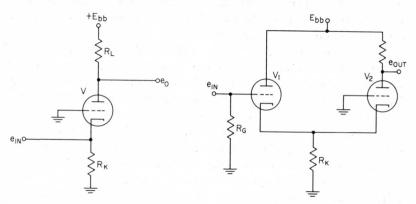

Fig. 12-11. Grounded-grid amplifier.   *Fig. 12-12. Direct-current amplifier.*

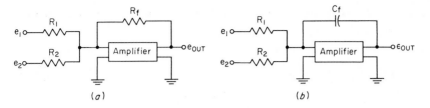

Fig. 12-13. Operational amplifiers.

the cathode resistor. This circuit has good high-frequency response, but its main use is for low-frequency or d-c amplification.

12-4 OPERATIONAL AMPLIFIERS

High-gain d-c amplifiers with feedback circuits can be used to perform certain mathematical operations. Known as *operational amplifiers,* they can be more specifically designated by the particular mathematical function involved: *summing amplifier, integrating amplifier,* and *inverting amplifier.* These are the basic units of analogue computers, where numbers are represented by d-c voltages.

If a feedback resistor is connected between the output and input terminals of the amplifier, and if several independent d-c signals are connected to the input terminal, each through a separate resistor, the result is a summing amplifier, shown in Fig. 12-13a. The output voltage is a function of the input voltages according to the following equation (Sec. A-13):

$$e_{out} = e_1 \left(\frac{R_f}{R_1} \right) + e_2 \left(\frac{R_f}{R_2} \right) + e_3 \left(\frac{R_f}{R_3} \right) + \cdots \qquad \textbf{12-11}$$

It can easily be seen that several d-c voltages, each representing a certain number, can each be multiplied by a factor determined by resistor values, and then the products can be added. This is the summing amplifier, but it can also multiply.

The operational amplifier usually has a phase reversal through it, so the output is actually a negative sum. If a single input signal is applied through a resistor, equal to the feedback resistor, the output will equal the input but will be reversed in polarity. This is the inverting amplifier; its only function is to change the sign of the input. A multiplying process could be combined with the inverting process.

If the feedback resistor R_f is replaced by a capacitor, as shown in Fig. 12-13b, the result is a *summing integrator;* the output signal is the time integral of the sum of all the input signals, each multiplied by a factor dependent upon resistor values. The equation for this circuit (from Sec. A-13) is given as

$$e_{out} = \int \left(\frac{e_1}{C_f R_1} + \frac{e_2}{C_f R_2} \right) dt \qquad \textbf{12-12}$$

These basic operational amplifiers can be connected so as to perform a series of mathematical operations in order to solve complex equations. The output voltage will usually vary with time, and the result can be read from a voltmeter, an oscilloscope, or a graphic recorder.

PROBLEMS

12-1   Explain the advantage of amplifying a signal before applying it to a diode comparator.

12-2   What is meant by the "common-mode effect" in a difference amplifier?

12-3   Discuss the use of a Schmitt circuit as a voltage comparator.

12-4   In the cathode follower of Fig. 12-7, assume that $R_g = 470$ kilohms, $R_K = 30$ kilohms, $E_{bb} = 150$ volts, and V is a 6SN7. ($C_{gp} = 3.8$ pf, $C_{gk} = 2.8$ pf, $C_{pk} = 0.8$ pf, $\mu = 20$, and $r_p = 10$ kilohms.) (a) What is the voltage gain? (b) What is the output resistance? (c) What is the input capacitance?

12-5   If R_K of Prob. 12-4 is decreased to 3 kilohms, what are the new values of (a) voltage gain, (b) output resistance, and (c) input capacitance?

12-6   Refer to Fig. 12-9. If $E_{bb} = 200$ volts, $R_g = 56$ kilohms, $R_1 = 5$ kilohms, $R_2 = 5$ kilohms, and the tube is a 6SN7, find (a) input resistance, (b) output resistance, (c) voltage gain, and (d) input capacitance.

12-7   If the value of R_2 of Prob. 12-6 is increased, does the input capacitance increase, decrease, or remain the same?

12-8   Name the characteristics of an emitter follower which make it of value.

12-9   What relationship does the output of the circuit of Fig. 12-13a have to e_1 and e_2? How does R_f influence the output?

12-10   What effect do the sizes of the input resistors in a summing integrator have on the output signal?

CHAPTER 13 *APPLICATIONS*

In the discussion of the individual types of circuits, reference was made to a number of commercial units. Some of these have been analyzed and discussed in the text; others have been presented as problems for the student to analyze.

Quite often a technician has no difficulty analyzing an individual circuit when it is isolated from the rest of a system; but when he sees the same circuit as one of many, all interconnected in a complete system, he may become confused and lost. For this reason a number of complete systems will be discussed in this chapter. These have been chosen for the individual circuits they contain and for the way they show how the various circuits, which have been discussed in the text, may be combined to perform useful operations.

Each piece of equipment will be first discussed in general terms to show its purpose and unique characteristics; then a block diagram will be presented and discussed; and finally, some of the individual circuits will be discussed in detail to show how they are like and unlike from the circuits discussed in previous chapters.

This chapter does not attempt to present system techniques. The scope of system analysis would embody another complete text. Nor are the systems chosen a cross section or a sample of the field. They have been selected mainly because of their adaptability to classroom use. Large systems such as radar units, television broadcast equipment, and telemetry transmission and modulation are not included. The following systems will be analyzed:

1. Electronic frequency meter
2. Transistorized oscilloscope
3. Pulse, sweep, and delay generator
4. Digital voltmeter

13-1 ELECTRONIC FREQUENCY METER

The frequency meter selected is a Hewlett-Packard Model 500B. The instrument can count sine waves, square waves, or pulses and can indicate the average frequency of random events. The Model 500B directly measures the frequency of an alternating voltage from 3 cps to 100 kc. It is suitable for laboratory measurement or production testing of audio and supersonic frequencies or for direct tachometry measurement with appropriate transducers. A recorder jack permits operation of a 1-ma recorder for continuous frequency record. The impedance characteristics of this terminal may be adjusted to match any 1,400-ohm (± 100 ohms) 1-ma recorder to the 500B meter circuit. The recorder jack also may be employed to drive a remote indicating meter.

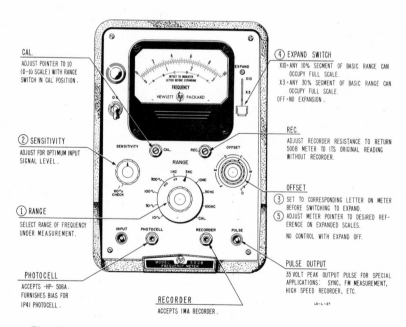

Fig. 13-1.   Front panel of the Hewlett-Packard 500B frequency meter.

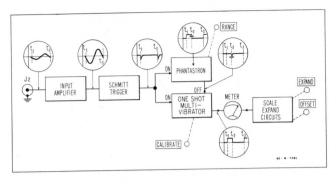

Fig. 13-2.   Block diagram of the Hewlett-Packard 500B frequency meter.

Besides indicating an applied frequency and providing a recorder output, the Model 500B provides two other types of measurements. First, it is designed to be able to expand its scale readings by factors of 3 to 10 times, an arrangement that facilitates measurements of frequency such as might be caused by line-voltage changes on frequency-generating circuits. Second, the instrument is designed to provide an output voltage which is proportional to the applied frequency. This signal from the PULSE terminal enables the instrument to be used as a wideband discriminator in applications where the measured signal contains very rapid frequency changes or frequency modulation. The discriminator voltage, when filtered, can be used to measure the amount of deviation in the signal as well as the rate and components of deviation. The front panel of the device is shown in Fig. 13-1.

BLOCK DIAGRAM

Figure 13-2 is a block diagram of the system, and Fig. 13-3 is a schematic of the system, excluding a regulated power supply. The signal to be measured, assumed here to be a sine wave, is applied at the input jack J_2. Once amplified, it is fed to a Schmitt trigger which produces a trigger pulse for each period of the input wave. It should be recalled from Chap. 6 that the output frequency of a Schmitt trigger is slaved to the input frequency. The output is a differentiated pulse for every period of the input wave, regardless of the configuration of the input wave. Hence, the input to the Schmitt trigger in Fig. 13-2 could have been a square wave, a sawtooth, or any periodic waveshape since the output would always be a pulse for each input period.

The output of the Schmitt trigger is fed to two circuits. It is fed to one half of a circuit which resembles a one-shot multivibrator and to a conventional phantastron circuit. The phantastron produces a reference

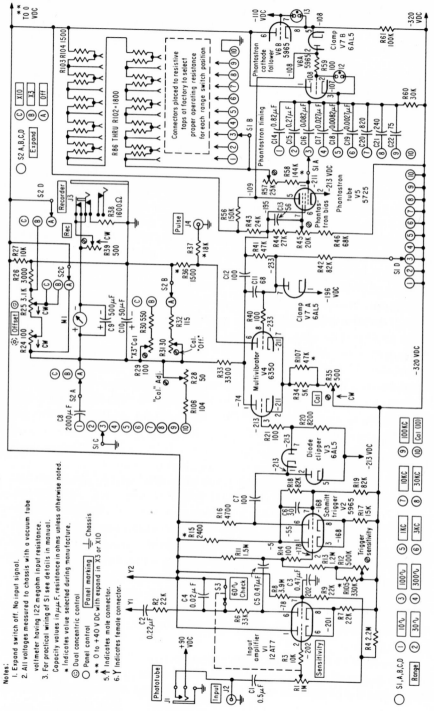

Fig. 13-3. Schematic diagram of the Hewlett-Packard 500B frequency meter.

pulse (depending upon the settings of the meter) which is coupled to the other half of the one-shot circuit. The output of the one-shot circuit drives a meter circuit which is essentially a bridge.

Refer to the schematic of Fig. 13-3. The following analysis discusses each segment of the block diagram, pointing out the components which make up the basic circuit and referencing these circuits to those analyzed in the text.

Input Amplifier V_1. V_1 is a conventional differential amplifier which amplifies the difference between voltages applied to its two grids. V_{1A} acts as a cathode follower driving the cathode of V_{1B}. Cathode followers were discussed in Chap. 12. V_{1B} acts as a grounded-grid amplifier with fixed bias provided by the divider network R_8, R_9, R_4. C_3 holds the V_{1B} grid at a-c ground. V_{1A} has no plate load. It therefore conducts more current than V_{1B} and has more influence than V_{1B} on the cathode bias developed across R_7.

A positive signal applied to the grid of V_{1A} causes increased conduction in V_{1A}, decreased conduction in V_{1B}, and a positive-going output at the plate of V_{1B}. The output from V_{1B} is coupled to the Schmitt trigger through C_5.

Schmitt Trigger V_2. V_2 is a Schmitt trigger, conventional in all respects. Capacitor C_6 is essentially a transpose or speed-up capacitor (Sec. 6-10). The positive-going portion of the trigger output is eliminated by one half of V_3 (pins 2 and 5) while the negative-going portion is differentiated by C_7 and R_{20} and passed through the other half of V_3 as a negative spike to the V_{4A} grid. Diode clippers were discussed in Chap. 4.

The sensitivity of the trigger is adjusted by R_{12}, which adjusts the no-signal voltage on the V_{2A} grid.

One-shot Multivibrator V_4. V_4 is a one-shot cathode-coupled multivibrator. In the no-signal condition V_{4A} conducts while V_{4B} is cut off. A negative spike from the trigger V_2 cuts off V_{4A}, causing a rapid switch in conduction to V_{4B} associated with multivibrators of this type (Sec. 7-1). However, V_4 is not a true multivibrator because it does not return to the no-signal state of its own accord. Recovery is determined by the action of the phantastron circuit V_5 to V_7.

Phantastron Circuit V_5, V_6, V_7. As a negative trigger spike drives the V_{4A} grid, a positive switching pulse appears on the V_{4A} plate. This pulse is coupled to the phantastron tube V_5 through C_{11} and C_{12}, starting a typical

Miller voltage rundown in the phantastron circuit (Sec. 9-8). At rundown start, the screen voltage on V_5 rises, holding the V_{4B} grid against the diode clamp V_{7A}, thus maintaining conduction in V_{4B} during the rundown period. At rundown completion, the screen voltage on V_5 decreases, cutting off V_{4B}. The period of the rundown is fixed by the RC time constant selected by S_1, the RANGE switch.

Phantastron action, therefore, causes V_{4B} to develop a current pulse during conduction which is stable in length. At the same time, degenerative action of the V_4 cathode resistor and the action of the clamp V_{7A} causes the current pulse to be stable in amplitude. One such stable pulse is passed through the meter circuit for each input cycle. The meter averages the pulses it receives and presents an indication proportional to average frequency.

Meter Circuit. When the EXPAND switch is placed in either X_3 or X_{10}, the meter shunts R_{32} and R_{30}, respectively, are removed, and the OFFSET control R_{24} and R_{25} is placed across the meter. This configuration is essentially a bridge.

The two halves of V_4 conduct alternately and represent two arms of the bridge. The input frequency determines the current ratio in which the tubes conduct. The bridge is balanced for the input frequency with the OFFSET control to keep the meter pointer on scale. Resistor R_{27} preserves the calibration of the meter circuit over the range of the OFFSET control.

13-2   TEKTRONIX MODEL 321 OSCILLOSCOPE

This oscilloscope is unique in that it can be powered from practically any power source which might be available: 105 to 125 volts or 210 to 250 volts, 50 to 800 cps; 11.5 to 35 volts d-c; internal flashlight dry cells; or internal rechargeable cells, either 2.5 or 4 amp-hr. It is lightweight, 17 lb, with batteries, and has a frequency response of 0 to 50 Mc. It is completely transistorized (except for the cathode-ray tube) and is an excellent instrument for portable work.

BLOCK DIAGRAM

The block diagram shown in Fig. 13-4 aids the overall description of the instrument.

The *vertical amplifier* amplifies the input signal and gives a balanced output to the deflection plates of the cathode-ray tube. A sensitivity as low as 10 mv per division is available. An internal voltage calibrator can be switched to the input of the vertical amplifier or can supply an external signal for probe calibration.

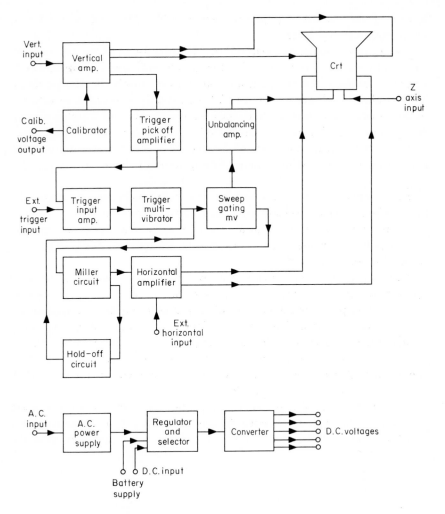

Fig. 13-4. Block diagram of the Tektronix Model 321 oscilloscope.

The *horizontal amplifier* can be used for the display of externally applied signals or will amplify the output of the horizontal-sweep circuits.

A *trigger pickoff amplifier* takes a signal from the vertical amplifier and applies it to the *trigger-input amplifier,* which, if necessary, inverts the phase of the trigger signal and drives the *trigger multivibrator.* This circuit generates the correct waveform for opening and closing the gate of the *sweep-gate multivibrator.* This gate circuit starts and stops the *Miller circuit,* which generates the sawtooth sweep for the horizontal time base. The trigger-input amplifier can also be driven from an externally applied signal. A *hold-off circuit* removes triggering pulses while the Miller circuit is generating a sweep signal.

The *a-c power supply* converts 120 or 240 volts a-c to about 16 volts d-c. The *regulator and selector circuit* will automatically switch in whichever supply voltage is highest: the rectified a-c, the battery supply, or the d-c input. The regulator and selector circuit will then supply a constant 10 volts d-c to the *converter*. This circuit then steps the voltage up and supplies a number of positive and negative values needed, from 6.3 to 3,350 volts.

A detailed discussion of some of the circuits of this instrument which are involved with pulse, switching, and timing signals follows.

Trigger-input Amplifier. This circuit serves two functions: it amplifies the trigger signal and, if necessary, inverts it. The trigger multivibrator requires a positive-going signal at its input. We wish to have a choice of triggering from a positive- or negative-going signal by throwing a switch to the corresponding position.

Two transistors are used in this amplifier. If a positive-going signal is applied at the input, the circuit is as shown in Fig. 13-5*a*. An emitter follower (Chap. 12) is directly coupled to a common-base amplifier (no phase shift). A variable base voltage of the common-base amplifier varies the quiescent value of its collector voltage. This is varied with the triggering level control and will control the point on the trigger signal at which the horizontal sweep begins. The way this is done will be discussed when the trigger multivibrator is considered.

If the trigger signal is negative-going, the circuit of Fig. 13-5*b* is used. The circuit change is made with the *slope switch*. Here, a common-emitter amplifier inverts the signal. The other transistor is used only as a d-c

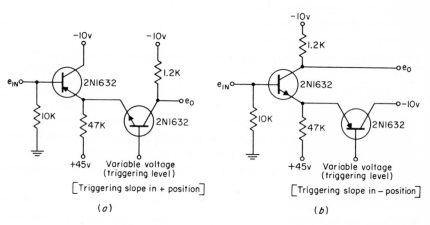

Fig. 13-5. Trigger-input amplifiers.

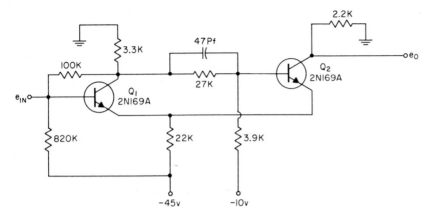

Fig. 13-6.   Trigger multivibrator.

emitter follower whose purpose is to vary the bias on the 2N169A amplifier and set its quiescent value of collector voltage. As was discussed in connection with the other circuit arrangement, this collector-voltage value determines the point on the trigger signal at which horizontal sweep begins.

Trigger Multivibrator. The trigger multivibrator is a Schmitt-trigger circuit which can be in either one of two stable states, depending on whether the input signal is above or below a certain level (Fig. 13-6).

The output of the trigger-input amplifier is directly coupled to the base of Q_1, and with no trigger signal Q_1 is cut off by the combination of base voltage from the previous stage and the emitter voltage developed by current flow through the 22-kilohm resistor. Q_2 is conducting at this time.

A positive-going signal from the trigger-input amplifier flips the multivibrator, at a particular point, into its other stable state: Q_1 conducting and Q_2 cut off. Because of the positive feedback in the circuit, the transition between stable states is very rapid regardless of how slowly the base signal of Q_1 may rise. As Q_2 cuts off, its collector voltage rises, and a positive step is created at the output.

When the signal at the base of Q_1 starts in the negative direction, Q_1 cuts off at a particular point, causing Q_2 to conduct, and a negative step at the output returns the output voltage to its original level.

This circuit, therefore, will take a trigger signal of any shape and change it to a rectangular waveform.

The triggering described causes the horizontal sweep to begin in synchronization with a certain level of the trigger signal, the particular level determined by varying the bias voltage on the trigger-input amplifier.

An *automatic* triggering mode is possible. This is accomplished by making the trigger multivibrator free-running, and synchronizing its frequency with the trigger signal. If no triggering signal is applied, the trigger multivibrator will oscillate at about 50 cps. The only change in the circuit of Fig. 13-6 is that a 2.2-μf capacitor is inserted in series with the input.

When triggering signals are absent, any change in the voltage on the collector of Q_1 is coupled back to the base circuit; but because of the 2.2-μf capacitor in the base circuit, there is about a 10-msec delay before the voltage change flips the multivibrator to its other stable state. For example, assume that Q_1 is cut off. Its collector voltage starts to rise. This voltage change is coupled through the 100-kilohm resistor to the base, but it takes about 10 msec until the base voltage has risen to a level that will cause Q_1 to start conducting. As Q_1 starts conducting, its collector voltage drops; this voltage change is coupled back to the base of Q_1, and after the 10-msec delay Q_1 goes into cutoff again. The total time of one cycle is about 20 msec, which gives a free-running frequency of about 50 cps. The output from the collector of Q_2 is a 50-cps square wave.

If a trigger signal higher in frequency than 50 cps is coupled through the 2.2-μf capacitor to the base of Q_1, the circuit can be triggered over a wide range of frequencies.

Sweep-gating Multivibrator.   Figure 13-7 shows the sweep-gating multivibrator which opens and closes the gate which starts and stops the sweep. This circuit can operate in either one of two ways, depending on the position of SW_1. If SW_1 is open, the circuit becomes a free-running multi-

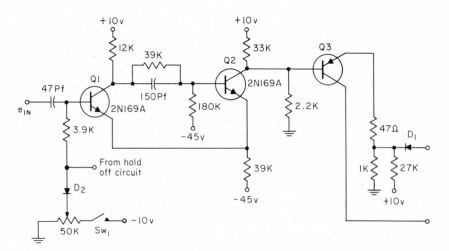

Fig. 13-7.   Sweep-gating multivibrator.

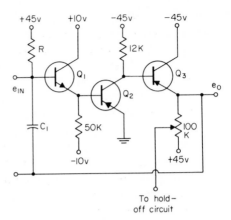

+45v +10v −45v −45v

R Q_1 12K Q_3

e_{IN} Q_2 e_0

C_1 50K   100 K

−10v   +45v

To hold−
off circuit

Fig. 13-8.   *Miller integrating circuit.*

vibrator and a sweep signal is generated with no input sync triggering. If SW_1 is closed, the multivibrator remains in a stable state until a trigger pulse is applied. The circuit which requires a triggering pulse will be considered first.

In its stable state, Q_1 is cut off and Q_2 is conducting. A positive pulse on the base of Q_1 forces the sweep-gating multivibrator into its second stable state with Q_2 cut off. The rise in collector voltage of Q_2 drives the base of Q_3 positive and cuts Q_3 off. Q_3's emitter goes positive, which reverse-biases D_1, opening the circuit which initiates the sweep.

The circuit remains in this stable state during the trace. The sweep signal is coupled back through the hold-off circuit to make the base of Q_1 go more and more negative until finally Q_1 goes to cutoff, Q_2 starts conducting, Q_3 starts conducting, and the trace portion of the sweep signal is terminated. The hold-off circuit keeps the base of Q_1 sufficiently negative that additional positive trigger pulses cannot trigger the sweep-gate multivibrator until the retrace is completed and the sweep circuits return to a state of equilibrium. Then Q_1 is returned to its original quiescent value where it can again be triggered by a positive pulse.

If SW_1 is closed, the base of Q_1 is not kept sufficiently negative to keep Q_1 at cutoff; so as soon as the hold-off voltage is removed, Q_1 starts conducting without any triggering pulse applied. The circuit then becomes free-running.

Miller Integrating Circuit. The actual horizontal-sweep signal is produced in the next circuit to be described (see Fig. 13-8). A very important requirement of the signal produced is that on the trace portion of the horizontal sweep the voltage must change linearly with respect to time. This voltage is produced by the timing capacitor C_1 charging through the timing resistor R. If the bottom end of the capacitor had a fixed potential, as the capacitor charged, its voltage would oppose the supply voltage and the charging current would be decreasing. This would result in a non-linear rise in voltage.

In the Miller integrator used in this oscilloscope, as the top end of the capacitor starts to go more positive, this change in voltage is amplified and inverted through the two emitter followers and the grounded-emitter amplifier, and the output is connected to the bottom end of the capacitor. Therefore, as the capacitor charges, the bottom end increases negatively by the same amount, keeping the top end at almost a constant potential. The timing resistor R, having an almost constant voltage across it, will be furnishing an almost constant charging current to the capacitor, making its voltage increase at a constant rate. (The discussion of the bootstrap circuit in Sec. 9-11 provides detailed theory.)

The output signal is taken from the bottom end of the capacitor and is thus a constantly changing voltage.

The input terminals of this circuit are connected to the switching terminals of the sweep-gating multivibrator (see Fig. 13-7). When the gate is open, the capacitor starts charging; and when the gate is closed, the capacitor discharges rapidly through the gate.

The length of time for the trace portion of the signal is determined by the setting of the 100-kilohm potentiometer at the emitter of Q_3. This setting determines how long it will take the voltage applied to the hold-off circuit to reach a certain level which will close the gate of the sweep-gating multivibrator.

Hold-off Circuit. As explained previously, the hold-off circuit (shown in Fig. 13-9) will keep triggering pulses from flipping the sweep-gate multivibrator during the retrace period and for a short time afterward. During the trace portion the emitter follower transfers the sawtooth waveform to the base of the input transistor in the sweep-gate multivibrator; and when

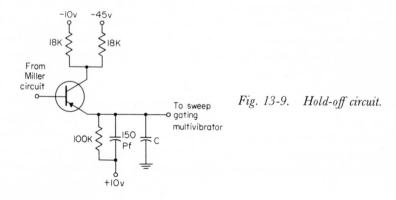

Fig. 13-9. Hold-off circuit.

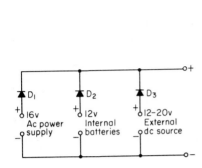

Fig. 13-10. *Automatic voltage selection.*

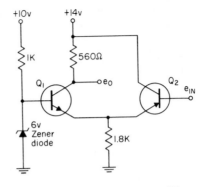

Fig. 13-11. *Difference amplifier.*

this transistor reaches cutoff, the sweep-gate multivibrator terminates the sweep.

During the trace time, the two capacitors in the hold-off circuit charge up; then during the retrace time they keep the base of the input transistor of the sweep-gate multivibrator sufficiently negative that triggering pulses have no effect. After a short time the capacitors have discharged sufficiently that they can no longer keep the sweep-gate multivibrator from being triggered.

The 50-kilohm potentiometer in Fig. 13-7 is called a stability control, and it keeps the base of Q_1 just negative enough to keep Q_1 from conducting. A positive trigger pulse can overcome this negative bias and can flip the sweep-gate multivibrator. This stability circuit is disconnected during the trace portion by diode D_2 being reverse-biased. Switch SW_1 can disconnect the -10-volt source from this circuit to make it free-running.

Automatic Voltage Selection. It has been mentioned that a variety of voltage-supply sources can be used to power this unit. If more than one source is connected at the same time, the highest potential is automatically selected and the others disconnected. Figure 13-10 shows this automatic-voltage-selection circuit. Whichever of the three sources is highest will make its particular diode conduct and will reverse-bias the other two diodes, removing the other two sources. For example, the a-c supply will put out about 16 volts, and that will back-bias D_2 by about 4 volts. If the external d-c supply is higher than 16 volts, both D_1 and D_2 will be reverse-biased. Otherwise, the a-c power supply will furnish the power.

Difference Amplifier. It is important that the input voltage to the voltage converter be maintained at a constant 10 volts, so a voltage-regulator circuit is used; an important part of this regulator circuit is the difference amplifier shown in Fig. 13-11. The input signal is compared with the

6 volts from the zener reference diode, and the output is proportional to the voltage difference. This output signal is then amplified and used to control the resistance of a transistor which is in series with the voltage to be regulated. The input to the base of Q_2 is a sample of the regulated voltage. Any change in this regulated voltage will thus cause a compensating change to counteract the original change.

COMPLETE SYSTEM

In order to develop skill in system analysis, the student should locate the various circuits just described in the complete schematic of the oscilloscope. Such a schematic can be obtained from the manufacturer.

13-3 PULSE, SWEEP, AND TIME-DELAY GENERATOR

The General Radio pulse, sweep, and time-delay generator Model 139-B is a multipurpose laboratory instrument designed to generate a variety of outputs for a given input repetition frequency. A periodic signal at its input can produce at the output a direct sync pulse, a delayed sync pulse, push-pull pulses with duration times ranging from 25 nsec to 1.1 sec at rates up to 0.25 ma, positive and negative linear ramp voltages of durations ranging from 3 μsec to 120 msec, and time delays from 1 μsec to 1.1 sec. The rise and fall times of the output transitions do not exceed 15 nsec.

BLOCK DIAGRAM

Figure 13-12 is a block diagram of the complete instrument. Assume that the periodic function at the input (PRF drive) is a sine wave. The input circuits produce a direct trigger signal and direct synchronizing signals. A front panel switch labeled TRIGGER SELECTOR connects the circuitry so that either a positive or a negative zero crossing will produce the output triggers. The trigger is available at the front panel of the generator and is also coupled to the delay circuits.

The delay circuits produce delayed triggers whose time of occurrence is referenced to the original trigger. Front panel controls allow a selection of delay from 1 μsec to 1.1 sec. In normal operation the coincidence system is not used. When it is used, two inputs are required to produce a delayed synchronizing signal. The first operates the delay circuits through the input circuits to open the coincidence gate. The second input pulse is fed into the COINCIDENCE DRIVE terminal and will cause the formation of the delayed trigger only when a gate is open.

The sweep circuits can be started by either the direct trigger pulse or the delayed trigger. These circuits produce (a) a positive and a negative ramp simultaneously up to a maximum amplitude of 135 volts in 3, 6, or

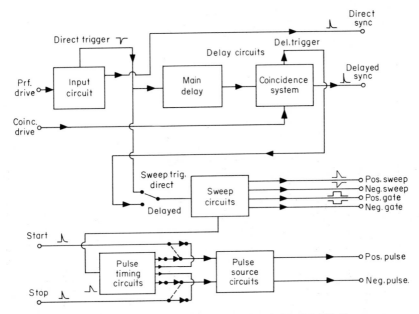

Fig. 13-12. Block diagram of the General Radio Model 139-B generator.

12 μsec and decimal multipliers thereof; and (b) positive and negative gate signals of the same duration as the sweeps. The ramps and gates are provided at the front panel; and in addition, a ramp signal is coupled to the input of the pulse timing circuits.

The pulse timing circuits are adjusted by front panel controls which predetermine the output-pulse duration and delay. These controls determine the formation times of the START and STOP triggers relative to the sweep and are used to start and stop the main pulse.

The pulses produced in the timing circuits are connected through the PULSE START STOP TRIGGERS switch to pulse-generating circuits. This switch will either (a) start and stop the output pulse at the time set on the front panel controls, (b) provide for externally generated pulses to start and stop the output pulse, or (c) permit the internally produced START and STOP triggers to be added to externally generated pulses to start and stop the output pulse.

The pulse source circuits are actually a bistable system which responds to START and STOP triggers.

CIRCUIT DESCRIPTION

The input-circuits block of Fig. 13-12 develops the basic trigger pulse. The equivalent schematic of this block is shown in Fig. 13-13. Diodes D_{102}

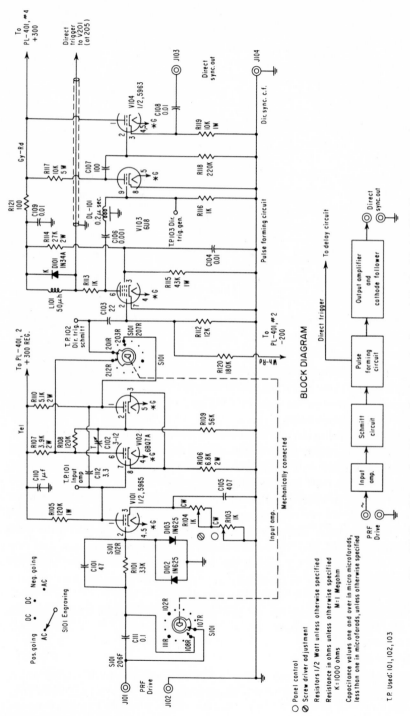

Fig. 13-13. Schematic of input circuits to the General Radio Model 139-B generator.

and D_{103} act as a clipper circuit providing a uniform input signal to V_{101} (a conventional amplifier). Duotriode V_{102} represents an ordinary Schmitt trigger. The following comparison with the circuit of Fig. 6-30 illustrates this case: $R_{107} = R_Z$, $R_{110} = R_5$, $R_{106} = R_k$, hysteresis resistors R_{108} and $R_{109} = R_3$ and R_4, and C_{102} is a transpose capacitor, made adjustable to compensate for tube changes and circuit aging. The output of the Schmitt trigger is coupled to the pulse-forming stage V_{103} where diode D_{101} clips one half of the differentiated square wave from the trigger. The trigger pulse is then amplified by V_{103} (triode portion). The trigger is coupled to the panel jack through cathode follower V_{104}.

The delay-circuits block of Fig. 13-12 is shown schematically in Fig. 13-14. The output from the Schmitt trigger is coupled to the input of a flip-flop consisting of V_{201} and V_{202}. This circuit is conventional in all respects. Compare the components of the circuit under discussion with those of the one in Fig. 6-20. Plate load resistors R_{203} and R_{204} equal R_2 and R_5. Coupling resistors R_{205}, R_{206}, R_{208}, and R_{207} are comparable to R_3, R_6, R_1, and R_4. R_{209} acts as bias (-50 volts of Fig. 6-20), and C_{203} and C_{204} are speedup capacitors. The pentode (high-gain) configuration provides faster switching. The output of the flip-flop is a square wave coupled to V_{203} through R_{211}. (C_{205} is also a speedup capacitor.) The sweep circuit of V_{203} is a slightly modified Miller integrator. It should be recalled that the Miller circuit requires a gate in order to initiate the rundown. Refer to the Miller circuit of Fig. 9-21. It was found that the values of R_1 and C determined the slope of the output. In this circuit R/C is selected by a front panel switch (S_{201}) to provide long or short duration times. The ramp output at the plate of V_{203} is coupled to the grid of V_{204} (a cathode follower) through R_{220}. The output of the cathode follower is directly coupled to the input of V_{205}. The circuit is labeled a DELAY AMPLITUDE COMPARATOR; however, the circuit is a conventional Schmitt trigger. The input triggering level is determined by R_{240}; hence the delay. The output square wave of the Schmitt trigger is differentiated through C_{230} and R_{244}, clipped and amplified through V_{204}. The delayed pulse is now returned to the input flip-flop (V_{202}), where the gate is turned off and the rundown of the Miller circuit stopped.

The delayed trigger is also coupled to the input of the coincidence system (block 3 of Fig. 13-12).

A monostable coincidence gate, adjustable from about 3 to 1,000 μsec, is a part of the delay circuit. The reset trigger produced by the main delay circuit opens this gate 1 μsec to 1.1 sec after the direct trigger. The coincidence gate permits time-selection operations.

In normal operation the opening of the coincidence gate produces the delayed synchronizing signal. However, with reduced sensitivity of the coincidence amplifier, the circuit can no longer be operated by the opening of the coincidence gate alone, and the circuits are pre-

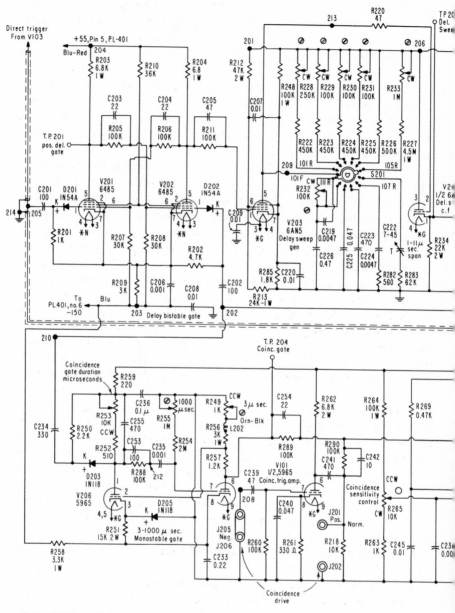

Resistors 1/2 Watt unless otherwise specified

Resistance in ohms unless otherwise specified
  K=1000 Ohms   M=1 Megohm

Capacitance values one and over in micro microfarads,
less than one in microfarads, unless otherwise specified.

O Panel control

⊘ Screw driver adjustment

Fig. 13-

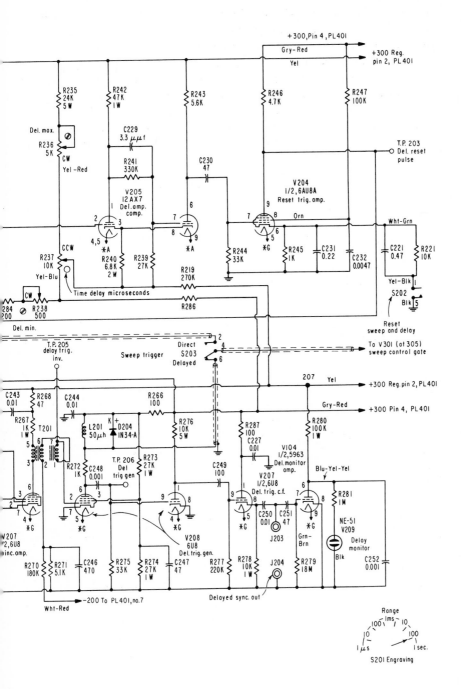

elay circuits; General Radio Model 139-B generator.

pared for coincidence operation. In this condition during the intervals in which the gate is open, the injection of a positive or a negative pulse at the appropriate COINCIDENCE DRIVE terminals will cause the coincidence amplifier to operate, resulting in the formation of the delayed synchronizing signal and delayed trigger. While the coincidence gate is open, as many delayed synchronizing signals and triggers will be produced as there are driving pulses to the coincidence circuit.

The sweep-circuit block of Fig. 13-12, similar in form to the main delay circuit, is shown in Fig. 13-15. The circuit consists of a bistable gate V_{301}

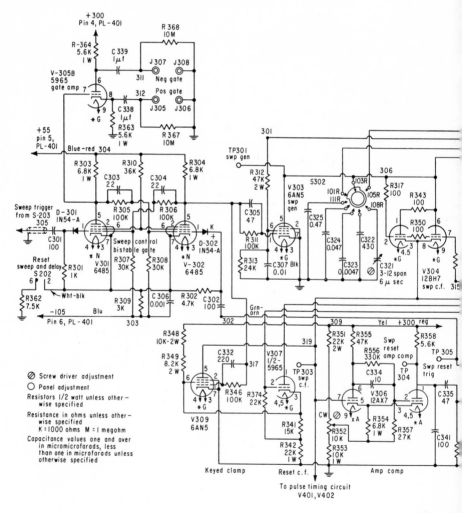

Fig. 13-

and V_{302}, a sweep generator V_{303}, an amplitude comparator, and a reset trigger amplifier, which produces the reset signal to close the gate. In this system, however, the sweep generator is a bootstrap circuit. It consists of a pentode which is turned off by the sweep gate to start the sweep, a cathode follower with a gain of nearly unity, a feedback diode, and a gated clamp circuit to control the initial sweep voltage. The linearly rising voltage waveform in this circuit is fed to the sweep-amplitude-comparator circuit, which switches when the sweep voltage reaches a preset 135 volts to form the reset trigger. In addition, the positive sweep voltage is fed (a) to the

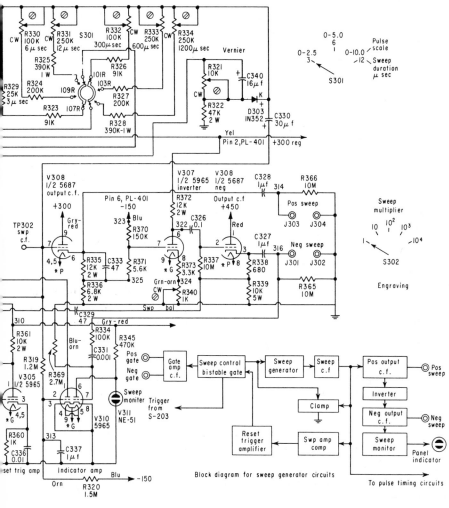

eep circuits; General Radio Model 139-B generator.

pulse-timing circuit, (*b*) to a cathode follower to provide positive sweep, and (*c*) through an inverter cathode follower to produce the negative sweep. The bistable sweep gate drives a phase-splitter, producing a push-pull waveform at the gate output terminals. The negative sweep at the output terminal drives a stage operating a neon indicator lamp to show that the sweep circuits are operating.

The sweep voltage operates two amplitude comparators (Fig. 13-16). The comparator at the lower voltage level produces the START trigger, while that at the higher voltage produces the STOP trigger. The d-c control voltages for these comparators are set by concentric panel controls for pulse duration and pulse delay. The triggers produced by the changes of state of the comparator circuits are differentiated and fed through a pair of cathode followers to the PULSE START STOP TRIGGERS switch, where they are fed to the pulse-generator circuit to time the pulse and to the START and STOP panel terminals. When the PULSE START STOP TRIGGERS switch is set to INTERNAL CIRCUITS (normal), these triggers operate a pair of amplifier stages, which shape them to drive the bistable-multivibrator circuit of the pulse source.

The START and STOP triggers operate a high-speed bistable gate circuit. This circuit drives a pair of amplifiers, which in turn operates a pair of drivers for the output stage. The push-pull output stage is a pair of beam tubes used as a current source with switched load resistors, across which the pulse of voltage is developed. The conducting output tube produces a current of 150 ma. Screen voltage on this stage is varied to control pulse amplitude.

The output system is balanced, and the push-pull pulses appear at coaxial connectors and parallel binding posts. The low-potential side of the load resistors is connected to an additional binding post normally grounded to the panel through a shorting link. Under these conditions the output pulses contain an a-c component negative with respect to ground. If the shorting link is removed, the d-c component of an external voltage (from any low-voltage laboratory supply or battery able to furnish 150 ma) can be varied by about 25 volts.

13-4 *AUTOMATIC D-C DIGITAL VOLTMETER; HEWLETT-PACKARD MODEL 405A*

This instrument measures positive or negative d-c voltages from 1 mv to 999 volts. It automatically zero-sets itself, chooses the proper voltage range and polarity, and displays the result in bright, clear numerals, complete with polarity sign and decimal point. It has an accuracy of ±0.2 per cent ±1 count. Input impedance is 11 megohms to d-c voltage. It samples the voltage being measured and displays the result every ⅕ to 2

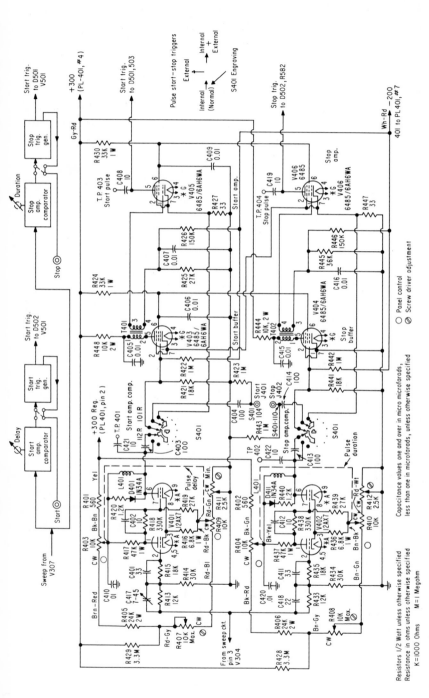

Fig. 13-16.   Pulse-timing circuits; General Radio Model 139-B generator.

sec, depending on the range being used. A hold control allows the range to be held and changed manually. Provisions are made to sample the voltage being measured on command of an externally applied pulse. Permanent printed records of the instrument measurements can be obtained by driving a digital recorder directly from the voltmeter.

Briefly, the theory of operation of this instrument is that it is a voltage-to-time converter. It measures the time required for an internally generated ramp voltage to increase from zero to a value which is proportional to the voltage being measured. The higher the input voltage, the longer the time interval required for this ramp voltage to reach the required level.

This time interval is measured by counting the number of cycles generated by a 50-kc oscillator. The total number of cycles occurring during this time interval is registered on three decade counters and is made to equal the voltage being measured.

A cycle of operation is as follows. Refer to the block diagram in Fig. 13-17. The sampling-rate generator starts the operation by triggering the relay-control multivibrator. This immediately triggers the feedback-gate multivibrator, and these two multivibrators zero-set the ramp voltage. After about 80 msec, the feedback-gate multivibrator returns to its stable condition. About 30 msec later the relay-control multivibrator returns to its stable state, triggering the delay multivibrator to apply the input signal to the difference amplifier. The delay multivibrator allows the relay to completely de-energize and then, after about 4 msec, it returns to its stable condition. This triggers the ramp-gate multivibrator, which starts the ramp voltage and opens the oscillator gate to start the count. The return of the delay multivibrator to its stable state is synchronized with the oscillator, so there is no count ambiguity at the start of the ramp.

When the ramp voltage equals the attenuated input signal, the output of the differential amplifier closes the oscillator gate, stopping the count, and the indicators display the value of the input voltage.

Two positions of the operation have been ignored but will now be described in detail. The first is the zero-setting of the voltmeter. When the relay-control multivibrator and the feedback-gate multivibrator are both on, a 1-mv level with polarity opposite to that of the input voltage is applied to the differential amplifier. One hundred per cent negative feedback is applied to the amplifier. This provides the initial conditions of the amplifier and the ramp voltage and zero-sets the voltmeter.

It was stated in the initial description of this instrument that it would automatically set the correct polarity and range. This is done by checking the outputs of the tens and hundreds counters. There are three counters, and it is desired that all three be used to display the voltage reading to three significant figures.

If there is no output from the tens counter, the hundreds counter is not being used, so the range is too high for the voltage being measured. If the hundreds counter produces an output, it means the count has exceeded 999, so the range is too low. The range is correct only when the tens counter produces an output but the hundreds counter does not.

These output signals are checked by the tens binary and the hundreds binary. At the start of the count both binaries are in their OFF condition. A signal from the tens counter will turn on the tens binary, which will

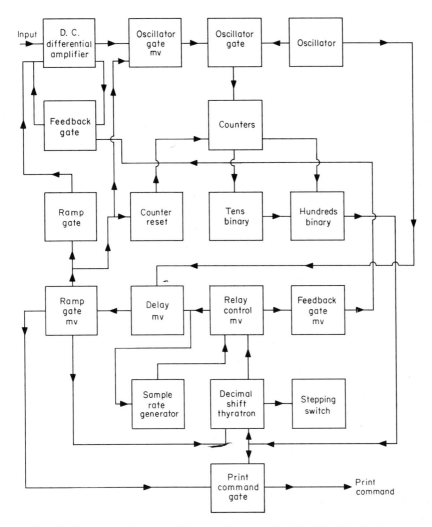

Fig. 13-17. Block diagram of Hewlett-Packard Model 405A digital voltmeter.

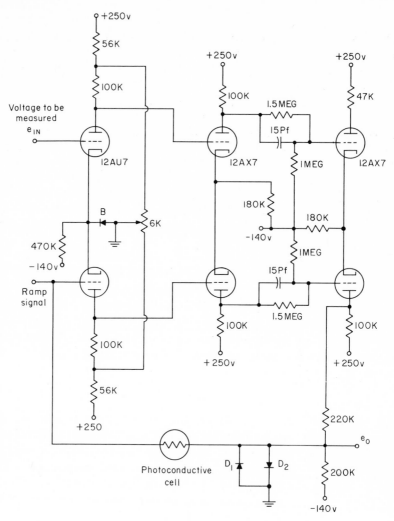

Fig. 13-18.   Differential amplifier.

then turn on the hundreds binary. Additional pulses from the tens counter will have no further effect. A signal from the hundreds counter will turn off the hundreds binary, but additional pulses will have no further effect.

If the voltage measurement ends with both binaries on, the range is correct. If the measurement ends with both binaries off, the range is too high. If the measurement ends with the tens binary on but the hundreds binary off, the range is too low. Thus, the state of the hundreds binary determines whether or not the range is correct. If it is on, the range is correct; if it is off, the range is wrong.

When the range switch is set for automatic operation, if the hundreds binary is off after a measurement, indicating an incorrect range, the decimal-shift thyratron fires and shifts to the next range. If this is incorrect, another range shift will be made; and this is repeated until the hundreds binary comes on, indicating a correct range.

A stepping relay, energized by the pulses from the decimal-shift thyratron, shifts ranges and polarity.

If the polarity is incorrect, the ramp voltage will never reach the input voltage level. Both the ramp-gate multivibrator and the oscillator-gate multivibrator will automatically return to their stable states, closing both gates about 30 msec after opening. This will cause a shift in the stepping relay, searching for a correct range and polarity.

Some of these circuits will now be analyzed in detail.

DIFFERENTIAL AMPLIFIER

The three-stage differential amplifier (shown in Fig. 13-18) amplifies the difference between the two input signals with a gain of about 1,000. The two diodes D_1 and D_2, connected to the output, allow a voltage swing of only about 1 volt. This means that there is a change in output voltage only when the two input signals are within about 0.5 mv of each other. As the ramp voltage equals and becomes greater than the voltage being measured, a 1-volt step signal is produced at the output.

MULTIVIBRATORS

It can be seen from the block diagram that there are five multivibrators in this instrument (not counting the counters and binaries). Three of these —the ramp-gate multivibrator, the relay-control multivibrator, and the feedback-control multivibrator—are plate-coupled monostable, with circuits as shown in Fig. 13-19. All three circuits are similar, with some variations in component values. V_1 is normally conducting, and V_2 is at

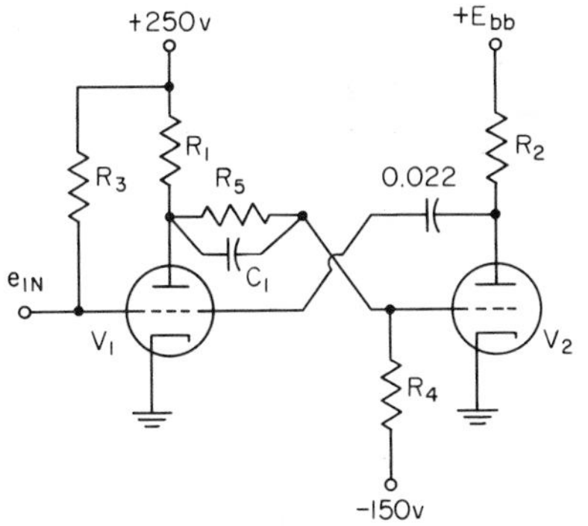

Fig. 13-19. Control multivibrator.

cutoff. A negative pulse to the input flips the multivibrator, and after a period of time it returns to the normal state.

The ramp-gate multivibrator supplies output signals from both plates, these signals going to the ramp gate. Only one output at a time is used, though, depending on the polarity of the d-c voltage to be measured.

The relay-control multivibrator has a relay coil in series with the cathode of V_2. Each time the multivibrator is triggered on, the relay coil is energized and the relay establishes the initial conditions at the input to the differential amplifier.

The feedback-gate multivibrator has a neon lamp connected across R_2. Each time the multivibrator is triggered on, the current through R_2 develops enough voltage drop to light the lamp. This lamp shines on the photoconductive cell (see Fig. 13-18), which provides 100 per cent feedback in the differential amplifier. This helps to establish the initial condition before a d-c voltage is measured.

The other two multivibrators—the oscillator-gate multivibrator and the delay multivibrator—are cathode-coupled as shown in Fig. 13-20. The normal state of the circuit has V_2 conducting, because its grid resistor R_2 is returned to $B+$; and V_1 is cut off because of the bias voltage developed across R_5.

The oscillator-gate multivibrator is a bistable circuit, requiring a negative pulse at input 2 to flip it on and then a negative pulse at input 1 to flip it off. The output signal is a positive pulse with a duration time equal to the on time of the multivibrator.

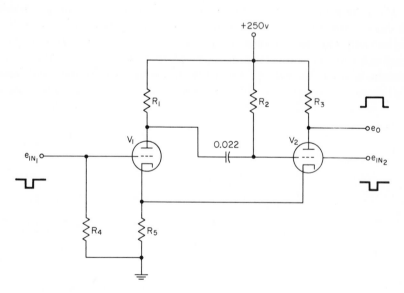

Fig. 13-20. Oscillator-gate multivibrator.

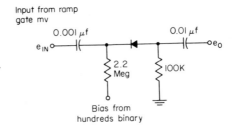

Fig. 13-21. Print-command gate.

The delay multivibrator has component values such that it is a monostable multivibrator with V_1 normally cut off and V_2 conducting. To trigger the circuit, a negative pulse from the relay multivibrator is applied to input 2. The circuit will automatically return to its stable state after about 4 msec, but only on the condition that there is a negative signal on input 1. A 50-kc sine wave from the oscillator is applied to input 1 so that the delay multivibrator returns to its stable state in synchronization with the negative peak of one of the sine waves from the oscillator.

GATING CIRCUITS

Three gating circuits are used in this instrument: the oscillator gate, the ramp gate, and a print-command gate, which is used only when a digital recorder is employed as the readout device.

The print-command gate is shown in Fig. 13-21. At the end of a count a negative pulse from the ramp-gate multivibrator is applied to the input of the print-command gate. If the decimal point and polarity are correct, the gate is open and the negative pulse goes through to cause the digital recorder to print the value of voltage being measured. If the decimal point and polarity are not correct, a positive bias from the output of the hundreds binary keeps the diode from conducting, and the gate is closed.

The ramp gate (Fig. 13-22) controls the charging and discharging of the ramp capacitor C_1. The gate is closed when the input from the ramp-

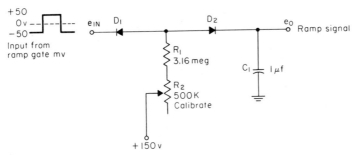

Fig. 13-22. Ramp gate.

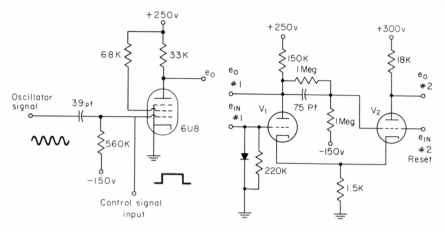

Fig. 13-23.   Oscillator gate.   Fig. 13-24.   Tens binary.

gate multivibrator is -50 volts on the cathode of D_2. The cathode of D_2 is at ground potential (C_1 is discharged), so D_2 is reverse-biased. When the input to the gate goes to $+50$ volts, D_1 is reverse-biased and D_2 becomes forward-biased through the R_1 and R_2 connection to the $+150$-volt source. The gate is now open and C_1 begins charging through R_1 and R_2 toward 150 volts. The charging time constant is about 3.5 sec, $(R_1 + R_2)C$, but the gate is open only about 0.03 sec. Therefore, the capacitor can charge to only about 1.5 volts maximum. This makes the ramp very linear and the voltage produced directly proportional to time [see Eq. (3-7)].

The gates just discussed were both diode gates. The oscillator gate is a pentode transmission gate (Fig. 13-23). The oscillator signal is continuously applied to the grid, but the -150-volt bias keeps the tube at cutoff. When the oscillator-gate multivibrator is turned on, the positive gating voltage applied to the control grid of the oscillator-gate tube opens the gate and lets the 50-kc sine wave through.

BINARIES

The purpose of the tens and hundreds binaries is to monitor the output counters to see whether the decimal point and polarity are correct or have to be shifted. These two binaries are identical. The circuit is shown in Fig. 13-24. This is a cathode-coupled bistable multivibrator. The output can be taken from either plate, and triggering can be accomplished at either grid. There is a difference between the tens and the hundreds binary circuits in the method of triggering and the plate from which the output is taken. In addition, reverse methods are used in designating the two binaries as being in the ON state or the OFF state.

In the tens binary, the ON state has V_2 conducting. It is used only to trigger the hundreds binary. The output of the tens binary is taken from the plate of V_2 and is a negative-going step as the binary is switched on. The tens binary is reset by a positive pulse applied from the delay multivibrator to input 2. It is switched on by a negative pulse from the tens counter, indicating that the tens counter has received at least 10 counts.

The hundreds binary is considered on when V_1 is conducting. It is triggered on by a negative pulse applied to its No. 2 input from the tens counter, when the tens binary is switched off; or it can be reset by a negative pulse from the hundreds counter, indicating that the hundreds counter has received at least 10 counts. The output is taken from the plate of V_1 in the hundreds binary.

The range and polarity of the instrument are correct if the count ends with the hundreds binary on. This state will give a negative output, which serves two purposes. It opens the print-command gate (see Fig. 13-21), and it keeps the decimal-shift thyratron from firing, which would shift the decimal point. If the hundreds binary is off, it indicates either that the tens binary was never shifted on (too low a count for the position of the decimal point) or that both binaries were turned on but the hundreds binary was shifted off again (too high a count for the position of the decimal point).

THYRATRONS

Three thyratron circuits are used in this instrument: the decimal-shift, the counter-reset, and the sample-rate.

The decimal-shift thyratron (Fig. 13-25) receives a positive pulse from the ramp-gate multivibrator at the end of each count. If the hundreds binary is on, it supplies a negative bias to the decimal-shift thyratron and the thyratron will not trigger, so the decimal point is not shifted. If the decimal point or polarity is incorrect, a positive bias is supplied from the

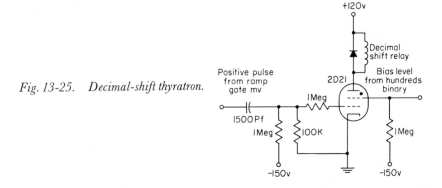

Fig. 13-25. Decimal-shift thyratron.

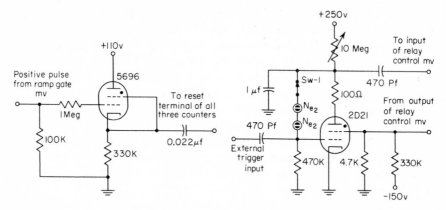

Fig. 13-26.   Reset thyratron.   Fig. 13-27.   Sample-rate thyratron.

hundreds binary and the thyratron fires, energizing the step relay, which shifts the decimal point to try a new count. This process continues until the correct position of the decimal point and the correct polarity are found.

The reset thyratron is a cathode-follower type of circuit which is fired by a positive pulse from the ramp-gate multivibrator at the start of the ramp signal. The circuit is shown in Fig. 13-26.

The sample-rate thyratron is the circuit that initiates each sampling count (Fig. 13-27). When it fires, a negative pulse triggers the relay-control multivibrator, which energizes the relay, which sets the initial condition. The relay-control multivibrator can also be triggered by a pulse from the decimal-shift thyratron. If this has taken place, a pulse from the relay-control multivibrator applied to grid 2 fires the sample-rate thyratron so it cannot fire again during a measurement started by the decimal-shift thyratron. If the sample-rate thyratron is not triggered by a pulse applied to grid 2 from the relay-control multivibrator, it can be fired by an external positive pulse applied to its 1 grid; or, if switch 1 is closed, an *RC* relaxation oscillator supplies positive pulses periodically to grid 1. The frequency of sampling on this "automatic" position is controlled by the 10-megohm potentiometer which controls the frequency of the relaxation oscillator.

APPENDIX

Refer to Fig. A-1a. The Kirchhoff voltage law states that at any instant of time

$$e_R + e_C - E = 0 \tag{A-1}$$

Ohm's law states that

$$e_R = iR \tag{A-2}$$

The fundamental relationship between capacitance, voltage, and current is

$$i = C\frac{de_C}{dt} \qquad \text{or} \qquad \frac{de_C}{dt} = \frac{i}{C}$$

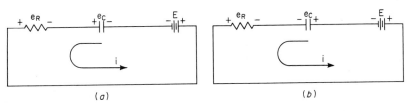

Fig. A-1.   *Charge or discharge of a capacitor through a resistor.*

289

Integrating both sides of this equation gives

$$e_C = \frac{1}{C} \int (i)\, dt \tag{A-3}$$

Substituting Eqs. (A-2) and (A-3) into Eq. (A-1) gives

$$iR + \frac{1}{C} \int (i)\, dt - E = 0$$

Differentiating this equation with respect to t yields

$$R \frac{di}{dt} + \frac{i}{C} = 0$$

Rearranging the equation and using $RC = \tau$ gives

$$\frac{di}{i} = -\frac{1}{\tau}\, dt$$

Integrating both sides of the equation yields

$$\ln i = -\frac{t}{\tau} + K$$

This equation can be written in exponential form:

$$i = \epsilon^{-(t/\tau + K)} = \epsilon^{-t/\tau} \epsilon^K$$

Let A equal the constant ϵ^K:

$$i = A\epsilon^{-t/\tau} \tag{A-4}$$

When $t = 0$, e_C equals its initial value E_{C0}, and

$$i = \frac{E - E_{C0}}{R}$$

Substituting these values into Eq. (A-4) gives

$$\frac{E - E_{C0}}{R} = A\epsilon^0 = A$$

Putting this value for A back into Eq. (A-4) yields

$$i = \frac{E - E_{C0}}{R}\, \epsilon^{-t/\tau} \tag{A-5}$$

This is the general equation for circuit current at any instant of time.

To find the capacitor voltage at any instant of time, it can be seen from Fig. A-1a that $e_C = E - iR$. Substituting Eq. (A-5) for i gives

$$e_C = E - (E - E_{C0})\epsilon^{-t/\tau} \tag{A-6}$$

This is the general equation for the charge or discharge of a capacitor through a resistor, when the initial voltage across the capacitor is in series opposing the supply voltage, as shown in Fig. A-1a.

If the capacitor's initial voltage is in series aiding the supply voltage, as shown in Fig. A-1b, the same derivation with polarities changed will give the following:

$$e_C = E - (E + E_{C0})\epsilon^{-t/\tau} \tag{A-7}$$

A-2 DERIVATION OF SPECIAL EQUATION FOR CHARGE OR DISCHARGE OF A CAPACITOR THROUGH A RESISTOR, FOR TIME PERIODS MUCH SHORTER THAN ONE TIME CONSTANT

The rate of charge or discharge of a capacitor can be calculated by taking the general equation (A-6) and differentiating it with respect to time:

$$\frac{de_C}{dt} = -(E - E_{C0})\epsilon^{-t/\tau}\left(-\frac{1}{\tau}\right)$$

$$= \frac{E - E_{C0}}{\tau}\epsilon^{-t/\tau}$$

The initial rate of charge can be calculated by letting $t = 0$:

$$\frac{de_C}{dt} = \frac{E - E_{C0}}{\tau}$$

Therefore, if the time period of charge or discharge is small, the change in capacitor voltage can be calculated from

$$\Delta e_C = \frac{E - E_{C0}}{\tau}t \tag{A-8}$$

By letting E_{R0} stand for the initial voltage across the resistor, $E_{R0} = E - E_{C0}$; and by substituting into Eq. (A-8),

$$\Delta e_C = \frac{E_{R0}t}{\tau} \tag{A-9}$$

A-3 CALCULATION SHOWING THE RESPONSE OF A LONG-TIME-CONSTANT CIRCUIT TO A SQUARE WAVE

It is assumed that the square-wave input is varying between 0 and 100 volts and has a period equal to 0.1τ. Therefore, $t = 0.05\tau$. (Each level of input voltage is applied for one-half the period.)

After the square-wave input has been applied for a certain length of time, the capacitor's voltage variations settle down to vary between two

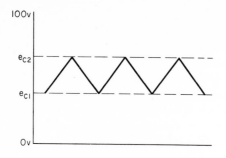

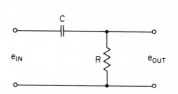

Fig. A-2. Response of a long-time-con- Fig. A-3. RC differentiating circuit.
stant circuit to a square wave.

limits (Fig. A-2). Because each time interval is short compared with the time constant of the circuit, it can be assumed that the capacitor charges and discharges at a linear rate; thus, the simplified Eq. (3-8) can be used:

$$\Delta e_C = \frac{E_{R0}t}{\tau} \tag{3-8}$$

Substituting $t = 0.05\tau$ gives

$$\Delta e_C = 0.05E_{R0} \tag{A-10}$$

Let the lower value of capacitor voltage be e_{C1} and the higher value, e_{C2}:

$$\Delta e_C = e_{C2} - e_{C1} \tag{A-11}$$

Substituting Eq. (A-10) into Eq. (A-11) gives

$$0.05E_{R0} = e_{C2} - e_{C1} \tag{A-12}$$

When the capacitor's charge begins to increase, $E_{R0} = 100 - e_{C1}$. Substituting this into Eq. (A-12) yields

$$0.05(100 - e_{C1}) = e_{C2} - e_{C1}$$
$$5 - 0.05e_{C1} = e_{C2} - e_{C1}$$
$$5 = e_{C2} - 0.95e_{C1} \tag{A-13}$$

When the capacitor's charge begins to decrease, $E_{R0} = e_{C2}$. Substituting this into Eq. (A-12) gives

$$0.05e_{C2} = e_{C2} - e_{C1}$$
$$e_{C1} = 0.95e_{C2} \tag{A-14}$$

By combining Eqs. (A-13) and (A-14), values can be found for e_{C1} and e_{C2}:

$$e_{C1} = 48.7 \text{ volts} \qquad e_{C2} = 51.3 \text{ volts}$$

A-4 DERIVATION OF THE EQUATION FOR AN RC DIFFERENTIATING CIRCUIT

Assume that the circuit in Fig. A-3 has a short time constant; that is, R and C are relatively small, or, more specifically, $X_c \gg R$. The voltage drop across the capacitor will be much larger than that across the resistor, so the current in the circuit will be determined by the capacitance. The fundamental relationship between current, voltage, and capacitance is

$$i = C\frac{de_{in}}{dt} \tag{A-15}$$

Ohm's law states that

$$e_{out} = iR \tag{A-16}$$

Combining Eqs. (A-15) and (A-16) gives

$$e_{out} = RC\frac{de_{in}}{dt} \tag{A-17}$$

which states that the output voltage is proportional to the time derivative of the input voltage.

A-5 DERIVATION OF THE EQUATION FOR AN RC INTEGRATING CIRCUIT

Assume that the circuit in Fig. A-4 has a long time constant; that is, $R \gg X_c$. The voltage drop across the resistor is much larger than that across the capacitor. The current in the circuit is determined by the resistance:

$$i = \frac{e_{in}}{R} \tag{A-18}$$

The output voltage is the voltage across the capacitor and is related to current by

$$i = C\frac{de_{out}}{dt} \tag{A-19}$$

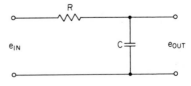

Fig. A-4.   RC integrating circuit.

Integrating Eq. (A-19) gives

$$e_{out} = \frac{1}{C} \int i \, dt \tag{A-20}$$

Substituting Eq. (A-18) for i in Eq. (A-20) gives

$$e_{out} = \frac{1}{RC} \int e_{in} \, dt \tag{A-21}$$

which shows that the output voltage is proportional to the time integral of the input voltage.

A-6 DERIVATION OF CURRENT AND VOLTAGE EQUATIONS FOR AN RL CIRCUIT

Kirchhoff's voltage law, applied to the circuit of Fig. A-5, gives

$$E = e_R + e_L \tag{A-22}$$

Ohm's law states:

$$e_R = iR \tag{A-23}$$

The fundamental relationship between inductance, voltage, and current is

$$e_L = L \frac{di}{dt} \tag{A-24}$$

Substituting Eqs. (A-23) and (A-24) into Eq. (A-22) gives

$$E = iR + L \frac{di}{dt}$$

which can be rearranged into the form

$$\frac{di}{i - E/R} = -\frac{R}{L} \, dt \tag{A-25}$$

Integrating Eq. (A-25) gives

$$\ln \left(i - \frac{E}{R} \right) = -\frac{R}{L} t + K$$

Expressing this in exponential form gives

$$i - \frac{E}{R} = \epsilon^{-(Rt/L+K)}$$

$$i - \frac{E}{R} = \epsilon^{-t/\tau} \epsilon^K \tag{A-26}$$

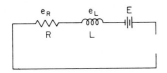

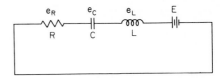

Fig. A-5.   Increase or decrease of cur-   Fig. A-6.   Current changes through an
rent through a coil.   RLC circuit.

where $\tau = L/R$. Let $\epsilon^K = A$, and Eq. (A-26) becomes

$$i = \frac{E}{R} + A\epsilon^{-t/\tau} \tag{A-27}$$

To evaluate A, substitute $i = I_0$, when $t = 0$, into Eq. (A-27):

$$I_0 = \frac{E}{R} + A$$

$$A = I_0 - \frac{E}{R}$$

Substituting this value of A into Eq. (A-27) yields

$$i = \frac{E}{R} + \left(I_0 - \frac{E}{R}\right)\epsilon^{-t/\tau} \tag{A-28}$$

Substituting Eq. (A-28) for i in Eq. (A-23) and then this result into
Eq. (A-22) gives

$$E = E + (I_0 R - E)\epsilon^{-t/\tau} + e_L$$

and solving for e_L yields

$$e_L = (E - E_{R0})\epsilon^{-t/\tau} \tag{A-29}$$

where E_{R0} is the initial voltage across the resistor.

A-7   DERIVATION OF THE CURRENT EQUATION FOR AN RLC CIRCUIT

Referring to Fig. A-6,

$$E = e_R + e_C + e_L$$
$$e_R = iR$$

$$e_C = \frac{1}{C}\int i \, dt$$

$$e_L = L\frac{di}{dt}$$

Combining these four equations gives

$$E = iR + \frac{1}{C} \int i \, dt + L \frac{di}{dt} \tag{A-30}$$

Differentiating Eq. (A-30),

$$0 = R \frac{di}{dt} + \frac{i}{C} + L \frac{d^2 i}{dt^2}$$

$$\frac{d^2 i}{dt^2} + \frac{R}{L} \frac{di}{dt} + \frac{1}{LC} i = 0 \tag{A-31}$$

This is a homogeneous linear second-order differential equation with constant coefficients. It can be solved in various ways (see A. E. Richmond, "Calculus for Electronics," pp. 368–370, McGraw-Hill Book Company) giving the resulting equation for i. If it is assumed that $R^2 \ll 4L/C$, the solution to Eq. (A-31) is

$$i = \frac{2E}{\sqrt{(4L/C) - R^2}} \, \epsilon^{-Rt/2L} \left[\sin \frac{\sqrt{(4L/C) - R^2}}{2L} t \right] \tag{A-32}$$

A-8 DERIVATION OF THE EQUATION FOR DETERMINING THE NUMBER OF CYCLES OF OSCILLATION TAKING PLACE IN A RINGING CIRCUIT

The number of cycles of oscillation taking place in a ringing circuit will be defined as the number taking place before their amplitude drops below $1/\epsilon$ times the initial amplitude. From Eq. (3-13) for the multiplying factor,

$$\epsilon^{-Rt/2L} = \epsilon^{-1} \qquad \frac{Rt}{2L} = 1 \qquad t = \frac{2L}{R} \tag{A-33}$$

Equation (3-12) for the angular velocity is

$$\omega = \frac{\sqrt{(4L/C) - R^2}}{2L}$$

Therefore the frequency of oscillation is

$$f = \frac{\omega}{2\pi} = \frac{\sqrt{(4L/C) - R^2}}{4\pi L} \tag{A-34}$$

The number of cycles taking place during time t is the product of frequency and time:

$$N = ft \tag{A-35}$$

Substituting Eqs. (A-33) and (A-34) into Eq. (A-35) gives

$$N = \frac{\sqrt{(4L/C) - R^2}}{4\pi L} \frac{2L}{R} = \frac{\sqrt{(4L/C) - R^2}}{2\pi R}$$

Dividing the numerator and the denominator by R yields

$$N = \frac{\sqrt{(4L/R^2C) - 1}}{2\pi} \tag{A-36}$$

From Equation (3-14) it was found that $Q^2 = L/R^2C$. Substituting this into Eq. (A-36) gives

$$N = \frac{\sqrt{4Q^2 - 1}}{2\pi} \tag{A-37}$$

If $Q \gg 1$,

$$N = \frac{\sqrt{4Q^2}}{2\pi}$$

$$N = \frac{Q}{\pi} \tag{A-38}$$

A-9 INPUT CAPACITANCE OF A TRIODE AMPLIFIER (MILLER EFFECT)

Refer to Fig. A-7. The voltage across the grid-plate capacitor is the sum of the input and output signals. The signal voltages are in series aiding because of the 180° phase reversal through the tube.

$$i_1 = \frac{e_{in} + e_{out}}{X_{gp}} \tag{A-39}$$

The voltage gain A equals the output signal divided by the input signal; hence,

$$e_{out} = Ae_{in} \tag{A-40}$$

The input signal appears across the grid-cathode capacitance, resulting in

$$i_2 = \frac{e_{in}}{X_{gk}} \tag{A-41}$$

The input reactance equals the input voltage divided by the input current, and the input current is the sum of the two components i_1 and i_2:

$$X_{in} = \frac{e_{in}}{i_1 + i_2} \tag{A-42}$$

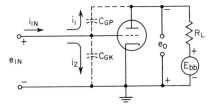

Fig. A-7. Conventional triode amplifier.

Substituting Eq. (A-40) into Eq. (A-39), then that result along with Eq. (A-41) into Eq. (A-42),

$$X_{in} \frac{e_{in}}{(e_{in} + Ae_{in})/X_{gp} + e_{in}/X_{gk}} \tag{A-43}$$

Dividing through by e_{in} and letting each reactance equal $1/\omega C$ gives

$$\frac{1}{\omega C_{in}} = \frac{1}{\omega C_{gp}(1 + A) + \omega C_{gk}} \tag{A-44}$$

Multiplying Eq. (A-44) by ω and inverting both sides of the equation gives

$$C_{in} = C_{gk} + (1 + A)\, C_{gp} \tag{A-45}$$

A-10 INPUT RESISTANCE OF A CATHODE FOLLOWER WITH SPLIT CATHODE RESISTOR

In Fig. A-8 the output voltage is divided across R_1 and R_2 so that

$$e_2 = e_{out} \frac{R_2}{R_1 + R_2} \tag{A-46}$$

$e_{out} = Ae_{in}$; hence Eq. (A-46) becomes

$$e_2 = \frac{Ae_{in}R_2}{R_1 + R_2} \tag{A-47}$$

The voltage across R_g is the difference between e_{in} and e_2. The current drawn from the input all flows through R_g and is

$$i_g = \frac{e_{in} - e_2}{R_g} \tag{A-48}$$

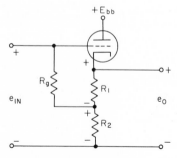

Fig. A-8. Cathode follower.

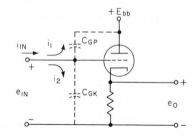

Fig. A-9. Input capacitance of a cathode follower.

Substituting e_2 from Eq. (A-47) into Eq. (A-48) gives

$$i_g = \frac{e_{in} - Ae_{in}R_2/(R_1 + R_2)}{R_g}$$

$$R_{in} = \frac{e_{in}}{i_g} = \frac{e_{in}}{[e_{in} - Ae_{in}R_2/(R_1 + R_2)]/R_g}$$

and dividing by e_{in} gives

$$R_{in} = \frac{R_g}{1 - AR_2/(R_1 + R_2)} \tag{A-49}$$

A-11 INPUT CAPACITANCE OF A CATHODE FOLLOWER

Refer to Fig. A-9. The input signal appears across the grid-plate capacitance, resulting in i_1. (The plate is grounded for a-c signals.)

$$i_1 = \frac{e_{in}}{X_{gp}} \tag{A-50}$$

The signal voltage across the grid-cathode capacitance is the difference between the input and output signals; these two voltages are in series opposing because there is no phase reversal. The resulting current is i_2. Assume that A_f equals the output signal divided by the input signal, $A_f = e_{out}/e_{in}$.

$$i_2 = \frac{e_{in} - A_f e_{in}}{X_{gk}} \tag{A-51}$$

The total input current is the sum of i_1 and i_2, and the input reactance is equal to the input voltage divided by the input current:

$$X_{in} = \frac{e_{in}}{i_1 + i_2} \tag{A-52}$$

Substituting Eqs. (A-50) and (A-51) into (A-52) gives

$$X_{in} = \frac{e_{in}}{e_{in}/X_{gp} + (e_{in} - A_f e_{in})/X_{gk}}$$

Dividing by e_{in} and letting each reactance equal $1/\omega C$ gives

$$\frac{1}{\omega C_{in}} = \frac{1}{\omega C_{gp} + (1 - A_f)\omega C_{gk}}$$

Multiplying by ω and inverting both sides of the equation,

$$C_{in} = C_{gp} + (1 - A_f)C_{gk} \tag{A-53}$$

Refer to Fig. A-10. If the feedback circuit shown as βe_o is disconnected, the gain of the stage without feedback is

$$A = \frac{e_o}{e_{in}} \tag{A-54}$$

With the feedback loop connected in the circuit, the gain becomes

$$A_f = \frac{e_o}{e_{in} - \beta e_o} \tag{A-55}$$

Solving Eq. (A-54) for e_o and substituting in Eq. (A-55),

$$A_f = \frac{A e_{in}}{e_{in} - A \beta e_{in}} \tag{A-56}$$

By factoring and canceling e_{in} of Eq. (A-56), the equation becomes, for voltage gain,

$$A_f = \frac{A}{1 - A\beta} \tag{A-57}$$

where $A_f \equiv$ voltage gain with feedback
$\quad\quad A \equiv$ voltage gain without feedback

The equation for distortion is

$$D_f = \frac{D}{1 - A\beta} \tag{A-58}$$

where $D_f \equiv$ per cent distortion with feedback
$\quad\quad D \equiv$ per cent distortion without feedback

The equation for output impedance is

$$Z_f = \frac{Z}{1 - A\beta} \quad \text{(voltage feedback)} \tag{A-59}$$

where $Z_f \equiv$ output impedance with feedback
$\quad\quad Z \equiv$ output impedance without feedback

$$Z_f = Z - R_f A \beta' \quad \text{(current feedback)} \tag{A-60}$$

where $R_f \equiv$ resistance in series with load to develop feedback voltage

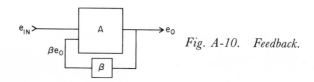

Fig. A-10.   Feedback.

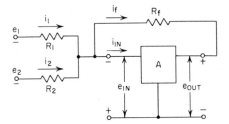

Fig. A-11.   Operational amplifier.

A-13   DERIVATION OF EQUATIONS FOR THE OPERATIONAL AMPLIFIER

THE SUMMING AMPLIFIER

A d-c amplifier is connected as shown in Fig. A-11; a resistor R_f is connected between the input and output terminals, and two independent d-c signals are connected to the input through separate resistors R_1 and R_2. The amplifier must have very high gain (50,000 or more), and therefore the input signal e_{in} will be very small. The input resistance will be very high, so the input current i_{in} will be negligible.

$$i_1 = \frac{e_1 - e_{in}}{R_1} \approx \frac{e_1}{R_1} \qquad i_2 = \frac{e_2 - e_{in}}{R_2} \approx \frac{e_2}{R_2}$$

$$i_1 + i_2 = i_f$$

$$\frac{e_1}{R_1} + \frac{e_2}{R_2} = i_f \tag{A-61}$$

Assuming a phase reversal through the amplifier, shown by the input and output polarities of e_{in} and e_{out} in Fig. A-11,

$$i_f = \frac{e_{out} + e_{in}}{R_f} \approx \frac{e_{out}}{R_f}$$

Substituting for i_f in Eq. (A-61) gives

$$\frac{e_1}{R_1} + \frac{e_2}{R_2} = \frac{e_{out}}{R_f}$$

Solving for e_{out} yields

$$e_{out} = e_1\left(\frac{R_f}{R_1}\right) + e_2\left(\frac{R_f}{R_2}\right)$$

If additional signals were applied to the amplifier input, each through its own resistor, the output signal would be

$$e_{out} = e_1\left(\frac{R_f}{R_1}\right) + e_2\left(\frac{R_f}{R_2}\right) + e_3\left(\frac{R_f}{R_3}\right) + \cdots \tag{A-62}$$

If the resistor R_f in Fig. A-11 is replaced by a capacitor C_f, the current through the capacitor is

$$i_f = C_f \frac{d(e_{out} + e_{in})}{dt} \approx C_f \frac{de_{out}}{dt}$$

Substituting for i_f in Eq. (A-61) gives

$$\frac{e_1}{R_1} + \frac{e_2}{R_2} = C_f \frac{de_{out}}{dt}$$

Solving for the derivative yields

$$\frac{de_{out}}{dt} = \frac{e_1}{C_f R_1} + \frac{e_2}{C_f R_2}$$

Integrating this equation gives

$$e_{out} = \int \left(\frac{e_1}{C_f R_1} + \frac{e_2}{C_f R_2} \right) dt + E_o$$

Additional inputs would result in

$$e_{out} = \int \left(\frac{e_1}{C_f R_1} + \frac{e_2}{C_f R_2} + \frac{e_3}{C_f R_3} + \cdots \right) dt + E_o \qquad \text{(A-63)}$$

where E_o = output signal at time $t = 0$

ANSWERS TO ODD-NUMBERED PROBLEMS

CHAPTER 1

1-1 (a) 2 μsec
     (b) 5 μsec
     (c) 11 μsec
     (d) 9.2 volts
1-3 (a) 0.8 μsec
     (b) 50

(c) *25* kc to 1.25 Mc
1-7 120 pf
1-9 12.82 per cent
1-11 6.37 cps to 20 kc
1-13 6.67 μsec

CHAPTER 2

2-1 (a) 10 ohms
     (b) 8 volts
     (c) 33.3 volts; 31.67 ohms
     (d) 8 volts
2-3 (a) 66.7 volts
     (b) 31.67 ohms
2-5 (a) 1.05 amp; 31.67 ohms
     (b) 8 volts

2-7 40.6 volts; 28.1 ohms
2-9 1.445 amp; 28.1 ohms
2-11 28.1 ohms
2-13 8.33 ohms
2-15 90 ohms
2-17 16.85 ohms
2-19 20 ohms
2-21 79.1 ma

CHAPTER 3

3-1 13.25 volts
3-3 1.25 sec
3-5 41.2 kilohms
3-7 256 μsec

3-9 2.5 msec
3-11 13.03 msec
3-13 0.3 volt
3-15 0.0123 μf

3-17   45.5 volts
3-19   0.463 sec
3-21   15 ma
3-23   45.5 volts
3-25 -11.88 volts
3-27   52.8 volts
3-29 (a) 0
      (b) 0.72 ma
      (c) 1.12 ma

(d) 12.5 volts
3-31   0.55 volt
3-33   198.6 μsec
3-35   200 μsec
3-39 (a) 9.13 kc
      (b) 11.62 ma
      (c) 0.15 msec
      (d) 1.37
      (e) 1.368

CHAPTER 4

4-1   2.5 volts
4-3   7.85 msec
4-5   Increased to 4 μsec

4-7   0.025 volt and 0.475 volt
4-15   35 volts p-p

CHAPTER 5

5-1   Active = 70 volts and 5.2 kilohms; cutoff = 300 volts and 30 kilohms
5-3 $\approx$22 volts
5-9   56 μsec
5-13 $I_{CBO} = 24$ μa; $I_{CEO} = 1.46$ ma
5-15   15 volts
5-17   None

5-19   7 volts peak-to-peak
5-21   130 μsec
5-23   25 μsec
5-25 $\approx$2 kilohms
5-27   330 ohms
5-29 $E = 15$ volts, $Z_g = 1.5$ kilohms; $E = 0$, $Z_g = 0$
5-31   10 volts

CHAPTER 6

6-1 (a) 2.5 ma
     (b) 13.8 volts
     (c) -1 volt
6-7   Across R_3 and R_6; $\approx$50 pf

6-9 (a) $\approx$0 volts
     (b) $\approx$0 volts
6-11   Plate, 242 volts; grid, -47 volts

CHAPTER 7

7-1 (a) 5.5 ma
     (b) 0 volts
     (c) -15 volts
     (d) 100 volts
7-5 (a) 10.3 msec
     (b) 78.8 msec
7-7 (a) 16 volts
     (b) 234 volts
     (c) 0 volts
7-9   71.6 msec

7-17   13.6 cps
7-19   1.515 cps
7-21 (a) 18.5 msec
      (b) 18.5 msec
7-25   18.5 msec
7-31 (a) $+3.15$ volts
      (b) 0.556 sec
7-33 $\approx$275 μa
7-37 (a) 78.4 cps
      (b) 10.41 msec

CHAPTER 8

8-1   309 pps

CHAPTER 9

9-1   0.151 μf

9-5   31.8 volts

9-7   306 cps

9-11   8.27 volts

9-13   0.0158 μf

9-15   13.2 volts

9-17   5.18 volts

9-19   (*a*) 38.6 volts

      (*b*) 42 volts

9-23   (*a*) 0 volts

      (*b*) 0 volts

CHAPTER 10

10-3   (*a*) 15

      (*b*) 13

10-11 9.06 volts

10-15 13

10-21 $E_R = 5$ volts; $E_F = 2$ volts

CHAPTER 11

11-1   (*a*) 707 ohms

      (*b*) 0.354 μsec

11-3   141.3 ft

11-5   (*a*) 0.195 in.

      (*b*) 16.65 nsec

11-7   0.1783 μsec; 0.169 μsec

11-9   83 ohms

11-11 40.1 pf/m

11-13 12.1

11-15 (*a*) 7.3

      (*b*) 0.4052 mh

CHAPTER 12

12-5   (*a*) 0.857

      (*b*) 428 ohms

      (*c*) 4.2 pf

INDEX